HUMAN AGING AND BEHAVIOR

Recent Advances in Research and Theory

Examines significant recent developments in research and theory on the alterations occurring in human performance from early maturity through middle age to old age. The contributions by several experimental psychologists and a team of clinical-social psychologists, describe their own research and summarize related discoveries. The population generally studied is the "average" man and woman; however, two chapters are included with specific samples. The first assesses the psychophysiological changes in aging pilots, and the second is devoted to the study of cognitive and personality variables in a selected group of aging college graduates.

Special attention is given to the relationship between behavioral and biological changes, and the relationship between diminished performance and reduced information processing capacity. In addition, chapters are included on the physiological correlates of response speed to language patterns, memory for verbal material, and ratings of health and social adjustment.

Human Aging
and Behavior

Recent Advances in Research and Theory

Contributors

Robert E. Canestrari, Jr.

F. I. M. Craik

D. R. Davies

Carl Eisdorfer

Patrick Rabbitt

Klaus F. Riegel

K. Warner Schaie

Charles R. Strother

Walter W. Surwillo

Jacek Szafran

George A. Talland

Human Aging and Behavior

Recent Advances in Research and Theory

EDITED BY

George A. Talland
Harvard Medical School
Boston, Massachusetts

Academic Press New York and London 1968

ACADEMIC PRESS INC.
111 Fifth Avenue, New York, New York 10003

United Kingdom Edition published by
ACADEMIC PRESS INC. (LONDON) LTD.
Berkeley Square House, London W.1

LIBRARY OF CONGRESS CATALOG CARD NUMBER: 68–16519

PRINTED IN THE UNITED STATES OF AMERICA

List of Contributors

Numbers in parentheses indicate the pages on which the authors' contributions begin.

Robert E. Canestrari, JR. (169), Research Unit on Aging, Veterans Administration Center, Hampton, Virginia

F. I. M. Craik (131), Birkbeck College, University of London, London, England

D. R. Davies (217), Department of Psychology, University of Leicester, Leicester, England

Carl Eisdorfer (189), Duke University, Durham, North Carolina

Patrick Rabbitt (75), Medical Research Council, Applied Psychology Research Unit, Cambridge, England

Klaus R. Riegel (239), Department of Psychology, University of Michigan, Ann Arbor, Michigan

K. Warner Schaie (281), Department of Psychology, West Virginia University, Morgantown, West Virginia

Charles R. Strother (281), University of Washington, Seattle, Washington

Walter W. Surwillo (1), Department of Psychiatry, University of Louisville School of Medicine, Louisville, Kentucky

Jacek Szafran[1] (37), Department of Experimental Psychology, Lovelace Foundation for Medical Education and Research, Albuquerque, New Mexico

George A. Talland (93), Harvard University Medical School, Massachusetts General Hospital, Boston, Massachusetts

[1]Present address: Department of Psychology, University of Southern California, University Park, Los Angeles, California.

Preface

Over the past decade there has been a notable growth in psychological research on problems related to aging, notable even more for an increase in sophistication and scientific rigor than in volume. As in other areas of psychological investigation, laboratory studies have been in the lead, and experiments testing hypotheses derived from theories have gained prominence over purely descriptive reports.

This development has undoubtedly been stimulated by an expanding awareness of the problems presented by a population with a long life expectancy, and it also reflects advances in the parent discipline of psychology and in related biological and social sciences. It owes much to the pioneer work of such psychologists as A. T. Welford in England and James E. Birren in this country, who have elected to dedicate their careers to gerontological research. For many years these two have been the spokesmen of their profession in the field of gerontology; their work and thought have been presented in a number of publications, and their influence, more particularly Welford's, on the authors here assembled is quite evident.

It is Welford's great contribution to gerontological research to have furnished it with a theory that has proved stimulating to psychologists, whether they wish to speculate about neural functions corresponding to the behavioral or limit their interest to the latter. This theory that analyzes the organism—or the central nervous system—in terms of its information-processing operations, has been borrowed from communication engineering, and has appealed to many psychologists who lean toward a cognitive position. In contrast to the strongest alternative position, from which behavior is viewed as a complex of S-R connections, the information-processing approach obviously attracts psychologists interested in the reasoning, planning human adult who masters his world by meeting its impact halfway, and whose mastery so often slips and even crumbles as he grows old.

Competence, skill, and efficiency depend on man's capacity to gather and apply information—memories, data in the perceptual environment, maps of contingencies. There is obvious promise in examining the mechanisms of information processing as the site of declining competence with age, and the more promise as some of these mechanisms may correspond to neural or other physiological systems that also deteriorate with advancing age.

Some endeavor to relate age-connected changes in performance to parallel changes in biological functions is implicit or explicit in most of the researches collected in this volume. Surwillo quite methodically sets out in search of a neurophysiological explanation of the loss of speed that is a well-established concomitant of advancing age; Eisdorfer arrives at one after a series of experiments on the effect of pacing upon learning. Szafran's behavioral tests are designed to probe the central functions of the nervous system and to compare them with psychophysiological data of peripheral function. Central function in these and the other chapters is equated with information-processing operations—coding, monitoring, transmitting, sorting, categorizing, organizing—the principal theme of Rabbitt's chapter, of my own, and Craik's. These last two shift the focus of inquiry to the deficit that occurs with age in memory and learning, the theme of Canestrari's and Eisdorfer's contributions. With his emphasis on the effects fast pacing exerts on older people. Eisdorfer prepares the reader for Davies' work on inspection tasks, which also reaches back to the problems of information processing. Riegel examines changes with age in a function that is generally believed to resist the assaults of the advancing years, the use of language. Schaie and Strother's contribution is the only one that did not originate in the experimental laboratory; it is a model example of survey research on the effects and problems of old age, psychological research that has been thriving along with performance tests of age-related changes.

The selection of the contributors has been avowedly biased; its aim was not so much to be representative, as to bring together some of the most rigorous and stimulating research in current gerontological psychology, research for which there is no adequate forum in the scientific journals. By allowing the authors sufficient space to present their work in detail, this Volume should do excellent service as a textbook in its field—where there is none—for each of the contributors has also thoroughly surveyed the research done and ideas advanced by other investigators that are relevant to his own work. In a good many problem areas, of course, the research presented here is the most comprehensive and advanced.

For readers more interested in the message psychological research has to offer on aging than in its attempts to grapple with theoretical problems and to construe tenable interpretations from its results, this volume promises cheer as well as caution. Schaie and Strother, and Szafran, who studied their subjects in life situations or with a view to their occupational skills, are quite encouraging about middle and old age. The rest of us who offer explanations for the loss of speed or deficiencies in memory and learning that appear in the course of aging are pretty far removed from the situations one is likely to encounter outside the laboratory. It is known, of course, that reaction times become slower, memory less reliable as one grows older; it is also known or believed that other gains will compensate for those losses. Experimental psychologists have little to report on those compensatory gains; this does not mean that they are illusory, they may be quite genuine but of a type that does not lend itself to demonstration in the laboratory. We all wish to know more about these gains, but we may as well face squarely the losses we risk by surviving early maturity and middle age, and by understanding these hazards try to minimize them.

Boston, Massachusetts   GEORGE A. TALLAND
October, 1967

Contents

Timing of Behavior in Senescence and the Role of the Central Nervous System

WALTER W. SURWILLO

Psychophysiological Studies of Aging in Pilots

JACEK SZAFRAN

Age and the Use of Structure in Transmitted Information

PATRICK RABBITT

Age and the Span of Immediate Recall

GEORGE A. TALLAND

Short-Term Memory and the Aging Process

F. I. M. CRAIK

Age Changes in Acquisition

ROBERT E. CANESTRARI, JR.

Arousal and Performance: Experiments in Verbal Learning and a Tentative Theory

CARL EISDORFER

Age Differences in Paced Inspection Tasks

D. R. DAVIES

Changes in Psycholinguistic Performances with Age

KLAUS F. RIEGEL

Cognitive and Personality Variables in College Graduates of Advanced Age

K. WARNER SCHAIE AND CHARLES R. STROTHER

Timing of Behavior in Senescence and the Role of the Central Nervous System

WALTER W. SURWILLO

Department of Psychiatry

University of Louisville School of Medicine

Louisville, Kentucky

I. Timing of Behavior and Old Age

An important factor common to all behavior is time. Whether a task or an activity is simple or complex, it takes time for it to be initiated, and it lasts for some interval. Simple responses have a latency and a duration, while more complex activities like learning involve, in addition, the programming of events into some temporal sequence.

Old age is distinguished by a general slowing in the timing of behavior. The adverse effect of age on speed of response is a commonplace observ-

1

ation and is probably one of the least disputed propositions in psychology. No matter what task is studied, latency tends to increase in old age. Birren (1959) has suggested that this finding is one of the "most fruitful points of departure" for exploring the nature of aged behavior. The present chapter will examine the factors associated with the longer response latencies in senescence, and will describe a mechanism and develop a theory to account for the phenomenon. Before turning to these matters, however, we shall first set the stage by briefly reviewing some of the evidence concerning the slowing in timing of behavior with age.

A. Simple Behavior

Simple reaction time (RT), which is at the bottom of the scale of behavioral complexity, has been studied extensively in relation to age. In the typical RT experiment, the subject (S) responds with a muscular contraction to a stimulus that is presented some interval after the occurrence of a warning signal. The experiment has been carried out with stimuli presented to the different sense modalities and with the responses elicited in various effectors (Bellis, 1933; Birren & Botwinick, 1955a; Elliot & Louttit, 1948; Forbes, 1945; Gavini, 1961; Miles, 1931; Obrist, 1953; Pierson & Montoye, 1958; Singleton, 1955; Welford, 1951; Welford, 1959). It seems to matter little which input route is employed or where the output is generated. All investigations have shown the same general picture of longer RT in groups of aged Ss than in similar groups of mature young Ss, or of positive correlations between RT and age in Ss over the middle thirties.

The studies just mentioned deal with speed of response to discrete events. In a simple RT experiment any trial is unrelated to the trials that precede it or to those that come after. As we might expect, age has similar adverse effects on continuous-performance tasks that involve the successive initiation of movements. Tapping or tallying with a manual counter are good examples. In an investigation of tally counting, Talland's (1962) Ss rhythmically pressed and released the key of a counter with the thumb, and worked as fast as possible at the task for 1 min. Rate of performance in this study dropped significantly from the young group to the intermediate-aged group and from the latter to the old group.

Choice or disjunctive RT is a step up the scale of behavioral complexity from simple RT. In the choice RT experiment, S is confronted with more than one possible stimulus and has a different response to go with each. Under these conditions, the effect of age is somewhat more complex.

The investigation of Suci, Davidoff, and Surwillo (1960) assigned a nonsense syllable to each of four pilot lamps that were mounted on a panel at the corners of a square matrix. The nonsense syllables were *bep, bix, buj,* and *boz*, and a group of young and an equal group of old *S*s learned to designate each lamp by its proper name. After preliminary training, an experiment was run in which the *S*s were required to respond as quickly as possible by naming the proper light whenever it flashed on. The vocal response in each case interrupted a chronoscope circuit and *S*'s response latencies were read from the chronoscope dial. The task was performed under conditions where the total number of lamps that were illuminated and, hence, the number of possibilities from which *S* chose his response, varied from one through four. One-, two-, three-, and four-lamp conditions represented 0.00, 1.00, 1.58, and 2.00 *bits* of stimulus information, respectively. [The bit is defined as the logarithm to the base 2 of the reciprocal of the *a priori* probability that a particular alternative will be selected. Thus, for example, with two alternatives, stimulus information equals $\log_2 (1/\rho) = \log_2 (1/0.5) = 1.00$ bit.]

Suci *et al.* (1960) found that in both young and old groups RT was an increasing linear function of the amount of stimulus information. When the data from the two groups were compared, the slope of the line describing the relation between RT and stimulus information proved to be significantly steeper for the old than for the young *S*s. This is illustrated for 0.00, 1.00, and 2.00 bits in Fig. 1, which shows that the difference between RT of old

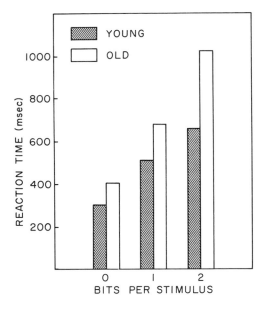

Fig. 1. Reaction time as a function of stimulus information and age. Young *S*s, 12 males, median age 18.5 years; old *S*s, 12 males, median age 63.0 years. Taken from a study by Suci *et al.* (1960) and used with the permission of the publisher.

and young Ss became larger as number of bits per stimulus increased. Decision time, therefore, turned out to be not only longer in old age but proportionally longer as amount of information associated with the decision increased.

B.   Complex Behavior

The adverse effect of age on timing of more complex behavior than the reaction tasks has been amply documented. A variety of different tasks have been investigated and the studies show that, in the main, old people require more time to complete the tasks, or finish fewer items in a given interval of time, than young people. We will mention only a few instances to serve as examples and to show the generality of the phenomenon under consideration.

Performance on a handwriting task was studied by Birren and Botwinick (1951) in groups of young normals, old normals, and senile patients. Subjects were required to write quickly, in their usual handwriting, lists of digits or words that were presented in large type on a test blank. Speed of handwriting, which was measured in terms of number of digits transcribed per second and number of words completed per 2 min, declined with age. It was also significantly slower in the group of senile patients than in the old normal subjects.

Speed of verbal association has been investigated in groups of young, middle-aged, and old Ss by Talland (1965). Two lists (A and B) of 10 items each were presented for word association under an instruction that called for S to respond, as quickly as possible, with any word that first happened to come to mind. The words in list B had logical opposites, whereas those in list A did not. Two other lists (C and D), also of 10 items each, were presented with the instruction to name the opposite of each word. List C consisted of words that had logical opposites, while list D was made up of the opposites of list B. Word-association time showed a tendency to increase with age, but significantly so only past middle age, and with the instruction to name the opposites of the stimulus words.

The time required to discriminate between two stimuli, or more generally, the speed of perception, also appears to be associated with age. Birren and Botwinick (1955b) required young and elderly Ss to judge which of two lines that were presented simultaneously by a tachistoscope was the shorter. Each S made a minimum of 48 judgments in a series where the pairs of lines differed in length from 1% to 50%. S responded as quickly as he could when a pair of lines was presented by saying "right" or "left" to indicate the side where the shorter line appeared. The vocal response interrupted a circuit connected to a chronoscope, from which the latency of S's response was determined. At all levels of difficulty of the judgments, a significant difference was found between speed of response of young and old groups. The elderly Ss, however, were proportionally slower as the judgment became more difficult. Thus, the difference in latency between young and old groups was 0.18 sec when the two lines differed in length by 50%, whereas the corresponding difference increased to 0.47 sec with only a 1% difference in length between the two lines.

Davies (1966) recently reported the results of an investigation in which several tests, among them the trail-making test, the perceptual maze test, and the digit code test, were administered to a large group of Ss in the third through the eighth decades. Performance on all three of these tests was found to decline significantly with age. Of particular interest in the present context is that performance scores on these tests involved time in one way or another. In the trail-making test the score was unity divided by the time required to complete the test, which is a measure of speed. The score on the perceptual maze test was number of mazes correctly solved in 12 min. Finally, number of items correctly coded in 2.5 min was taken as the measure of performance on the digit code test.

Although the total time required to learn a task or activity has long been an important variable in studies of learning in old age, the effects of presentation rate, or pace, on verbal-learning performance in senescence have only recently attracted interest. Canestrari (1963) and Eisdorfer, Axelrod, and Wilkie (1963) compared learning performances under paced conditions of old and young groups of Ss and found that differences between the groups were greater at faster paces than at slower paces. In Canestrari's (1963) paired-associate study each S performed at: a fast pace, in which anticipation and inspection intervals were 1.5 sec long; a slow pace, in which each interval lasted for 3.0 sec; and a self-determined pace, in which Ss were permitted to extend the time whenever it appeared necessary. The largest and smallest age differences were found to occur at the fast-pace and self-paced conditions, respectively. Eisdorfer *et al.* (1963) concluded from their own study of paced learning that the prevalence of errors and, hence, the poor performance of old Ss at a fast pace resulted from insufficient time to produce learned responses. This suggested that age decrement in paced verbal learning was a performance deficit rather than a learning deficit.

To test this hypothesis, Arenberg (1965) employed measures of errors in a paired-associate study that could not be attributable to insufficient time for S to respond. Arenberg's findings indicated that age decrements in paired-associate learning at fast presentation rates were not the result of performance deficits. The evidence strongly suggests that the search mechanism, which undoubtedly plays an important role in the process of recall, is slowed in old age.

II. Peripheral Factors in the Slowing of Senescent Behavior

Numerous studies have been made of various organs and organ systems in an effort to account for the slowing of senescent behavior. In reviewing this research, we shall concentrate on those studies that relate to simple behavior since therein, we believe, lies the key to the general problem of slowing in old age.

A.   Peripheral Nerve Conduction

Several studies (Norris, Shock, & Wagman, 1953; Sommer, 1941; Wagman & Lesse, 1952) of conduction velocity in human motor nerve have shown that speed of transmission of the nervous impulse is slowed in old age. By means of recorded electromyograms (EMGs) that were elicited in response to percutaneous electrical stimulation of the ulnar nerve at two or three points on the arm, Wagman and Lesse (1952) showed that maximum conduction velocity of motor fibers of human ulnar nerve was reached before age 10 and started to decline as early as age 50. Mean conduction velocity was 58.4 m/sec in Ss aged 20–30 years, 51.4 m/sec in Ss aged 60–82 years, and the difference between the two velocities was statistically significant. Using the same method with a group of 175 Ss, Norris et al. (1953) reported a drop in conduction velocity from 58–59 m/sec for Ss in their thirties to 48–49 m/sec for those in their eighties. With a conduction pathway 1 m in length, these velocities correspond to durations of 0.017 and 0.021 sec, respectively. Thus, the decrease in conduction velocity of approximately 10 m/sec in old age would amount to an increase of only 0.004 sec in RT. As pointed out by these investigators, such a change could account for only 4% of reported reductions in speed of voluntary reactions between 30 and 80 years of age.

In an ingenious experiment concerned with the same question, Birren and Botwinick (1955a) investigated speed of finger, jaw, and foot reactions to auditory stimuli. They hypothesized that if changes in the peripheral pathways were primarily involved in the slow RT of old age, then the RTs observed when the foot responded would be disproportionately slow compared with those observed when the finger or jaw responded. For all three conditions, RT of the elderly Ss proved to be significantly slower than RT of the young Ss, but there was no relation between difference in speed of response of the groups and length of the peripheral path involved in the responses. This study, therefore, is in agreement with all the others in showing that peripheral conduction is not an important factor in the slowing of senescent behavior.

B.   Synaptic and Neuromuscular Delay

Although synaptic delay has not been directly compared in humans, Wayner and Emmers (1958) have measured synaptic delays for the monosynaptic flexor hallucis longus reflex in groups of 117-, 276-, 445-, and 822-day-old rats. Synaptic delay increased progressively and significantly over this age range from a mean value of 0.97 msec in the youngest group to a mean value of 1.36 msec in the oldest group. Birren (1955) has shown that the startle reaction of rats to a loud auditory stimulus or to an electric shock is about 20 msec slower in old animals than it is in young adult rats. Since the age difference in synaptic delay is only a small percentage of this value, it appears that age differences at the synapse can account for only a very small percentage (about 2%) of the slowing of responses in senescence. It would appear that the same is probably true in the case of neuromuscular delay, which has been shown to have a duration of only 0.5–1.0 msec in mammalian striated muscle (Eccles & O'Connor, 1939).

C.   Sensory Mechanisms

It is possible that some portion of the longer response latency of old age is produced at the level of the sense organs. Such an effect could, for example, result from a slower activation of the sense organ concerned with the initiating stimulus. Weiss (1956a) concerned himself with this possibility in an experiment designed to determine whether there were age differences in the latency of response of the retina. Latency of the A-wave of the electro-retinogram (ERG) was recorded as an index of retinal functioning, since this electrical sign of activity appears to represent the initial response of the eye to a light stimulus. Two groups of Ss, one aged 18–37 years and the other 66–76 years, were studied, using five different intensities of light as a stimulus. Ss had their pupils dilated with neosynephrine, and a contact lens, which was fitted with an electrode, was applied after tetracaine anesthesia. ERGs were recorded on the screen of an oscilloscope and latencies were determined from photographs of the tracings. The findings in this study showed no significant differences in latency of A-wave of the ERG between young and old Ss.

Kumnick's (1956) work with pupillary responses also suggests the absence of age differences in timing at the level of the sense organ. It was found in this investigation that latency of pupil constriction in response to light and sound stimulation was unchanged with age over the range of 7.5–90.8 years.

D.   Motor Time

If, in an RT experiment, an EMG is recorded from the muscle that elicits the response, the electrical activity from this muscle is found to lead (precede in time) the mechanical response. The delay, or time interval, between EMG response and mechanical response has been termed *motor time* and has emerged as another possible source of the longer response latencies associated with senescence. In an experiment investigating this motor component of RT, Weiss (1956b) recorded EMGs from the extensor muscle of the forearm while S responded, by lifting his finger as quickly as possible, to a 1000-cycle tone that occurred after a variable warning interval (see also Birren, 1959, pp. 151–152). Motor time, which was taken as the time between a consistent increase in muscle action potentials from the forearm and the breaking of a circuit by an overt finger movement, proved to be remarkably constant for both young and elderly Ss. The difference between motor times for the groups of 14 young and 10 old Ss that were studied was very small, and it was concluded that the motor component contributed little to the slowing of RT with increased age.

A preliminary investigation in the present writer's laboratory (unpublished research reported here was carried out while the writer was at the Gerontology Branch of the Baltimore City Hospitals) suggested that motor time was somewhat more variable, from subject to subject, than had been reported. Since the number of cases in Weiss's (1956b) study was small, the matter was reinvestigated. One hundred males, aged 28–99 years, were tested in an RT experiment where S responded to a suprathreshold 250-cycle tone by pressing a button, as quickly as possible, with the thumb. Stimuli were presented at random intervals over a loudspeaker; they were sounded without the usual foreperiod and warning signal. A pair of electrodes was attached to the radial side of the palmar surface of the hand, over flexor pollicis brevis, and EMGs were recorded on the chart of a polygraph along with signals corresponding to the presentation of the stimulus and the initiation of S's mechanical response (see Fig. 2). Average value of motor time for the group was 48 msec, with a range of 21–108 msec. While motor time showed considerable variation from subject to subject in this study, the variance was not associated with age and, in this respect, our results confirmed Weiss's (1956b) earlier findings. Thus, the Pearson product-moment correlation (r) between age and average motor time was only 0.092, which was not significantly different from zero. There is no evidence, therefore, that motor time contributes to the slowing of RT in senescence. This conclusion has recently been further corroborated by Botwinick and Thompson (1966) and Weiss (1965).

III. The Central Nervous System in the Slowing of Senescent Behavior

The previous section showed that, on the basis of presently available evidence, age differences in the various peripheral processes cannot account

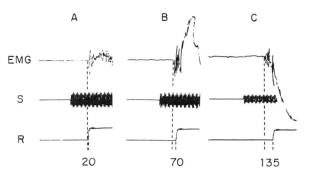

Fig. 2. Determination of motor time in an RT experiment. The signal in the middle (S) tracing indicates that a stimulus has been presented. Upper (EMG) tracing muscle action potentials recorded from flexor pollicis brevis; lower (R) tracing: upward deflection is pressure of S's thumb on response button. Numbers at bottom are motor times in milliseconds of three different subjects (A, B, and C) as determined from the samples shown. Amplitude of this signal in tracing S corresponds, in each case, to 100 μV in the EMG tracing.

for, or contribute little to, the slowing of RT in old age. It is clear, therefore, that we must search elsewhere for the changes to explain this phenomenon. As Talland (1965) has observed, we hardly need to be told to examine the central neural processes in this search. It is our belief that, at present, the cerebral cortex is the best place to look.

A.   The Electroencephalogram (EEG) and Old Age

As may be readily seen from an inspection of Fig. 3, one obvious difference between the EEGs of old and young persons is in frequency of the alpha rhythm. Slowing of the alpha rhythm in senescence was first noted by Berger (1933) in patients with senile dementia, but was regarded by him as a purely pathological phenomenon that bore no relation to the process of aging. Davis (1941) reported the presence of slow alpha rhythms in EEGs of elderly psychiatric patients and, in contrast with Berger's view, suggested that the senescent EEG was shifted toward the slow end of the frequency spectrum relative to the EEGs of young adults. Subsequent research has confirmed Davis's hypothesis that the EEG becomes slower in old age, and the question now concerns the magnitude of this difference.

The alpha rhythm, which is the dominant rhythm of the waking EEG, has usually been defined as a sequence of waves, principally from the occipital region of the cortex, that are readily attenuated by visual stimulation and have a frequency of 8–13 cps. In studies of old age, this bandwidth needs to be extended at the lower end, since frequencies of 7 cps and less are seen in the very old. Frequencies of this order were recorded in the dominant rhythm of the 99-year-old S shown in Fig. 3. In normal young

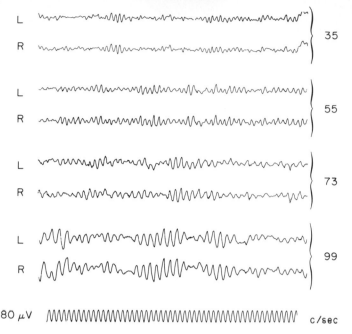

Fig. 3. Slowing in frequency of dominant (alpha) rhythm of the EEG with age. Numbers at the right are ages of the Ss; the letters L and R refer to recordings from left and right hemispheres, respectively. Recordings were made from pairs of surface leads over occipital and frontal areas; Ss were alert but had their eyes closed. Reproduced with the permission of the publisher from Surwillo (1963a, Fig.1).

adults under resting conditions, average frequency of the alpha rhythm is 10.2–10.5 cps (Brazier & Finesinger, 1944). Corresponding average values for old persons are significantly lower: Obrist (1954) reported a mean of 9.1 cps for residents of an old age home in the seventh and eighth decades, and 8.6 cps for those beyond age 80; Mundy-Castle, Hurst, Beerstecher, and Prinsloo (1954) reported a mean of 9.4 cps for normal control Ss with an average age of 75 years. More recently, in a study of a group of 256 elderly community volunteers, Busse and Obrist (1963) reported a significant downward shift in alpha frequency of more than a half cycle between two groups of Ss aged 60–74 and 75–94 years.

In all these studies, the EEGs were principally resting records made while Ss were lying quietly, with the eyes closed, allegedly doing nothing. Since it has been shown that frequency of the EEG varies with an S's level of alertness (Roth, 1961), the resting records from a group of Ss might not all correspond to the same organismic state and, hence, might not be directly comparable. Thus, at one extreme, S could become drowsy and fall asleep during the recording session, while at the other he could use the period of inactivity during recording to mentally review some problem or plan some activity. If in the former case S happened to be a young person, and in the latter an old person, a fundamental difference in alpha frequency between the two Ss could be substantially attenuated. To overcome this problem, EEGs can be recorded during periods while S is engaged in the performance of a standard task under conditions of high motivation. In Fig. 4, average values of EEG period obtained under non-resting conditions are plotted against age for a group of 98 healthy community volunteers aged 28–99 years. EEG period, or duration of the alpha cycle, is the reciprocal of frequency. Both terms henceforth will be used interchangeably, but all statistics involving EEG will be reported in terms of period, since this unit of measurement is linear with respect to time. To facilitate conversion from one unit of measurement to the other, Table I gives the relation between frequency of alpha rhythm and duration of an alpha cycle.

The data plotted in Fig. 4 were obtained from "on-line" EEGs that were recorded in the interval of time between the presentation of an auditory stimulus and the initiation of S's response during the course of a simple RT

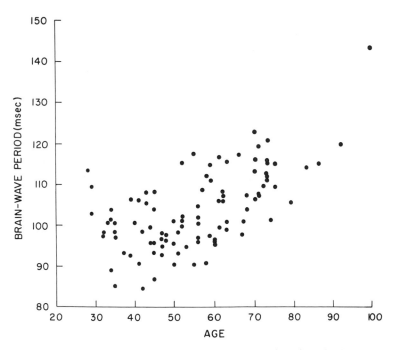

Fig. 4. Period of nonresting alpha rhythm as a function of age in 98 healthy community (male) volunteers. Adapted from Surwillo (1963a, Fig. 3) and used with the permission of the publisher.

TABLE I

DURATION (PERIOD) OF ONE CYCLE FOR FREQUENCIES IN THE ALPHA-RHYTHM BAND

Frequency (cps)	Period (msec)	Frequency (cps)	Period (msec)
6	167	10	100
7	143	11	91
8	125	12	83
9	111	13	77

experiment. The Pearson r between alpha period and age was 0.60, which was highly significant. Using the method of least squares, a straight line was fitted to the points which had the equation

$$P = 0.408 \text{ Age} + 80.82$$

where P = duration of the alpha cycle in milliseconds. From this equation we see that alpha period increases with age at the rate of about 4 msec per decade.

Since the rate of change in duration of alpha cycle just cited was based on cross-sectional data, it is impossible to determine whether the apparent slowing in alpha frequency represents a true change with age or is the result of a selective dropout of Ss who have the higher-frequency EEGs in the population. Obrist, Henry, and Justiss (1961) have provided evidence that favors the hypothesis of a *change* in frequency of the alpha rhythm with age. Their longitudinal study of the alpha rhythm showed that two thirds of a group of mentally "normal" old persons underwent progressive reductions in alpha frequency over a 10-year period. In one of the Ss studied, alpha showed a dramatic decline from 9.4 cps at the age of 79 to 8.0 cps at age 89. Dropouts due to death occurred more often among Ss with slow rhythm than among those with fast rhythms. These investigators pointed out that an alpha frequency of 9 cps in an elderly person could represent a substantial reduction in frequency from some earlier level.

B. Period of the EEG as a Mechanism in Timing: A Hypothesis

The finding that alpha period changed at the rate of 4 msec per decade and, hence, could increase by 20 msec per cycle between the ages of 30 and 80 suggested that the EEG might be implicated in the slowing of RT in old age. As a first step, we endeavored to discover whether RT and duration of the alpha-rhythm cycle were related. In an investigation first reported in 1960 (Surwillo, 1960, 1961), a statistically significant rank-order correlation of 0.81 was found between RT and alpha period in a group of 13 Ss aged 18–72 years. The EEGs were on-line recordings of the dominant rhythm, and the measure of period was based on the average duration of waves occurring between the stimulus, which was a supraliminal 250-cycle tone, and the response, which was a sound uttered by S. These results led to the formulation of a hypothesis that period of the alpha rhythm, or some multiple of the alpha cycle, serves as the master timing mechanism in behavior.

The basic tenet of this hypothesis is that time in the domain of the central nervous system is reckoned in terms of the alpha cycle. Just as the oscillations of a pendulum, a wheel, or a crystal serve to time events in the physical domain so, we hypothesize, can the oscillations that are seen in the alpha rhythm of the EEG time events that occur in the brain.

It is worth pointing out that the general concept of the EEG as a timing mechanism in the brain is not new. It had its origin in the speculation, first propounded by Bishop (1933; 1936), that the alpha rhythm is associated with a cortical excitability cycle. With evidence later appearing in support of this speculation (Bartley, 1940; Bates, 1951; Chang, 1951, 1952; Jasper & Andrews, 1938a; Kibbler, Boreham, & Richter, 1949), the original concept was elaborated into a number of related hypotheses. Lindsley (1952), for example, proposed that the alpha activity cycle was a basic metabolic or respiratory rhythm of the individual brain cells that served as a means of pulsing and coding sensory impulses. In a similar vein, Walter (1950, 1953) suggested that the alpha rhythm was the reflection of a central regulating mechanism for coordinating afferent and efferent signals. In this hypothesis, alpha rhythm was thought to possess a scanning function analogous to that of television. More recently, Wiener (1958) proposed that the alpha rhythm served the function of a "clock" in the organization of behavior.

Although the hypothesis associating the alpha cycle with timing in the central nervous system has been current for over 30 years, the consequences of this hypothesis for behavior in general and aged behavior in particular have not been extensively explored. Let us, for a moment, consider simple RT in an individual S. Between the presentation of the stimulus and the initiation of S's response, a given number of previously programmed events must be run off. If, following our hypothesis, we assume that each of these events requires that some portion of an alpha wave pass by before it is carried out, then the interval that elapses between stimulus and response will be determined and defined by the total number of alpha cycles traced out in this interval. As long as the number of alpha cycles corresponding to this interval remains constant from trial to trial, latency of response will appear to be constant when viewed in the realm of the central nervous system. Cycle-to-cycle variations in duration of alpha waves will not, in this domain, affect latency of responses, since the alpha cycle is the unit in terms of which duration is measured.

If we turn now to the physical domain and time the same responses against a clock, cycle-to-cycle variations in alpha frequency, according to our hypothesis, will appear as trial-to-trial variations in latency of S's responses. This variability in RT, it will be seen, results because, of the two clocks being compared, the biological "clock" is not nearly as precise a timing instrument as our physical devices for measuring time. The hypothesis concerning the alpha rhythm and timing, therefore, provides a mechanism to account for variability in an individual's RTs. If it gives a true picture of reality, we should expect to find positive correlations between simple RT and period of alpha cycle in individual S's. Note, however, that the hypothesis does not require that all of the variance in an individual's distribution of RTs be accounted for by variations in period of the alpha cycle. Thus, trial-to-trial differences in total number of alpha cycles in the interval between stimulus and response will introduce into the measures of RT, variance that is uncorrelated with period of the alpha rhythm.

The same mechanism can be employed to explain differences in RT between different Ss and, hence, to account for the slowing of simple RT in old age. Figure 5 shows the essentials and workings of the mechanism with two hypothetical Ss, one a young adult with fast (12 cps) alpha and the other an elderly S with slow (8 cps) alpha. Assume that exactly two alpha cycles are required to run off all events that must take place in the interval between the presentation of a stimulus (S in Fig. 5) and the initiation

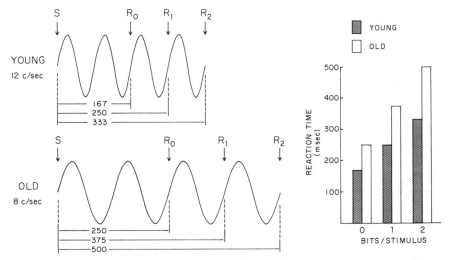

Fig. 5. Comparison of EEGs and RTs of two hypothetical Ss, one a young adult with an alpha rhythm of 12 cps and the other an elderly person with an alpha rhythm of 8 cps. S indicates the time of presentation of a stimulus; R_0 is the response in a simple RT experiment; R_1 and R_2 are the responses under conditions of 1.00 and 2.00 bits of stimulus information, respectively. Numbers below the waves are the hypothetical RTs in milliseconds, and these values are shown in the graph at the right.

of S's response (R_0 in Fig. 5). Let us also assume that, as shown in Fig. 5, the stimulus occurs at the same phase of the wave in both Ss. The latter simplifies the demonstration and is a necessary assumption, since Callaway (1962), Callaway and Yeager (1960), and Lansing (1957) have found that simple RT is a function of the phase of the alpha cycle in which a stimulus falls and a response is elicited. RT in Fig. 5 for the young and old Ss is exactly 2 alpha cycles long, but the latency is 167 msec in the young S and 250 msec in the old S. Thus, the difference of 42 msec in duration of 1 cycle of the alpha rhythm (see Table 1) between the young and old Ss becomes a difference (to the nearest millisecond) of $250 - 167 = 83$ msec when spread over 2 cycles.

Figure 5 also shows the result when our hypothesis is applied to an RT experiment in which choice is involved. It is well known that choice, or disjunctive, RT is longer than simple RT. Let us assume that the processing of each bit of stimulus information by the brain requires exactly one alpha cycle. Thus, in Fig. 5, the response for the zero-bit condition (simple RT) occurs at R_0, while the responses for the 1.00- and 2.00-bit conditions occur at R_1 and R_2, respectively. Durations of the waves and, hence, latency of the responses in milliseconds are shown in the graph at the right of the figure. Note that, in our two hypothetical Ss, RT increases as a function of the amount of stimulus information (number of bits per stimulus). Of greater consequence in the present context, however, is the fact that RT increases more rapidly in old than in young Ss. As a result of this difference, the old S is seen to require more and more time to elicit a response than the young S as number of bits per stimulus increases. This is exactly what happened with real Ss in the investigation reported by Suci et al. (1960), which was discussed in Section I, A of the present chapter. A comparison of the graphs in Figs. 1 and 5 shows a striking similarity between the real and the hypothetical data. The hypothesis concerning alpha rhythm and timing, therefore, provides a possible mechanism to account for the increasingly longer RTs in old age as amount of information associated with a decision is increased.

Obrist (1965) has pointed out that any hypothesis that suggests possible mechanisms for senescent changes in speed of response must explain not only the lengthening of RT itself, but also the considerable increase in its variability. Several investigations (Gavini, 1961; Goldfarb, 1941; Obrist, 1953; Pierson & Montoye, 1958) have reported that variability in RT within individuals increases with age, as well as variability between individuals. Goldfarb (1941) observed that variability within an individual's responses at ages 35–54 was about twice as great as at ages 18–44. Substantially the same findings were reported in an experiment by Pierson and Montoye (1958). The study by Obrist (1953) was designed to produce RTs with values as close as possible to the physiological limit and with minimum variability.

To this end, attempts were made to control for practice effects, fluctuations in motivation, fatigue, and possible variations in performance due to sensorimotor factors. In spite of these controls, however, mean RT variability within individuals increased by about 50% from a group of 25 Ss with a mean age of 27.5 years to a group of 59 Ss with a mean age of 80.6 years.

Because the increased variability of RT in old age appears to be a genuine finding, it is necessary to examine the hypothesis we have proposed concerning slowing of RT in old age to determine whether it can also account for age increases in variability of RT. Within the framework of this hypothesis, variability in an individual's distribution of RTs has two possible sources. One of these sources, namely, cycle-to-cycle variations in frequency of the alpha rhythm, was discussed earlier in this section. The second possible source of variability in RT is trial-to-trial variation in the total number of alpha waves required to run off the events that must take place in the interval after the stimulus is presented but before S's response is elicited. Which of these sources can account for the greater variability, or larger standard deviation of RT (σ_{RT}), in elderly individuals?

In order for the first-mentioned source of variability in RT to play a role in the larger σ_{RT} of old age, old individuals must show greater cycle-to-cycle variation in duration of their alpha waves (more variability in frequency of the alpha rhythm) than young individuals. In an investigation by Mundy-Castle *et al.* (1954), standard deviation of alpha rhythm frequency was computed and found to be 0.98 and 1.11 cps, respectively, in two groups whose average age was 22 and 75 years. Although these findings suggest that variability of alpha rhythm frequency may be increased in old age, the magnitude of the difference hardly seems large enough to account for the larger σ_{RT} that is reported in senescence.

The effect on σ_{RT} of trial-to-trial variation in total number of alpha waves may be examined by referring again to Fig. 5. Assume, as before, that we have two hypothetical Ss, a young adult with a fast (12 cps) alpha rhythm

TABLE II

Effect of Variation in Number of Alpha Cycles within an
RT Interval on RT Variability (Hypothetical Data)

Type of S	Alpha frequency (cps)	RT in 2 waves[a] (msec)	RT in 3 waves[b] (msec)	Max. RT − min. RT (msec)
Young	12	167	250	83
Old	8	250	375	125

[a] R_0 in Fig. 5.
[b] R_1 in Fig. 5.

and an elderly person with a slow (8 cps) alpha rhythm. Let us say that the stimulus in the simple RT experiment in which these Ss participate always falls in the same phase of the alpha wave, and that in one trial both Ss respond after exactly 2 cycles have gone by (R_0 in Fig. 5), and in another trial after exactly 3 cycles (R_1 in Fig. 5). The RTs observed under these conditions are tabulated in Table II. Note that, although the same assumptions have been applied to both young and old Ss, the range of RT is greater in the old than the young S, and that the difference between maximum and minimum RT is increased by about 50% in the elderly person. Since the latter is a measure of variability, we should expect also to find a larger σ_{RT} in a distribution of responses from the old S. Our hypothesis concerning timing and the alpha rhythm, therefore, can account for increased variability of RT, as well as increased RT, in senescence. Indeed, in the context of our hypothesis, variability differences in responses of old and young individuals appear to be a necessary consequence of differences in frequency of the alpha rhythm.

IV. Testing the Hypothesis

As we pointed out earlier, the hypothesis that was proposed and developed in Section III, B has certain consequences with respect to the relation of age, duration of alpha cycle, and behavior. In the present section we will examine the experimental evidence that has been brought to bear on this hypothesis and will see how the hypothesis holds up in the laboratory.

A.   EEG Period and Simple RT

Surwillo (1963a) investigated the relation of age, duration of alpha cycle, and simple RT in a group of 100 community volunteers aged 28–99. Two questions of primary importance for our hypothesis were attacked. One purpose of this study was to discover whether trial-to-trial variations in an individual's RT were associated with duration of the alpha cycle; that is, to test the hypothesis that RT is positively correlated with period of the alpha rhythm within individuals. A second purpose was to determine if the slowed alpha rhythms of senescence could actually account for the longer RTs of old age.

The 100 Ss were tested in a simple RT experiment in which they were asked to press a button as quickly as possible whenever a supraliminal 250-cycle tone was presented over a loudspeaker. The tones, which occurred at random, had a duration of approximately 3.0 sec; since no forewarning or "ready signal" announced their presentation, the RTs recorded in the experiment were for "unalerted" responses. S performed the task while resting comfortably in a recumbent position, with the eyes closed, in a darkened room. A test period consisted of three separate 10-min sessions separated by intervals of rest; during each session about 30 stimuli were presented. First and second sessions were identical, but about halfway through the third session the duration of the tone changed abruptly to only 0.3 sec. *S*, who had been told about this change beforehand, was asked to exert the greatest possible effort to produce the fastest responses when the tones became short. Since in the first two sessions *S*s frequently became sleepy, data from all three sessions combined provided a sample of RTs over the whole arousal continuum, from drowsiness to high-level alertness.

On-line EEGs were recorded from two pairs of surface electrodes; one pair was attached over the occipital and frontal areas of the left hemisphere,

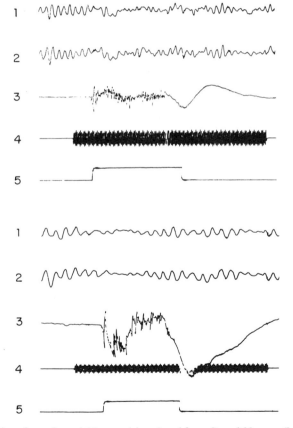

Fig. 6. Tracings from *S* aged 35 years (above) and from *S* aged 99 years (below), showing recordings of on-line EEGs. Channels 1 and 2, EEGs from left and right hemispheres, respectively; channel 3, EMG, flexor pollicis brevis; channel 4, stimulus marker; channel 5, response marker. Note the marked difference in frequency of alpha rhythm between the young and old *S*s.

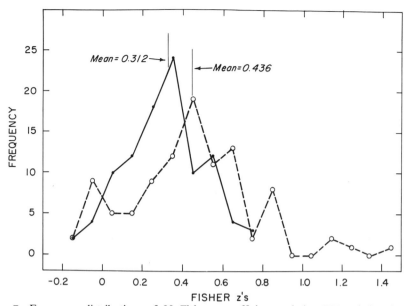

Fig. 7. Frequency distributions of 99 Fisher z coefficients relating RT and duration of alpha wave in on-line EEGs within individuals. Solid line shows coefficients computed from data for all three sessions combined. Dashed line represents coefficients derived from data of third session, where Ss performed under conditions of high motivation. Reproduced with the permission of the publisher from Surwillo (1963a, Fig. 4).

the other pair over the same areas of the right hemisphere. Electrode locations corresponded roughly to $0_1–Fp_1$, and $0_2–Fp_2$ in the "10–20" International System. These recording sites were chosen because they yielded maximum alpha activity in the tracings and because they were approximations to monopolar placements with respect to alpha rhythm. Separate channels recorded the occurrence of the tones and the initiation of S's responses on a polygraph chart along with the EEG tracings, and a third channel recorded the EMG from flexor pollicis brevis, which was the precursor of the mechanical response. Figure 6 shows a sample from two different Ss of the kind of recordings that were obtained.

Period of the alpha rhythm was determined from measurements of average duration of waves occurring between stimulus and response in each trial. The logic behind selection of this particular time for the measurement of alpha was based on the simple premise that behavior and central nervous activity are temporally contiguous and that the temporal aspects of today's behavior cannot be analyzed by reference to yesterday's or tomorrow's central nervous activity. A manual method of measurement was employed in which all waves that were not identified as artifacts, regardless of their durations, were included in the measurement. Although waves outside the conventional alpha-rhythm frequencies were not deliberately excluded, the large majority measured turned out to be in the alpha band. Only the tracing from the dominant hemisphere was measured and considered in the analysis.

A Pearson product-moment r between the distribution of RTs and the corresponding distribution of alpha-cycle durations was determined for 99 of the 100 Ss. Since these r's were based on data from all three sessions of the test combined, they showed degree of association between the variables over the whole arousal continuum. The solid line in Fig. 7 is the frequency distribution of these coefficients after the r's had been transformed into Fisher z's. Ninety-three of the 99 coefficients proved to be positive and average z was 0.312, which corresponded to an r of 0.302. Since standard error of the mean was only 0.02, our mean of 0.312 was clearly greater than zero, thus providing evidence of a positive correlation between RT and duration of alpha cycle within individuals.

Using data from only that portion of the third session when Ss performed under highly motivated conditions, average values of RT and average values of alpha-rhythm period were computed for each S. It was argued that, if the slowed alpha rhythm of senescence were responsible for the longer RTs of old age, then the positive correlation between RT and age that was sure to be found would vanish if period of the alpha rhythm were held constant. To test this proposition, the data were subjected to a partial correlation analysis. Although a correlation of only 0.19 was found between RT and age in this study, this r proved to be statistically significant. When period of the alpha rhythm was partialled out, however, this positive correlation vanished, as had been predicted.

B.   EEG Period and Response Variability

In a companion study using the same data of the experiment reviewed in Section IV, A, Surwillo (1963b) investigated the role played by frequency of the alpha rhythm in σ_{RT}. Using only data from that portion of the third session of the previous study where Ss performed under conditions of high motivation, σ_{RT} was determined for each of the 100 Ss tested. Values ranged from 5.1 through 80.5 msec, with a mean of 29.4 msec. The Pearson product-moment correlation between σ_{RT} and age (which, it will be recalled, ranged from 28 through 99 years) was 0.26 and was statistically significant. If, as we argued in Section IV, A, the greater within-individual variability of alpha-rhythm frequency in senescence was not large enough to account for the increased σ_{RT} in old age, then the positive correlation between σ_{RT} and age should still remain significant, even after variability of alpha-rhythm frequency has been partialled out. Partial correlation analysis of the data revealed that this was indeed the case. Although r between σ_{RT} and age was reduced to 0.19 when alpha variability was held constant, the latter co-efficient was still statistically significant.

If, on the other hand, our hypothesis concerning the function of duration of alpha cycle in timing of behavior were valid, we should expect the positive r between σ_{RT} and age to vanish with frequency of alpha rhythm held constant across the whole group. The investigation by Surwillo (1963b) confirmed this latter prediction. As in the previous study, period of the alpha rhythm was held constant, or partialled out, by means of partial correlation analysis. Under these conditions, the positive correlation between σ_{RT} and age vanished, and again we were confronted with strong evidence in favor of our hypothesis.

C. EEG Period and Disjunctive RT

The relation of age, duration of alpha cycle, and disjunctive RT was examined by Surwillo (1964a) in a group of 54 healthy community volunteers, aged 34–92. As in the previously described study, the auditory channel was used to present the stimulus and S gave his response by pressing a button with his thumb. The auditory system was used for the input mainly because of methodological considerations. In a preliminary investigation, visual stimulation from low-level neon lamps was attempted. Although we found it possible to record low-amplitude ($< 25~\mu$V) alpha rhythms under these conditions, frequent artifacts associated with blinking and rolling of the eyes made the technique impractical. By avoiding the visual channel and keeping the eyes closed, however, these problems were easily avoided. On the other hand, use of the auditory system made it more difficult to design a task that was suitable for testing the hypothesis under investigation.

The test period, in which each of the 54 Ss participated, was divided into four separate 10-min sessions that were separated by intervals of rest. Before testing began, each S familiarized himself with the difference between a 250-cycle and a 1000-cycle tone, and adjusted the intensity of the latter until it was judged to be as loud as the former, which was well above S's threshold. In the first session Ss were told that, from time to time, high or low tones would be presented without warning over a loudspeaker, and that all tones regardless of pitch were to be responded to by pressing the response button as quickly as possible. Each of the 30 tones that were presented lasted for approximately 3.0 sec, and the 1000-cycle and 250-cycle tones appeared in random order with the restriction that each occurred the same number of times during the session. In the second session a total of 36 stimuli were presented; the first 16 appeared like those in the previous session, while the last 20 tones were only 0.3 sec long. The short tone served the same purpose it had in the experiment reported in Section IV, A, namely, as a prearranged signal for S to produce responses that, from the standpoint of speed, were as close as possible to the physiological limit.

The third and fourth sessions required a disjunctive reaction, and *S*s were instructed to press the button only whenever the high (1000-cycle) tone occurred. In the third session, *S* had an opportunity to practice and the tones were again 3.0 sec long. The fourth session began with more practice and concluded with a test period that consisted of 26 stimuli. All of the latter were 0.3 sec long; one half were 1000-cycle tones and the other half were 250-cycle tones, presented in random order. As was the case in the second session, the short tone signaled *S* that the fastest possible responses were called for.

On-line EEGs were recorded and measured in the same manner as described in the study discussed in Section IV, A. Average values of simple RT, disjunctive RT, and alpha period for both conditions were determined for each of the 54 *S*s tested. These values are plotted in Fig. 8, where each open circle was derived from a mean number of eleven observations, and each solid circle from a mean number of sixteen observations from the same

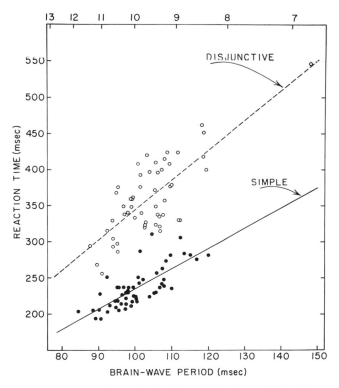

Fig. 8. RT as a function of period of alpha rhythm for a disjunctive response (open circles, broken line) and for a simple response (solid circles, solid line). Numbers at the top of the graph refer to the corresponding alpha frequencies in cycles per second. Reproduced with the permission of the publisher from Surwillo (1964a, Fig. 1).

group. Straight lines fitted to each of the distributions by the method of least squares yielded slopes of 4.18 and 2.80 for the disjunctive RT and the simple RT conditions, respectively. If the time required by S to make his decision (that is, to decide whether the 250-cycle or the 1000-cycle tone was sounded) were positively correlated with period of the alpha rhythm, then the slope of the line describing disjunctive RT should be significantly steeper than the slope of the line for simple RT. In the absence of a correlation, on the other hand, the lines should be parallel. A statistical test revealed that the slope of 4.18 was significantly steeper than the slope of 2.80 and, as a consequence, we had evidence that slower alpha rhythms were associated with increased decision time, and vice versa.

In order to determine the relation between age and the time consumed in making the decision, average values of simple RT were subtracted, in each case, from the corresponding averages of disjunctive RT. The Pearson product-moment correlation between age and these difference scores was 0.26, which, on the hypothesis that old people require more time than young people to make a decision, was statistically significant. To discover the role played by duration of the alpha cycle in this relationship, we again resorted to the method of partial correlation analysis. If differences in period of alpha rhythm were responsible for the increased time consumed by old persons in making a decision, then our r of 0.26 should vanish with period of the alpha rhythm held constant. Since this was precisely what happened when the analysis was carried out, the findings were in agreement with our hypothesis concerning the alpha rhythm as a timing mechanism in behavior.

D.   EEG Period and Complex Behavior

While it is not the purpose of this section to review all of the evidence concerning EEG period and complex behavior that might be relevant to our hypothesis, we would like to briefly mention a few studies to round out the picture. One major shortcoming of many studies of brain potentials in relation to complex behavior stems from the fact that the EEGs studied were usually clinical tracings, or recordings, made at some time before or after the behavior of interest to the investigator was observed. We have touched on this point earlier in the present chapter. It is true, of course, that the recording of on-line EEGs poses formidable methodological problems. On the other hand, the interpretation of an organism's behavior by reference to a sample of its EEGs recorded at some other time and under totally different conditions poses even greater problems. The opportunities here for research are numerous and the returns potentially exciting.

Denier van der Gon and van Hinte (1959) reported a study in which speed of handwriting was examined in relation to frequency of the alpha rhythm. Sixty-nine unselected psychiatric patients were tested and an average value of alpha frequency was obtained for each from clinical EEGs. Speed of writing was determined by having the Ss write the test word "momom" a number of times and taking an average of the rate after hesitations in writing were discounted. These authors reported the presence of a low positive correlation (the actual value of the coefficient was not cited) between speed of writing (words per second) and frequency of alpha rhythm in the group of 69 patients. When, however, patients with abnormal EEGs and patients who wrote the test word dysrhythmically, or with more than two interruptions per word, were excluded, a Pearson product-moment correlation of 0.84 was reported. The latter, which was based on the 28 patients who were left after the exclusions, is significant by the conventional statistical test.

The first study that we know of in which on-line EEGs were investigated during learning was reported by Obrist (1950). This investigator examined the EEGs from monopolar occipital tracings of fifteen college students while they learned a list of sixteen nonsense syllables by the serial anticipation method. The syllables were presented orally, at the rate of one syllable every 4 sec, until S reached the criterion of one perfect recitation of the list. Each trial was initiated by a 4-sec rest interval and a signal to anticipate the first nonsense syllable. Under these conditions, a correlation of 0.60 was obtained between alpha frequency of individual Ss and their rate of learning. Obrist pointed out that this finding suggested that frequency changes in the EEG might be meaningfully related to the learning process.

More recently, Thompson and Obrist (1964) recorded EEGs from parieto-occipital electrodes while seventeen college students learned twelve nonsense syllables by the serial anticipation method. EEGs were analyzed by means of a Burch Period Analyzer, which gave the number of waves per unit time for frequencies 8.5–12.5 cps, for frequencies greater than 12.5 cps, and for the first derivative of the tracing. Comparisons were made of these measures for the learning condition, a rest control condition, and for a control period during which an attempt was made to replicate the sensory and motor aspects of the experimental conditions without requiring any learning. In the latter, the letters ABC were played from prerecorded audio tape at 4-sec intervals and were repeated by S following each presentation. Significant changes were observed in the EEGs recorded during verbal learning as compared with the nonlearning control conditions. Activity in the frequency band 8.5–12.5 cps decreased during learning, whereas activity over 12.5 cps, and the derivative measure, or "superimposed activity," increased. These changes, moreover, proved to be maximal at a critical time in the learning process, namely, when S first began to anticipate the nonsense syllables correctly.

Although the findings considered in this section were not based on a large sample of Ss, they indicate clearly the potential importance of EEG frequency in the understanding of complex behavior. From the standpoint of our hypothesis concerning alpha rhythm and timing of behavior, they suggest that the alpha cycle may very well be implicated in timing of higher-order activity as well as in the simpler behavior that was examined earlier.

E.   EEG Period as a Possible Causal Factor in Behavioral Slowing

The evidence presented thus far in Section IV has been largely inferential. Although the findings reviewed indicate that frequency of the alpha rhythm and the temporal aspects of behavior are closely associated, they obviously permit no conclusions concerning cause-and-effect relationships. Indeed, the longer RT and the increased duration of the alpha cycle in old age may be due simply to the effect of some other factor that controls the variation in the EEGs as well as variation in RT. Thus, for example, Obrist (1964) and Obrist, Sokoloff, Lassen, Lane, Butler, and Feinberg (1963) have presented evidence that one of the important factors underlying the slowing of senescent EEGs is a reduction of cerebral oxygen uptake. The well-known findings of McFarland (1932, 1937) that anoxia produced by sudden ascents to high altitudes resulted in longer RTs certainly make it reasonable to speculate that cerebral anoxia may produce senescent slowing in RT by virtue of its effect on the electrical activity of the cortex.

In order to obtain some insight into this important question, Surwillo (1964b) attempted to modify frequency of the EEG by experimental procedures, while *simultaneously* measuring RT. In this study, frequency of the alpha rhythm was manipulated by means of repetitive photic stimulation known as photic "driving." It is well known that frequency changes can be induced in the EEG by flicker. We argued that, if the duration of the alpha cycle and RT were causally linked, then RT and period of the photic driving signal should be positively correlated whenever the waves, recorded from the cortex in the interval between stimulus and response, were synchronized with the flashes. As we discovered, however, this hypothesis was not easy to test.

Photic driving was attempted with a total of 48 Ss over a range of 6–15 flashes per second. Of those tested, all but five Ss failed to show evidence of synchronization with the flashing light or manifested synchronization over only a very narrow range of flash rates while taking part in the RT experiment. In the five Ss whose EEGs could be synchronized within an average range of 4 flashes per second, correlations between RT and period of the driving signal under conditions of EEG synchronization were all positive and ranged from 0.10 to 0.55. In a control group composed of Ss whose EEGs showed synchronization with the flashing light under resting conditions but not while taking part in the RT experiment, these correlations proved to be negative as well as positive, and showed no trend. It is hardly necessary to point out, of course, that these findings are limited as far as generalizations are concerned and at best are only suggestive of a causal relationship between duration of alpha cycle and simple RT. This experiment was, however, recently replicated and our findings confirmed at Duke University [Waszak (1965), personal communication], where correlations of 0.271 ($N = 48$) and 0.542 ($N = 67$) were obtained in two different Ss.

V.   Timing in the Central Nervous System and the Perception of Time

We can scarcely examine the topic of the present chapter without recalling the old adage that time goes by faster in old age, and inquiring whether the alpha rhythm plays a role in this phenomenon as well. Two lines of evidence, one from the realm of time perception and age and the other from time perception and the concept of an internal clock, suggested that this might be a fruitful line of inquiry. The idea that time passes more rapidly with advancing age appears to have originated in this century when William James (1901, p. 625) observed that the years seem to pass more rapidly as we grow older. Since then, similar confirmatory observations have been made from time to time. Thus, for example, Lecomte du Noüy (1937) considered the apparent acceleration of time in old age to be a "commonplace observation," and Nitardy (1943) proposed that the phenomenon was a "universal experience." Although there was a conspicuous lack of empirical evidence in support of this proposition, it provided an interesting hypothesis to test in the laboratory.

The concept of an internal clock, or some cyclic physiological process controlling the experience of time, has been a recurrent theme in theories of time perception since Hoagland (1933, 1935) postulated that judgment of time was mediated by the reaction rate of some chemical pacemaker in the central nervous system. Hoagland contended that *subjective* time becomes accelerated as physiological activity speeds up, and based this hypothesis on his own and the earlier discovery by Francois (1927) that hyperthermia was accompanied by the experience of time passing slowly. Recent findings have both confirmed and denied these observations. Kleber, Lhamon, and Goldstone (1963) reported a significant relationship between hyperthermia and judgments of time, whereas Bell & Provins (1963) failed to find any clear association between time estimation and changes in body temperature.

Gooddy (1958) considered the alpha rhythm of the EEG to be the ultimate clock in the organism's sense of time. Several facts argue for a relationship between time perception and duration of the alpha cycle. Hyperthermia, which, as mentioned earlier, has been associated with acceleration of subjective time, was shown by Hoagland (1936) and Jasper and Andrews (1938b) to be accompanied by an increase in frequency of the alpha rhythm. Lansing and Trunnell (1963) and Hermann and Quarton (1964) found significant correlations between alpha frequency and thyroid level, with higher frequencies associated with hyperthyroidism, while Kleber *et al.* (1963) reported that hyperthyroidism was accompanied by an acceleration in subjective time. Anliker's (1963) report that estimates of 3-sec intervals were longer when his *S*s were drowsy than when they were alert is interesting when it is recalled that the EEG typically shows a shift in the direction of lower-frequency activity with drowsiness (Cobb, 1963).

Since, as will be recalled from Fig. 4, average frequency of the alpha rhythm in persons over 80 years of age may fall to 8 cps, slowing down of this clock could have a profound effect on an elderly person's estimates of time. If, for example, an estimate of 1 min by a young adult with alpha frequency of 10 cps were based on the passage of 60×10, or 600, alpha waves, we should expect an estimate of 1 min by an elderly person with alpha frequency of 8 cps to encompass $600 \div 8$, or 75, sec. Because the internal clock, according to this proposition, is running slower in the old than in the young person, *subjective* time becomes slow by comparison with physical time in old age. As a consequence, physical time appears to pass by more rapidly to the old person. To check this proposition, an experiment was carried out in which we tested the hypothesis that time intervals estimated by persons with slow alpha rhythms would be longer than those produced by persons with alpha rhythms that were considered normal or fast with respect to frequency.

Two groups of 20 *S*s each were tested. One group was composed of adult males, each with an average frequency of alpha rhythm of less than 9 cps as recorded while the *S*s took part in a simple RT experiment. These *S*s were all 70 years of age and older. The second group also consisted of adult males, but in this case each had an average alpha frequency greater than 10 cps when recorded under the same conditions; *S*s in this group were 35 years of age and younger. EEGs were recorded from occipital areas of left and right hemispheres and the tracing from the dominant hemisphere was used to obtain measures of alpha frequency. All *S*s were volunteers living in the community who held, or had retired from, academic, scientific, technical, or administrative positions primarily in the government service.

Time estimates were made by the *S*s using the production method of temporal judgment. In this technique, *S* is asked to hold a telegraph key closed for the period of time that he judges is equal to the duration stated by the experimenter. In the experiment presently under examination, the interval estimated was 30 sec. The actual duration of the interval produced was measured to the closest 0.01 sec by a chronoscope that was activated when S closed the telegraph key. The findings in this experiment were surprising since they completely rejected the hypothesis under investigation. Time intervals estimated by Ss with slow alpha rhythms were not longer than the same intervals estimated by Ss with normal-to-fast alpha. Both groups judged the 30-sec interval very accurately, with the slow-alpha group yielding an average estimate of 29.07 sec and the fast-alpha group giving an estimate of 29.46 sec. It seemed clear that the substantial difference in alpha frequency between the groups had no influence on the Ss' estimates of time, at least not on their estimates of short intervals of time made under laboratory conditions.

The results of this investigation raised another issue, however, which completely overshadowed its original purpose. Since one of the groups tested was old and the other young, our findings seriously put to question the notion that time passes more rapidly as we grow older. To clarify this issue experimentally, Surwillo (1964c) tested the hypothesis that time is perceived to move at a faster rate with advancing age.

Three groups of 40 males each, all of whom were community volunteers principally from the professions, were tested. The groups had mean ages of 37.5, 56.1, and 73.7 years. Each S estimated intervals of 30, 60, and 180 sec by the production method of temporal judgment described earlier. Three estimates were obtained for each interval, and S's score was the mean of these values. No feedback concerning S's performance on the task was given during the course of the experiment.

Results of this experiment were unequivocal in showing that there was no systematic increase with age in the duration of the estimated time intervals. Indeed, none of the mean estimates for the groups differed significantly from the standard intervals of 30, 60, and 180 sec. As a consequence, the hypothesis that time is perceived to move at a faster rate with advancing age was rejected. On the other hand, in generalizing this conclusion to longer time intervals, we need to be cautious. Thus, although it seems more parsimonious to postulate that what is true of a short interval will also obtain in the case of a long interval, length of interval could be a crucial variable.

We would like to return to the results of the previous experiment for a moment. It should be recognized that, although our findings in that study showed no differences in time estimates between the two groups of Ss, they do not necessarily offer conclusive evidence against the possible role of alpha rhythm in time perception. The old Ss tested in this investigation were individuals who had retired from professional positions but were extremely active in some pursuit that required day-to-day budgeting of their time and effort. It could be argued that, because of the importance of time in the activities of these individuals, they had many opportunities over the years in which to compare and recalibrate their internal clock against a physical standard. The ready availability of timepieces in our culture and the great emphasis that is placed on punctuality would suggest that this possibility needs to be explored.

VI. The EEG and Timing of Involuntary Responses

Although human behavior readily becomes more complex and the behavioral scientist usually shows greater interest in its more complex forms, the investigation of simple behavior can frequently yield important clues to our understanding of general principles. It was with this in mind that we undertook the investigation of involuntary responses when the question was recently raised regarding the generality of our hypothesis concerning timing of behavior to other than voluntary responses. If our hypothesis holds for timing in general, then, to the extent that the cerebral cortex is implicated, it should hold for timing of involuntary responses as well as for voluntary responses. Attenuation (or "blocking," as it has been called) of the alpha rhythm of the EEG, and the galvanic skin response appeared to present interesting possibilities for study. In this section we shall be concerned with an investigation of the latency of alpha attenuation. Latency of galvanic skin responses is currently under investigation.

Attenuation of the alpha rhythm, or blocking, is probably the best-known phenomenon in EEG research. It occurs whenever S is stimulated, and it appears as a drop in amplitude of the on-going alpha rhythm some interval after the presentation of a stimulus. The phenomenon is produced by almost any kind of a stimulus and appears to be an involuntary response to adequate stimulation. Surwillo (1966) investigated the latency of this response in relation to duration of the alpha cycle in a group of 90 healthy community volunteers aged 17–91 years. The alpha rhythm was blocked by high-intensity pulses of white light, 1 sec in duration, that were flashed in front of S's face while he reclined in a darkened room with the eyes closed. EEGs were simultaneously recorded from a pair of transverse occipital (surface) electrodes that corresponded to O_1–O_2 in the "10–20" International System, and a marker signal from the photic stimulator was recorded on the chart along with the EEG tracing. During the test session, S was presented with twenty-five flashes that occurred more or less at random over a period of 8 min. Figure 9 gives an example of the tracings that were recorded from two different Ss.

Alpha attenuation was defined as a decrease in peak-to-peak amplitude of the tracing to a value $\leq 25\%$ of the amplitude recorded at the instant of the flash. The latent time of alpha attenuation was determined by measuring the linear distance between beginning of the flash marker signal and end of

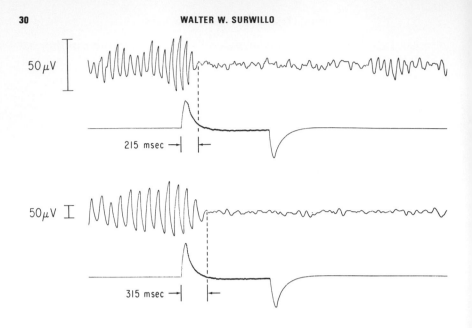

Fig. 9. The relation of latency of alpha attenuation (blocking) to alpha-rhythm period, data from two different Ss. In each case: upper tracing EEG recorded from transverse occipital electrodes $(O_1 - O_2)$; lower tracing, marker signal from photostimulator (upward deflection indicates flash "on," downward deflection flash "off"). Numbers directly under marker-signal tracings are attenuation latencies. Average duration of alpha cycle in interval between flash "on" and start of alpha attenuation: above, 80 msec; below, 122 msec. Reproduced with the permission of the publisher from Surwillo (1966, Fig. 1).

the first half-wave that occurred in the EEG tracing after the flash, which met the criterion for alpha attenuation. Average period of the alpha rhythm was determined for the waves recorded in each of these intervals, and an average value over the whole test was computed for each S along with averages of attenuation latency. Since the manner in which attenuation latency was measured produced a spurious positive correlation between latency of alpha attenuation and period of alpha rhythm, we resorted to a regression-type analysis instead of the correlation-type analysis that was used earlier in studying the relation between RT and alpha period. The regression line fitted to the data from our 90 Ss yielded the equation

$$AL = 3.36\,P - 30.78$$

where AL was attenuation latency and P was alpha period. Since the spurious relationship mentioned had the equation

$$AL = 0.5P.$$

the hypothesis that latent time of alpha attenuation and duration of alpha cycle were related was tested by comparing the slopes by t test. Since the slope of 3.36 was significantly steeper than the slope of 0.5, it was concluded that the variables were related and that period of the alpha rhythm plays a role in speed of the involuntary response.

The increased RTs characteristic of senescence are, as would have been expected, also paralleled by increased latency of attenuation of the alpha rhythm of the EEG. The Pearson product-moment correlation between latency of alpha attenuation and age in the sample of 90 Ss that was studied was 0.20, which, on the hypothesis that latency increases in senescence, was significant. This correlation closely matches the r of 0.19 between simple RT and age that was mentioned earlier (Section IV, A) and the r of 0.26 between decision time and age (see Section IV, C).

VII Conclusions and Implications

This chapter has dealt with the phenomenon of slowing that is characteristic of senescent behavior. We have been concerned chiefly with the longer response latencies of old age and have examined the various factors, both peripheral and central, that are associated with this slowing. Since peripheral factors were shown not to be adequate to account for the age differences in response speed, emphasis was placed on the role of the central nervous system. A theory was formulated in which period of the alpha rhythm of the EEG was hypothesized to be the master timing mechanism in behavior. It was shown in the context of the theory how slowing of this timing mechanism could account for (1) the slower reactions or longer response latencies that are characteristic of senescence, (2) the progressively greater time required by elderly individuals to handle increased amounts of stimulus information, and (3) the increased variability of response speed in old age.

Several aspects and implications of the proposed theory were tested in the laboratory. We found that age differences in latency of an involuntary response, as well as age differences in latency and variability of simple voluntary responses, could be accounted for by differences in duration of alpha cycle in individuals' EEGs. A study in which alpha frequency was modified experimentally suggested the possibility of a causal relationship between response latencies and duration of alpha cycle. The relation of perception of time to age and its possible association with period of the alpha rhythm was also examined. In this case, our findings not only revealed that the perception of time probably was not governed by the alpha cycle, but also that healthy elderly community volunteers did not observe time to pass by more rapidly than young individuals.

Although our theory concerning the slowing of behavior in old age was supported, in the main, by the empirical findings presented in this chapter, it is worth noting certain limitations inherent in the evidence that was reported. In the first place, all the studies that tested various aspects of the theory employed an experimental design in which reactions to stimuli were obtained only in the presence of well-developed EEG activity. Second, only samples with well-defined (usually alpha) waves in the interval between stimulus and response were included in the analyses. Whereas such selection seemed justified and in some instances became a necessary expedient, any procedure that involves arbitrary selection of data imposes restrictions of interpretation that cannot be ignored. We cannot say, for example, what if any relation obtains between response latency and period of the alpha rhythm when the EEG is desynchronized. It is clear, however, that although we cannot ignore these limitations, the theory brings some very much needed order into a body of otherwise unorganized facts and observations. As with other theories, its value rests on its ability to generate new hypotheses and to withstand the test of new research.

REFERENCES

Anliker, J. Variations in alpha voltage of the electroencephalogram and time perception. *Science*, 1963, **140**, 1307–1309.

Arenberg, D. Anticipation interval and age differences in verbal learning. *J. abnorm. Psychol.*, 1965, **70**, 419–425.

Bartley, S. H. The relation between cortical response to visual stimulation and changes in the alpha rhythm. *J. exp. Psychol.*, 1940, **27**, 624–639.

Bates, J. A. V. Electrical activity of the cortex accompanying movement. *J. Physiol.*, 1951, **113**, 240–257.

Bell, C. R., & Provins, K. A. Relation between physiological responses to environmental heat and time judgments. *J. exp. Psychol.*, 1963, **66**, 572–579.

Bellis, C. J. Reaction time and chronological age. *Proc. Soc. exp. Biol.*, 1933, **30**, 801–803.

Berger, H. Ueber das Elektrenkephalogramm des Menschen. Fünfte Mitteilung. *Arch. Psychiat. Nervenkr.*, 1933, **98**, 231–254.

Birren, J. E. Age differences in startle reaction time of the rat to noise and electric shock. *J. Geront.*, 1955, **10**, 429–432.

Birren, J. E. Sensation, perception and modification of behavior in relation to the process of aging. In J. E. Birren, H. A. Imus, & W. F. Windle (Eds.), *The process of aging in the nervous system.* Springfield, Ill.: Charles C. Thomas, 1959. Pp. 143-165.

Birren, J. E., & Botwinick, J. The relation of writing speed to age and to the senile psychoses. *J. consult. Psychol.*, 1951, **15**, 243–249.

Birren, J. E., & Botwinick, J. Age differences in finger, jaw, and foot reaction time to auditory stimuli. *J. Geront.*, 1955, **10**, 429-432. (a)

Birren, J, E., & Botwinick, J. Speed of response as a function of perceptual difficulty and age. *J. Geront.*, 1955, **10**, 433–436. (b)

Bishop, G. H. Cyclic changes in excitability of the optic pathway of the rabbit. *Amer. J. Physiol.*, 1933, **103**, 213–224.

Bishop, G. H. The interpretation of cortical potentials. *Cold Spr. Harb. Sympos. quant. Biol.*, 1936, **4**, 305–319.

Botwinick, J., & Thompson, L. W. Premotor and motor components of reaction time. *J. exp. Psychol.*, 1966, **71**, 9–15.

Brazier, Mary A. B., & Finesinger, J. E. Characteristics of the normal electroencephalogram. I. A study of the occipital cortical potentials in 500 normal adults. *J. clin. Invest.*, 1944, **23**, 303–311.

Busse, E. W., & Obrist, W. D. Significance of focal electroencephalographic changes in the elderly. *Postgrad. Med.*, 1963, **34**, 179–182.

Callaway, E., III. Factors influencing the relationship between alpha activity and visual reaction time. *Electroenceph. clin. Neurophysiol.*, 1962, **14**, 674–682.

Callaway, E., III, & Yeager, C. L. Relationship between reaction time and electroencephalographic alpha phase. *Science*, 1960, **132**, 1765–1766.

Canestrari, R. E., Jr. Paced and self-paced learning in young and elderly adults. *J. Geront.*, 1963, **18**, 165–168.

Chang, H. T. Changes in excitability of cerebral cortex following single electric shock applied to cortical surface. *J. Neurophysiol.*, 1951, **14**, 95–112.

Chang, H. T. Cortical response to stimulation of lateral geniculate body and the potentiation thereof by continuous illumination of retina. *J. Neurophysiol.*, 1952, **15**, 5–26.

Cobb, W. A. The normal adult E.E.G. In D. Hill & G. Parr (Eds.), *Electroencephalography*. New York: Macmillan, 1963. Pp. 232–249.

Davies, Ann D. M. Measures of mental deterioration in ageing and brain damage. Paper presented at Collo. Psychol. Functioning in Normal Ageing and Senile Aged, Semmering. Austria, June, 1966.

Davis, Pauline A. The electroencephalogram in old age. *Dis. nerv. Syst.*, 1941, **2**, 77.

Denier van der Gon, J. J., & van Hinte, N. The relation between the frequency of the alpha-rhythm and the speed of writing. *Electroenceph. clin. Neurophysiol.*, 1959, **11**, 669–674.

Eccles, J. C., & O'Connor, W. J. Responses which nerve impulses evoke in mammalian striated muscles. *J. Physiol.*, 1939, **97**, 44–102.

Eisdorfer, C., Axelrod, S., & Wilkie, Frances L. Stimulus exposure time as a factor in serial learning in an aged sample. *J. abnorm. soc. Psychol.*, 1963, **67**, 594–600.

Elliot, F. R., & Louttit, C. M. Auto braking reaction times to visual vs. auditory warning signals. *Proc. Ind. Acad. Sci.*, 1948, **47**, 220–225.

Forbes, G. The effect of certain variables on visual and auditory reaction times. *J. exp. Psychol.*, 1945, **35**, 153–162.

Francois, M. Contribution à l'étude du sens du temps: La température interne comme facteur de variation de l'appréciation subjective des durées. *Année psychol.*, 1927, **28**, 186–204.

Gavini, Helene. Les temps de réaction simple chez les hommes et les femmes de 55 à 85 ans. In *Le vieillissement de fonctions psychologiques et psychophysiologiques*. Paris: Centre National de la Recherche Scientifique, 1961. Pp. 97–105.

Goldfarb, W. An investigation of reaction time in older adults and its relationship to certain observed mental test patterns. *Teach. Coll. Contr. Educ.*, 1941, No. 831.

Gooddy, W. Time and the nervous system: The brain as a clock. *Lancet*, 1958, No. 7031, 1139–1144.

Hermann, H. T., & Quarton, G. C. Changes in alpha frequency with change in thyroid hormone level. *Electroenceph. clin. Neurophysiol.*, 1964, **16**, 515–518.

Hoagland, H. The physiological control of judgments of duration: Evidence for a chemical clock. *J. gen. Psychol.*, 1933, **9**, 267–287.

Hoagland, H. *Pacemakers in relation to aspects of behavior*. New York: Macmillan, 1935.

Hoagland, H. Some pacemaker aspects of rhythmic activity in the nervous system. *Cold Spr. Harb. Sympos. quant. Biol.*, 1936, **4**, 267–284.

James, W. *Principles of psychology. Vol. I*. London: Macmillan, 1901.

Jasper, H., & Andrews, H. L. Brain potentials and voluntary muscle activity in man. *J. Neurophysiol.*, 1938, **1**, 87–100. (a)

Jasper, H. H., & Andrews, H. L. Electro-encephalography: III. Normal differentiation of occipital and precentral regions in man. *Arch. Neurol. Psychiat., Chicago*, 1938, **39**, 96–116. (b)

Kibbler, G. O., Boreham, J. L., & Richter, D. Relation of the alpha rhythm of the brain to psychomotor phenomena. *Nature (London)*, 1949, **164**, 371.

Kleber, R. J., Lhamon, W. T., & Goldstone, S. Hyperthermia, hyperthyroidism, and time judgment. *J. comp. physiol. Psychol.*, 1963, **56**, 362–365.

Kumnick, Lillian S. Aging and the latency and duration of pupil constriction in response to light and sound stimuli. *J. Geront.*, 1956, **11**, 391–396.

Lansing, R. W. Relation of brain and tremor rhythms to visual reaction time. *Electroenceph. clin. Neurophysiol.*, 1957, **9**, 497–504.

Lansing, R. W., & Trunnell, J. B. Electroencephalographic changes accompanying thyroid deficiency in man. *J. clin. Endocr.*, 1963, **23**, 470–480.

Lecomte du Noüy, P. *Biological time*. New York: Macmillan, 1937.

Lindsley, D. B. Psychological phenomena and the electroencephalogram. *Electroenceph. clin. Neurophysiol.*, 1952, **4**, 443–456.

McFarland, R. A. The psychological effects of oxygen deprivation (anoxemia) on human behavior. *Arch. Psychol.*, 1932, **22**, No. 145, 1–135.

McFarland, R. A. Psycho-physiological studies at high altitude in the Andes. IV. Sensory and circulatory responses of the Andean residents at 17,500 feet, *J. comp. Psychol.*, 1937, **23**, 191–258.

Miles, W. R. Correlation of reaction and coordination speed with age in adults. *Amer. J. Psychol.*, 1931, **43**, 377–391.

Mundy-Castle, A. C., Hurst, L. A., Beerstecher, D. M., & Prinsloo, T. The electroencephalogram in the senile psychoses. *Electroenceph. clin. Neurophysiol.*, 1954, **6**, 245–252.

Nitardy, F. W. Apparent time acceleration with age of the individual. *Science*, 1943, **98**, 110.

Norris, A. H., Shock, N. W., & Wagman, I. H. Age changes in the maximum conduction velocity of motor fibers of human ulnar nerves. *J. appl. Physiol.*, 1953, **5**, 589–593.

Obrist, W. D. Skin resistance and electroencephalographic changes associated with learning. *Summaries of doctoral Dissertations*, Northwestern Univer., 1950, **18**, 607–610.

Obrist, W. D. Simple auditory reaction time in aged adults. *J. Psychol.*, 1953, **35**, 259–266.

Obrist, W. D. The electroencephalogram of normal aged adults. *Electroenceph. clin. Neurophysiol.*, 1954, **6**, 235–244.

Obrist, W. D. Cerebral ischemia and the senescent electroencephalogram. In E. Simonson & T. H. McGavack (Eds.), *Cerebral ischemia*. Springfield, Ill.: Charles C. Thomas, 1964. Pp. 71–98.

Obrist, W. D. Electroencephalographic approach to age changes in response speed. In A. T. Welford & J. E. Birren (Eds.), *Behavior, aging and the nervous system*. Springfield, Ill.: Charles C. Thomas, 1965. Chapter 13.

Obrist, W. D., Henry, C. E., & Justiss, W. A. Longitudinal study of EEG in old age. *Excerpta med. Int. Congr.*, 1961, Ser. No. **37**, 180–181.

Obrist, W. D., Sokoloff, L., Lassen, N. A., Lane, M. H., Butler, R. N., & Feinberg, I. Relation of EEG to cerebral blood flow and metabolism in old age. *Electroenceph. clin. Neurophysiol.*, 1963, **15**, 610–619.

Pierson, W. R., & Montoye, H. J. Movement time, reaction time, and age. *J. Geront.*, 1958, **13**, 418–421.

Roth, B. The clinical and theoretical importance of EEG rhythms corresponding to states of lowered vigilance. *Electroenceph. clin. Neurophysiol.*, 1961, **13**, 395–399.

Singleton, W. T. Age and performance timing on simple skills. In Int. Assoc. Geront, 3rd Congr., London, 1954, *Old age in the modern world.* Edinburgh: E. & S. Livingstone, 1955. Pp. 221–231.

Sommer, J. Synchronisierung motorischer Impulse und ihre Bedeutung für die neurophysiologische Forschung. *Z. ges. Neur.*, 1941, **172**, 500–530.

Suci, G. J., Davidoff, M. D., & Surwillo, W. W. Reaction time as a function of stimulus information and age. *J. exp. Psychol.*, 1960, **60**, 242–244.

Surwillo, W. W. Central nervous system factors in simple reaction time. *Amer. Psychologist*, 1960, **15**, 419.

Surwillo, W. W. Frequency of the "alpha" rhythm, reaction time and age. *Nature (London)*, 1961, **191**, 823–824.

Surwillo, W. W. The relation of simple response time to brain-wave frequency and the effects of age. *Electroenceph. clin. Neurophysiol.*, 1963, **15**, 105–114. (a)

Surwillo, W. W. The relation of response-time variability to age and the influence of brain wave frequency. *Electroenceph. clin. Neurophysiol.*, 1963, **15**, 1029–1032. (b)

Surwillo, W. W. The relation of decision time to brain wave frequency and to age. *Electroenceph. clin. Neurophysiol.*, 1964, **16**, 510–514. (a)

Surwillo, W. W. Some observations on the relation of response speed to frequency of photic stimulation under conditions of EEG synchronization. *Electroenceph. clin. Neurophysiol.*, 1964, **17**, 194–198. (b)

Surwillo, W. W. Age and the perception of short intervals of time. *J. Geront.*, 1964, **19**, 322–324. (c)

Surwillo, W. W. On the relation of latency of alpha attenuation to alpha rhythm frequency and the influence of age. *Electroenceph. clin. Neurophysiol.*, 1966, **20**, 129–132.

Talland, G. A. The effect of age on speed of simple manual skill. *J. genet. Psychol.*, 1962, **100**, 69–76.

Talland, G. A. Initiation of response, and reaction time in aging and with brain damage. In J. E. Birren & A. T. Welford (Eds.), *Behavior, aging, and the nervous system: Biological determinants of speed of behavior and its changes with age.* Springfield, Ill.: Charles C. Thomas, 1965. Pp. 526–561.

Thompson, L. W., & Obrist, W. D. EEG correlates of verbal learning and overlearning. *Electroenceph. clin. Neurophysiol.*, 1964, **16**, 332–342.

Wagman, I. H., & Lesse, H. Maximum conduction velocities of motor fibers of ulnar nerve in human subjects of various ages and sizes. *J. Neurophysiol.*, 1952, **15**, 235–244.

Walter, W. G. The twenty-fourth Maudsley lecture: The functions of the electrical rhythms in the brain. *J. ment. Sci.*, 1950, **96**, 1–31.

Walter, W. G. *The living brain.* London: Duckworth, 1953.

Wayner, M. J., Jr., & Emmers, R. Spinal synaptic delay in young and aged rats. *Amer. J. Physiol.*, 1958, **194**, 403–405.

Weiss, A. D. The relation of A-wave latency of the electroretinogram to human aging. *J. Geront.*, 1956, **11**, 448–449. (a)

Weiss, A. D. The motor component of auditory reaction time as related to age. *Amer. Psychologist*, 1956, **11**, 374. (b)

Weiss, A. D. The locus of reaction time change with set, motivation, and age. *J. Geront.*, 1965, **20**, 60–64.

Welford, A. T. *Skill and age.* London: Oxford Univer. Press, 1951.

Welford, A. T. Psychomotor performance. In J. E. Birren (Ed.), *Handbook of aging and the individual.* Chicago, Ill.: Univer. of Chicago Press, 1959, Pp. 562–613.

Wiener, N. Time and the science of organization. (First part.) *Scientia (Milano)*, 1958, **93**, 199–205.

Psychophysiological Studies of Aging in Pilots*

JACEK SZAFRAN†

Department of Experimental Psychology,

Lovelace Foundation for Medical Education and Research

Albuquerque, New Mexico

I. Introduction

It has not been very easy to find a convenient arrangement for the different parts of this paper. To avoid possible misunderstanding later, let it be stated at the outset that the author had set three aims before himself in constructing the presentation: First, to introduce a relatively novel kind of data, some of them not previously published, to those who are interested in aging, whether as gerontologists or merely as curious persons; second, to defend a particular concept that has emerged from his attempts to come to terms with the experimental results, even though he recognizes that their quality is limited by various deficiencies and uncertainties; and third, to prepare the way for a reappraisal of some of the classical material on aging.

* Based in part on postgraduate seminars presented at the Rossmoor-Cortese Institute for the Study of Retirement and aging, University of Southern California, March, 1966, and at the School of Public Health, University of California at Los Angeles September 1966.

† *Present address*: Department of Psychology and Institute for the Study of Retirement and Aging, University of Southern California, Los Angeles, California.

II. The Problem

Before describing the research objectives and methods, a word should be
said about the subjects whose "aging profile" will be discussed herein. They
are all professional (i.e., airline, military, and test) pilots, ranging in age
from the late twenties to the early sixties and participating in a psychophysiological study of the possible effects of aging sponsored by the United States
Public Health Service at the Lovelace Foundation. The measurement and
analysis of progressive age changes in this particular professional group has
been undertaken for two reasons: (1) because of the special advantages that
this group may offer for the important differentiation between the effects of
aging per se and those of cumulative pathology; there are relatively few aging
studies in which the occupational and health status of the subjects has been
clearly defined; (2) because early detection of deteriorative trends in flying
personnel in command of high-performance aircraft has become a major
cause for concern among the aviation medical consultants. Clearly in an
exercise of this kind the investigators are obliged to steer a course midway
between the purely academic and purely applied considerations. On an a
priori basis it is conceivable that although aging may have a direct effect on
flying performance, the latter is not very sensitive to it, so that, fortunately,
the overall changes with time in the relevant functions and skills can remain,
within some well-defined limits, of little consequence. Indeed, in some areas,
a critical perusal of the literature bears out the impression that "skill prog-
nosis for age becomes steadily more and not less favorable as we come to
understand better the nature of the changes that take place" (Bartlett, 1951,
p. 216) in normally healthy individuals.

   At present the program of research is about halfway toward achieving its
aim of initial examination of 500 subjects. Some impression of the sample of
volunteers recruited to date may be obtained by comparing its age distribution with that of the "parent population" of airline pilots (Schreuder,
1966). It will be seen from Fig. 1 that, despite an unnecessarily large number
of subjects in the younger decades—due in part to the inclusion of military
and test pilots—and bearing in mind the requirements of random sampling,
the older sector of the available range is reasonably well represented.

   At the risk of doing some injustice to a few of its finer points, the object
of the investigation as a whole can be said to be to consider, from the standpoint of the disciplines of cardiovascular and pulmonary physiology as well
as experimental psychology, the following proposition: Given the chronological age of a highly trained individual who is engaged in a profession
demanding high standards of bodily and mental fitness, would it be feasible
to estimate his "physiological age"—whatever this may mean on rigorous
definition—and to proceed to elucidate in some detail his position regarding
the traditionally expected "inevitability" of reduced or impaired capacities

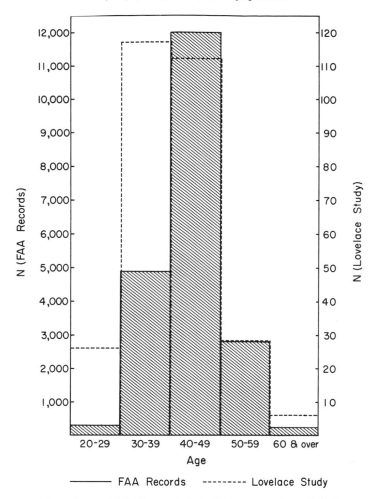

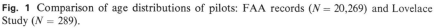

——— FAA Records --------- Lovelace Study

Fig. 1 Comparison of age distributions of pilots: FAA records ($N = 20{,}269$) and Lovelace Study ($N = 289$).

in later adult life? Clearly, if legitimate, this is a question at once of theoretical and practical import, for unfavorable predictions of every kind hold the center of the stage in gerontological research at almost every level. Needless to say, it was recognized from the very beginning of the effort that, as ever, there were bound to be many problems of technique and interpretation in assessing, in the necessarily "reduced" or frankly artificial situations afforded by the laboratory, the subtle variations occurring through adulthood with advancing years. Are these assessments likely to be accepted as valid when the significance of the conclusions to which they might lead is considered? The position taken on this difficult point was the usual one—that it should not deter us from trying. And although it was hoped that when the initial cross-sectional comparison could eventually be supplemented by the necessary longitudinal data, the work might conceivably help to provide a rational basis for adopting a retirement policy for flying personnel, no illusions were entertained about the likelihood of the fundamental question remaining unanswered.

Among the many possible investigations that might have been undertaken from the standpoint of psychology, the program of laboratory experimentation sketched in the following sections acknowledges the well-known findings on age changes in the resolving power of sensory detectors, the efficiency of access to information near the time of its input, and the speed of response (A. T. Welford, 1958; Birren, 1964). But it also draws on the important guidelines established by the theory of skill as existing in point of time—the human operator must be able to relate his actions at any given moment to what has just happened before and what is about to happen afterward (Bartlett, 1947). Yet he is limited for speed as well as for the number of simultaneous discriminations. It accords with this view that the effects of aging on high-grade skills should be sought principally in those aspects of sequential performance that call for the exercise of judgment and decision. Although the cerebral mechanism of these processes is not yet understood, it must probably be envisaged as having sufficient "plasticity" to permit some degree of variation in the details of executive responses for optimum efficiency.

The problems of human skill, once it is recognized that there is a set of problems concerning the constellation of abilities which is so laboriously acquired through practice and experience, can be approached systematically within the conceptual framework of information theory. The underlying assumption here is, of course, that the central nervous system resembles other communication systems in that intelligence is being processed through it. Admittedly, the question of what exactly is meant by the term information processing when applied to the central nervous system is somewhat controversial. Nevertheless, although the details of the wiring diagram of the information flow are not fully known at present, it is quite clear that the brain is well designed for complex coding operations (Craik, 1947; Hick, 1951; Crossman, 1964; Young, 1964).

It is not always realized that because of the technological ingenuity of engineers, the human operator of modern control systems, particularly in aviation, has become progressively less concerned with continuous manual monitoring, and correspondingly more concerned with the interpretation of a large variety of signals for action that may originate from different sources simultaneously or in rapid succession. Insofar as control in this sense must involve transfer of information, the emphasis is on sustained readiness for quite complex judgments and decisions, many of which have to be made within very restricted time limits if they are not to become antiquated in relation to a rapidly changing display. Since in all judging and deciding the individual is inevitably faced with uncertainty about what to expect, as well as about what action to prefer, certain average properties of perceptual choices, such as the increase in response latency with increase in input entropy, become relevant in this context because they must, in some sense, reflect the rate at which the brain can gain information in its attempt to structure the sensory inflow (Hick, 1952). In the theory of the human operator of control systems the concept of "channel capacity" is held to be fundamental, since the efficiency of coding and decoding operations performed by the brain or its outposts must be assumed to depend very intimately on the entropy of messages in time being less than the overall capacity of the system. This formulation has in turn suggested the desirability, in principle, of evaluating reserve channel capacity in the face of "information overload" and reduced signal-to-noise ratio (Szafran, 1963, 1964, 1965c).

III. Techniques

Presenting in a single chapter an investigation that, with its three disciplines, stretches over many different measurements, requires considerable selection and omission. For the present purpose it will be quite sufficient to note that between 7:00 A. M. and noon, ultralow-frequency ballistocardiogram stroke volume (Klensch, 1961) and other indices of cardiovascular status, recorded before and after exercise, as well as oxygen uptake and heart rate at maximum effort (Luft, Cardus, Lin, Anderson, & Howarth, 1963; Luft, 1967), are investigated, followed by psychological appraisal from 1:00 P. M. to 5:30 P. M.

The design of the psychological experiments is intended to reflect the particular feature essential for flying, namely, making high-speed decisions and detecting low-probability and low-intensity signals, as well as the ability to receive and retain significant amounts of information in the course of routine control procedures. Prima facie this would appear to be a reasonable enough abstraction from the real-life situation, although doubtless there are others equally feasible. It is impossible to be certain about any of them, however, since the principal difficulty in specifying sufficient conditions for the performance of a high-grade skill is that the operator usually does not know how he does what he does (Bartlett, 1947).

Information theory assesses the amount of information in events in terms of the uncertainty that they resolve when they do actually happen; this "selective potential" of events and messages constitutes their information content (Cherry, 1957; Kay and Szafran, 1963). Different events are, of course, likely to contain different amounts of information, but what is of interest is the average amount of information that can be expected from a given source. In other words, signals that might have occurred within the context of a particular skill, but did not, are also to be taken into account when estimating rates of performance and internal consistency. At first sight, it may appear unreasonable that an appraisal of this kind should depend on the probability of each class rather than on its physical characteristics or its "meaning." The statistical advantages are considerable, however, for it thus becomes possible to treat the number of alternatives eliminated (in binary units per unit of time, or bits per second) as a measure of the rate of gain of information. Experimentally, if the signals are arranged in a random sequence, the average response latency should be found, to a good approximation, proportional to the logarithm of the number of equivalent choices or, in other words, to the minimum quantity of information that must be extracted from the input to identify it (Hick, 1951). To the extent that a decision preceding any action is the choice of one from a set of alternatives, this suggests that information is gained at a constant rate in serial operations (Hick, 1952).

Consequently, one type of experiment in the Lovelace Study is concerned with the timing characteristics of high-speed sequential decisions. It takes the form of recording in some detail—in milliseconds, together with error rates, employing the SETAR (N. T. Welford, 1953)—latencies of responses in multichoice tasks of known information content and observing their altered characteristics under various conditions of increased task load. The technique consists of introducing subsidiary tasks (Poulton, 1958; Schouten, Kalsbeek, & Leopold, 1962) and measuring their effects on the performance of the concurrent main task. The statistical comparison of average rates of gain of information—calculated from the ratio of information content of signals to response latencies, in bits per second—with and without overload, is tentatively regarded as yielding an estimate of reserve channel capacity. Except for certain unimportant details of instrumentation, the primary task is a conventional one in which the subject is presented with a random sequence of neon-light signals generated by an automatic programmer, and is required to identify them one by one and then to operate an appropriate control, of the microswitch type, with maximum speed and minimum error. The intersignal intervals vary randomly over the range of 0.50–5.00 sec (or 0.75–3.25 sec, in cases of delays in the testing schedule), in steps of 0.50 sec (or 0.25 sec), in runs of some 300 (or 150) in length, each signal having an equal probability of occurrence in ensembles of three, five, and eight alternatives, so that at any moment the subject is uncertain which signal is likely to occur and when. With some subjects, particularly test pilots and senior airline pilots, data are also obtained for a twelve-choice task. In addition, whenever extra time can be found, supplementary information on central refractoriness is also sought. The experimental procedure in this case consists of recording response latencies to sequences of random signals, about 200 in length, arranged in sets of two, four, six, and eight equivalent choices, the intersignal intervals (S_1–S_2) being 100, 200, 250, 300, 750, 1250, and 2250 msec. After excluding the few unavoidable errors in recording resulting from an occasional overlap between successive events exceeding the capacity of the buffer storage of the SETAR, some 20–25 response times to the second signal (R_2) at each interval for every subject are available for estimating the rate of gain of information.

The overload tasks are designed to tax the subject's short-term memory and his ability to tolerate an interference with the aural monitoring of speech. Specifically, one such task (referred to later in tables and figures as subtask M) requires the subject to watch a succession of symbols, letters, and numbers projected onto the center of the primary task display (each presentation lasting some 4 sec) and to recall the material presented two stages earlier (Kay, 1953). The task has been included because of the importance that is attached to sequential recall in the psychological literature on skill and aging (A. T. Welford, 1958). The other type of subsidiary task (referred to as subtask DF) requires the subject, in addition to executing the responses in the primary task, to describe the successive characteristics of display and control, using a few simple code words; something approaching a stress situation is imposed by arranging for a delay of 0.18 sec in the auditory feedback from the subject's speech production (Lee, 1950; Zangwill, 1960). This task has been introduced because it is felt that in present-day flying the voice link with the ground control stations constitutes an important part of the pilot's job and from certain points of view could be suspected of being at least potentially capable of interfering with the main task of keeping the aircraft under control. Obviously this general comment does not exhaust other possibilities for the selection of secondary tasks. It is, however, assumed that neither type of task used here has been ill-chosen for the purpose of gauging the extent to which an increase in information load may swamp the man whose skill should on general grounds be susceptible to the effects of aging.

In the sensory-perception studies the following procedures are employed on a routine basis:

1. measurement of visual accommodation, using the Costenbaden Accomodometer;

2. determination of the critical flicker fusion frequency (CFF) and the minimum perceptible interflash interval (IFI); in both cases the Grass PS 2 Photo-Stimulator is used, with a circular test area subtending an angle of 0.2 deg and the luminance reaching the level of 20 mL; flash duration is fixed at 10 μsec and independent of frequency;

3. recording of the course of dark adaptation, employing the Goldmann-

Weekers Adaptometer and their recommended test standards, i.e., light preadaptation at 2500 lx, brightness of test field at 6 lx, and a striped test figure with 100% contrast.

In addition, tachistoscopic recognition thresholds, using a three-channel electronically controlled instrument, and fluctuations of auditory thresholds, employing Bekesy's (1947) method and the Grason-Stadler Type E 800-4 Audiometer, are investigated in some detail, particularly with regard to the question of "threshold resistance" in the presence of deliberately introduced noise or under conditions of divided attention.

More specifically, in the case of Bekesy audiometry, the subject sits in a double-walled soundproof room, listens through TDH-39 earphones, and is required to "track" his threshold over the range of frequencies 250–8000 cps at an attenuation rate of 2.5 dB/sec. Initially, threshold fluctuations of a pulsed tone, with an interruption rate of 2.5 per second and a rise-decay time of 25 msec, are recorded for each ear; an additional tracing, employing a continuous tone, is obtained for the "worse" ear, i.e., the one showing more hearing loss. Following this conventional procedure, noise audiometry is investigated in the following manner: for the "better" ear (the one showing less hearing loss), the subject is required to retrace his pulsed-tone thresholds when 50-dB and 80-dB sound pressure level (SPL) re. 0.0002-microbar wide-spectrum white noise is presented to the contralateral ear; for the worse ear only the 80-dB SPL level of white noise is employed and the tone is a continuous one. In addition, for the worse ear, fixed-frequency pulsed-tone tracings are obtained for that part of the range which shows the most pronounced hearing loss. Whenever possible, pairs of audiometric tracings, each run lasting approximately 7 min, are interspaced with other tests so as to minimize the effects of practice and transfer. Following Bekesy's (1947) original recommendation, threshold values are interpolated between peaks and troughs in the tracings, i.e., the "just not heard" and the "just heard" tones, respectively.

In the case of the tachistoscopic perception studies, recognition thresholds are obtained at exposures of 0.2 msec, with field luminances being held constant at approximately 10 mL and the display—consisting of shapes, numbers, letters, and words—subtending a visual angle of about 2 deg (condition S). On some occasions, "visual noise" patterns of the type described by Julesz (1961) are exposed, for the same duration as the signal card and immediately following it, in an attempt to "erase" some of the information contained in the afterimage (condition VN). In other runs the subject is required to monitor a subsidiary auditory task of the vigilance type: he listens to two tones of different frequencies, one of which is occasionally interrupted, and has to acknowledge the occurrence of this event by operating an appropriate hand switch (condition DA). In all three conditions input information varies between groups of 10 cards from 2.8

bits/symbol to 76.5 bits/symbol, the subject being told in advance about the relevant characteristics of each symbol group. To simplify computer analysis, information transmitted is assessed at only four points of input entropy (low, 3.2 and 5.0 bits/symbol; intermediate, 17.7 bits/symbol; and high, 45.9 bits/symbol) by considering the ratio of the number of symbols correctly recognized to the maximum number of possible identifications, in bits per symbol.

The data from the different experiments are punched on IBM cards and all further quantitative analyses are carried out with the aid of a computer.

IV. Findings

The discussion of findings is intended to highlight the most characteristic and striking trends so far observed and to emphasize the essentially pre-liminary nature of the interpretations that can be offered at this stage of the work. It should be noted that the number of subjects referred to in the discussion of the different experiments is unequal because not all of the necessary equipment was available at the time the main study was initiated.

A.   Visual Accommodation

Figure 2 makes it quite clear that the prediction of a reduced ability of the older eye to focus sharp images on the retina at short viewing distances has been fully sustained in the present study. In line with the classical results

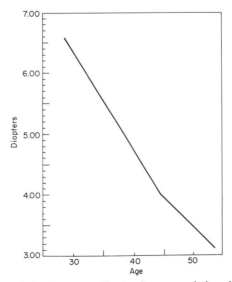

Fig. 2. Visual accommodation (mean amplitude of accommodation plotted against age).

of Duane (1922), the correlation coefficient between age and amplitude of accommodation is found to be $r = -.71, p < .001$. It should be mentioned that for about one third of our subjects ($N = 159$) an independent clinical assessment is available in which a different measuring instrument (Prince's Rule) was employed. In spite of certain minor discrepancies, the two sets of data are essentially similar ($r = .80, p < .001$). In agreement with the results of Bruckner (1959), the mean values for the younger half of the sample are around 6 diopters and for the older half about 4 diopters.

Theories of presbyopia usually emphasize the diminished elasticity of the crystalline lens and anatomical changes in the ciliary muscle, but there are suggestions that genetic, dietetic, and climatic factors may also be implicated (Rambo and Sangal, 1960). Even so, it seems exceedingly doubtful— particularly perhaps in the light of other data reported later— whether anything further could be extrapolated from these variations to provide an "index of aging" in the visual pathway (Weale, 1963).

B. Critical Flicker Fusion Frequency and Minimum Perceptible Interflash Interval

It will be seen from Fig. 3 that although temporal discrimination is necessarily limited by intensity discrimination, the data on CFF ($N = 189$) and IFI ($N = 161$) (intercorrelated at the level of $r = -.40, p < .001$) fail to

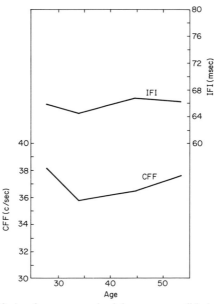

Fig. 3. Critical flicker fusion frequency and minimum perceptible interflash interval (mean thresholds plotted against age).

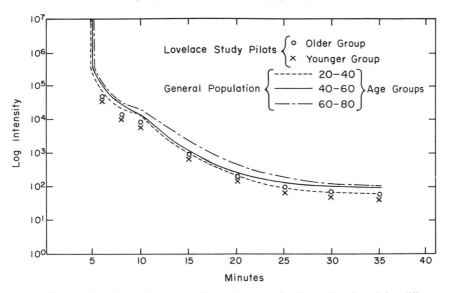

Fig. 4. Dark adaptation (Goldmann-Weekers) (mean log intensity plotted for different age groups against time in the dark).

confirm the expected change of threshold with age. The values of correlation coefficients are very small indeed: $r = .04$ for the CFF and $r = .13$ for the IFI; not significant. It should be added that for about one fourth of our subjects these estimates of the temporal resolution of the visual system are also available employing a version of the classical psychophysical method, after the manner of the technique of Bekesy (1947) for the continuous recording of auditory threshold fluctuations. Although the variance tends to increase somewhat in this case, the correlation between average values obtained by the conventional and the tracking methods is of the order of $r = .80$ ($p < .001$) for the CFF and $r = .60$ ($p < .001$) for the IFI.

Unfortunately, because of technical limitations, it was not possible to vary systematically the levels of light-time in the flicker cycle, as recommended by McFarland, Warren, & Karis (1958). To this extent the present evidence can perhaps be regarded as not fully conclusive, though it may be noted that the negative finding is not an isolated one (e.g., Landis and Hamwi, 1956).

C. Dark Adaptation

As shown in Fig. 4, the determination of threshold energies in the course of dark adaptation ($N = 197$) confirms the expected correlation with age at both alpha and terminal points ($r = .25, p < .001$, and $r = .16, p < .05$, respectively). However, since the data also reveal lower average values for the pilots than those quoted for the general population employing the same adaptometer (Fankhauser and Schmidt, 1957), it seems permissible to infer that as an occupational group pilots are better observers and consequently are able to extract information more efficiently even at very low levels of signal-to-noise ratio (Szafran, 1965b, 1966c).

It is instructive to reflect, in this connection, that although the classical theory of vision relates sensitivity of the eye to concentration of rhodopsin—leading to explanations of age changes in dark adaptation in terms of retinal metabolism (McFarland and Fisher, 1955)—newer theories postulate constant efficiency of the retina and a variable gain mechanism acting as an amplifier between retinal receptors and optic nerve fibers (Barlow, 1956; Rushton, 1957). In the case of dark adaptation it may be supposed that time is required to "reset" the gain mechanism to its maximum value, the gradual improvement in seeing following the increase in amplification (Rose, 1948). On this view of visual discrimination it is tempting, but perhaps rash, to expect that the more experienced an observer—e.g., a professional pilot—the less amplification would be needed to present the information to the brain.

On general grounds, as well as within the framework of any particular theory of aging, it should be borne in mind that measurements of the resolving power of the sensory systems must inevitably reflect not only the properties of the peripheral detectors but also the intelligent use of perceptual skills (Weale, 1963). The relevance of this point to the problems at issue in the present study will become apparent later.

D.   Tachistoscopic Recognition Thresholds

In the tachistoscopic experiments $(N = 90)$ it is found that the channel capacity curves are remarkably near perfect transmission of information up to about 20 bits. They drop by some 20%–25% in the presence of "visual noise," and there is a similar change of the order of up to 20% under conditions of division of attention. This trend is in line with other findings which suggest that diverting attention away from a high-information signal is likely to produce an effect resembling a reduction in its intensity (Broadbent and Gregory, 1963). The relevant data are summarized in Fig. 5, from which it will be seen that there is some lowering of performance with increasing age at the higher levels of information input, reflecting the well-established fact that the aging eye, because of miosis and lenticular yellowing, requires more light (Weale, 1963). The individual differences in this respect are, however, larger than group differences over the age range 28–61 and none of the correlation coefficients attain the level of statistical significance ($r = -.15$ in the control condition; $r = -.05$ in the visual noise condition and $r = -.07$ in the divided attention condition). Paradoxically,

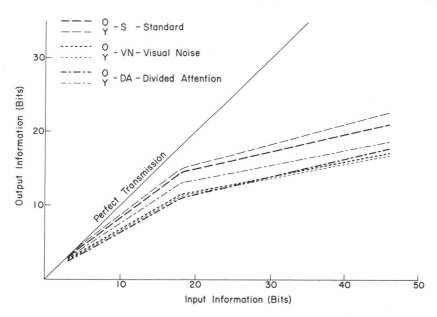

Fig. 5. Channel capacity curves for recognition of shapes, numbers, letters, and words at 0.2-msec exposure (output information plotted against input information, in bits, for younger and older subjects).

a comparison of information-transfer functions in the presence of visual noise suggests that it is the younger pilots, i.e., those under 40 years of age, who may be more embarrassed by this reduction of the signal-to-noise ratio. They show a relative loss of the order of up to 25% as compared with that of up to only 20% for the over-40 group. In other words, the older pilots appear to adopt a more "canny" or otherwise more efficient strategy for signal detection, one that outweighs at least some of the limitations imposed by the peripheral end of the visual pathway. Their capacity to deal with the equivocal odds under conditions of divided attention is lower than that of the younger group essentially for the same reason, but very likely also because this involves short-term retention and recall (up to 20% relative loss, as compared with about 15% for the younger pilots; on the other hand, the proportion of signals missed in the subsidiary auditory task, of the order of 10% on the average, is not directly related to age: $r = .14$, not significant). In spite of these disadvantages, however, the differential values for information transfer under the visual noise and divided-attention conditions, as compared with the control, do not reveal any substantial decline with age ($r = -.13$, not significant).

A relationship can probably be traced between these data and the statistical theory of sensory thresholds which assumes that the human observer of faint or very brief signals can vary in confidence about his judgments and that shifts in the criterion which he must use in arriving at a decision may be promoted by training and further enhanced by experience (Tanner and Swets, 1954). As compared with classical psychophysics, the novelty of this theory consists in regarding the brain as a rather "noisy" communication channel, in which decisions about sensory input must be based on information in some way distorted by random neural activity within the central nervous system itself. Hence, the decision mechanism has to test hypotheses, so to speak, to distinguish between the states of "noise alone" and "noise plus signal." It is assumed that the ease or difficulty of deciding between the hypotheses depends on the likelihood ratio of the two probability functions involved, the problem for the brain being to find the smallest acceptable ratio for signal identification.

In physical communication systems the lower level of signal power possible to maintain a given rate of transmission of information is set by the level of noise in the channel. It is instructive to reflect that the human observer shows a comparable falling off and lower limit as the physical power of signals impinging on his sense organs is reduced, and that his ability to resolve small differences of signal power also appears to be limited in a similar manner. This is a good enough excuse to regard sensory systems as being subject to the same kind of limitations as any man-made instrument (Craik, 1940; Rose, 1948; Gregory, 1956). If valid, the analogy suggests that the existence of sensory thresholds might be due to the presence of neural noise, or that, at least, such thresholds might be more efficiently described in this way (Barlow, 1956).

In an elegant and carefully controlled experiment, Gregory (1956, 1957) has attempted to treat the visual threshold as a problem of discriminating an information source from a noisy background, and has shown that there are age differences in the value of k of the rewritten Weber's law: $\Delta I/(I + k) = C$, a constant that can be attributed to neural noise. He argues that the level of neural noise of the visual system increases with age. Similarly, in a study of information intake and discrimination in relation to age, Crossman and Szafran (1956) have felt obliged to conclude from their data showing "easily discriminable" signals to be relatively more affected than "difficult" ones— each category defined quantitatively in terms of a "confusion function" (Crossman, 1955)—that changes in performance with age should be attributed to neural noise somewhere early in the chain of perceptual mechanisms, probably before discrimination. Their argument is based on the supposition that if a random disturbance is added to all signals before discrimination, something like this effect could be expected, for the ratio would be little altered if nearly unity but much altered if near zero. They postulate, in effect, an increasing level of neural noise, which would tend to obscure all differences between signals or states, and offer the speculation that in physiological terms the noise might be an increased rate of spontaneous firing of neurons, or an increased likelihood for neighboring neurons to excite one another by nonsynaptic pathways.

If this were a valid explanation, it should follow that differential thresholds are likely to be much less affected by aging than absolute ones. This tentative prediction is also being tested for the auditory system.

E. Bekesy Audiometry

In the auditory perception studies ($N = 246$) the important feature of more efficient use of perceptual skills by professional pilots as compared with the general population becomes once again apparent. Figure 6 contrasts the average hearing threshold levels at four frequencies observed in the Lovelace Study with the corresponding estimates for the "better" ear reported in several large-scale surveys in the United States (National Health Survey, 1965). There has been some question as to whether or not Bekesy thresholds, assessed conventionally by midpoints between audibility and inaudibility, are in fact strictly comparable to those obtained by traditional audiometric techniques. For example, Corso's (1956) results suggest that the midpoint estimates may be too high, the inaudibility points giving a better fit. However, these discrepancies appear to be explicable in terms of the instructions given to the subjects (Hirsch, 1962). In a well-controlled study by Burns and Hinchcliffe (1957) in which the instructions were identical to those received by the pilots, a substantial measure of agreement was found between the two sets of measurements.

As in the National Health Survey (1965), the left ear shows more pronounced hearing loss than the right ear in a greater proportion of cases, and the dissimilarity between the two ears becomes more striking for the higher tones. This trend is depicted in Table I, from which it will also be seen that the present data suggest a possible increase of the effect with age. The reason for this is not clear, but possibly it has something to do with the fact that pilots move from the right-side seat in the cockpit to the left-side one when they are promoted to full captain rank, and that therefore the left ear becomes more exposed to engine noise and vibrations. On the other hand, this may prove to be an entirely irrelevant consideration.

It is of greater theoretical import that—dividing the sample at the age of 40—the older pilots, as compared with the younger, do not show the traditionally expected more severe change of the effective threshold in the presence of white noise input to the contralateral ear. Signal detection under these suboptimal circumstances appears to be uncannily efficient and, in spite of increased presbyacusia, there is no evidence of any disproportional loss in auditory discrimination with advancing age (at 80-dB SPL white noise level, $r = -.08$ for the better ear and $r = -.07$ for the worse ear; not sig-

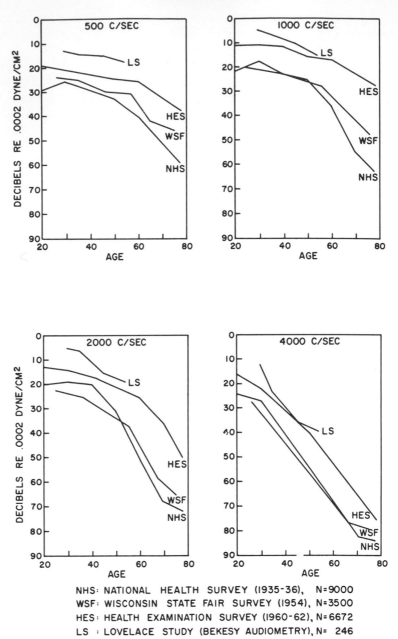

NHS: NATIONAL HEALTH SURVEY (1935-36), N=9000
WSF: WISCONSIN STATE FAIR SURVEY (1954), N=3500
HES: HEALTH EXAMINATION SURVEY (1960-62), N=6672
LS : LOVELACE STUDY (BEKESY AUDIOMETRY), N= 246

Fig. 6. Comparison of average hearing thresholds by age at four frequencies (500, 1000, 2000, and 4000 cps) for the "better" ear: National Health Survey, Wisconsin State Fair Survey, Health Examination Survey, and Lovelace Study.

TABLE I

PROPORTION OF SUBJECTS WITH THRESHOLD DIFFERENCES ($\Delta > 5$ dB)
BETWEEN THE TWO EARS[a]

Frequency (cps)	National Health Survey (1965) (standard audiometry)		Lovelace Study (Bekesy audiometry)	
	Right ear worse (%)	Left ear worse (%)	Right ear worse (%)	Left ear worse (%)
250	—	—	20.6	10.5[b]
500	15.9	11.5	16.9	11.5
750	—	—	14.9	12.8
1000	10.7	9.8	13.5	14.9
1500	—	—	17.2	19.3
2000	13.2	17.6	15.9	29.1[b]
3000	14.7	22.1	18.6	37.8[c]
4000	18.0	23.6	20.3	38.9[c]
6000	23.1	27.1	25.7	36.5[d]
8000	—	—	24.3	33.8[d]

	Lovelace Study data by age groups							
Age group:	20–29 ($N=22$)		30–39 ($N=93$)		40–49 ($N=97$)		50–60 ($N=34$)	
Worse ear:	Right	Left	Right	Left	Right	Left	Right	Left
250	19.2	0.0[d]	16.4	13.8	23.7	9.6[d]	20.0	10.0
500	11.5	7.7	12.9	12.1	19.3	10.5	26.7	16.7
750	11.5	11.5	10.3	13.8	15.8	11.4	30.0	13.3
1000	7.7	19.2	11.2	15.5	15.8	14.9	13.3	6.7
1500	23.1	15.4	15.5	14.7	16.7	21.0	23.3	26.7
2000	7.7	23.1	12.9	21.5	18.4	33.3[d]	20.0	43.3
3000	19.2	42.3	20.7	32.8	15.8	41.2	26.7	40.0
4000	11.5	50.0[d]	27.6	26.7	18.4	47.4[c]	13.3	40.0[d]
6000	30.8	30.8	24.1	35.3	32.5	33.3	6.7	56.7[c]
8000	30.8	19.2	27.6	29.3	22.8	35.1	16.7	56.7[c]

[a]Health Examination Survey ($N = 6672$) and Lovelace Study ($N = 246$).
[b]Difference significant at 1% level.
[c]Difference significant at 0.1% level or better.
[d]Difference significant at 5% level.

nificant). The average differences between the pulsed-tone thresholds in quiet and in noise for the better ear are shown in Figs. 7 and 8. Of course, pulsed tones would tend to facilitate identification of signal in the presence of noise because the effect of adaptation is negligible (Harbert and Young, 1962). The corresponding values for the continuous tone in the worse ear are given in Fig. 9. It is not easy to assess the precise significance of the

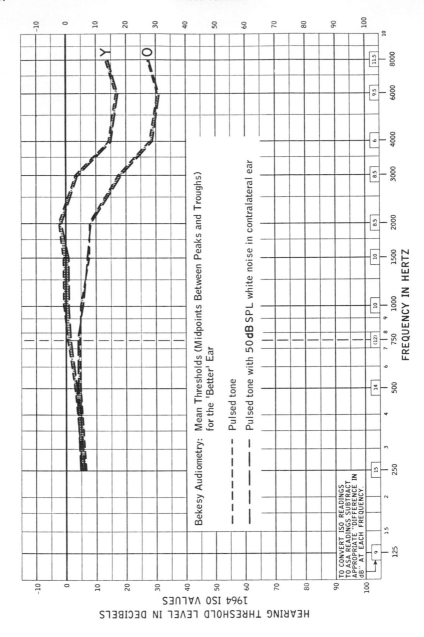

Fig. 7. Bekesy audiometry: Mean thresholds for the better ear (pulsed tone, in quiet and with 50-dB SPL white noise in the contralateral ear: average values for younger and older subjects).

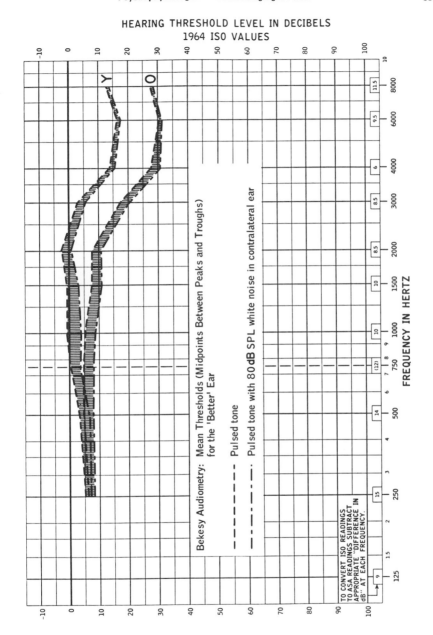

Fig. 8. Bekesy audiometry: Mean thresholds for the better ear (pulsed tone, in quiet and with 80-dB SPL white noise in the contralateral ear: average values for younger and older subjects).

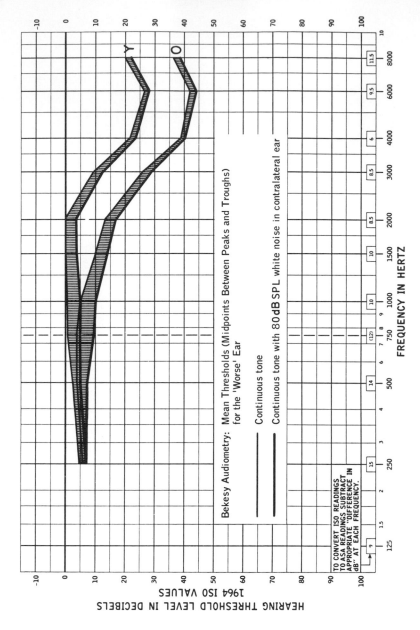

Fig. 9. Bekesy audiometry: Mean threshold for the worse ear (continuous tone in quiet and with 80-dB SPL white noise in the contralateral ear: average values for younger and older subjects).

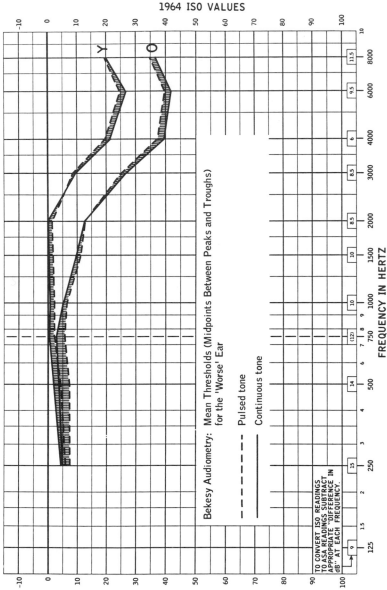

Fig. 10. Bekesy audiometry: Mean thresholds for the worse ear (pulsed and continuous tone in quiet: average values for younger and older subjects).

overall trend, but it is noteworthy that it seems to be in line with other reports that older pilots can deal quite efficiently with auditory inputs in the presence of noise (McFarland and O'Doherty, 1959; Bragg and Greene, 1963). Whether the concept of critical bandwidths (Fletcher, 1940) could satisfactorily account for these effects is conjectural, for much more rigorous control would be required than has proved feasible in the present study. On the other hand, when we examine the small discrepancy between mean levels of peaks and troughs in the tracings for the continuous and pulsed signals in the worse ear (shown in Fig. 10), we see that the average threshold values for the older subjects, as compared with those for the younger, do not seem to support an explanation in terms of recruitment phenomena, as favored by McFarland and O'Doherty (1959). Moreover, the threshold difference is negatively correlated with age ($r = -.22, p < .01$). Furthermore, if we accept the original suggestion of Bekesy (1947) that a reduced amplitude of tracing is likely to be observed where loudness recruitment is present, such differences as can be discerned between the pulsed and continuous signals over the critical range of frequencies showing hearing loss (i.e., 3000–8000 cps) reveal again a negative correlation with age ($r = -.26$, $p < .01$). On the average, the width of the tracings for the younger subjects is of the order of 9 dB in the case of pulsed tone and 7 dB in that of a continuous one. For the older subjects, the corresponding values are around 8 dB in both cases. Studies by Palva (1956) suggest that whereas the normal envelope of the Bekesy audiogram is about 7–10 dB, in cases of recruitment it is less than 5 dB wide. The diagnostic significance of the amplitude of the Bekesy tracing has been challenged by Jerger (1962), but supported by Hirsch (1962).

What is rather surprising, and could not have been predicted from the classical data on binaural masking, is that the difference between the fixed frequency tracings obtained under quiet and 85-dB SPL white noise conditions ($N = 65$; age range 29–61) *in favor of the latter* appears to be positively correlated with age ($r = .31$, $p < .05$). Some representative individual records are shown in Fig. 11, and 12. It is not too much to say that the understanding of why this should be so presents a major problem for clinical audiology, particularly since extraordinarily little is known about the nature of high-tone deafness. A conventional theory, based on clinical and pathological findings, is that there may be two types of presbycusis: one in which the lesion is in the organ of Corti at the basal turn and another in which a partial atrophy of the nerve supply, again at the base of the cochlea, is more marked (Crowe, Guild, & Polvogt, 1934). Why aging processes should selectively affect the basal end of the cochlea is not understood at present (Schuknecht, 1955). An unusual point of view is that nerve deafness might be caused by raised level of random neural activity associated with damage to the hair cells (Gregory, 1957).

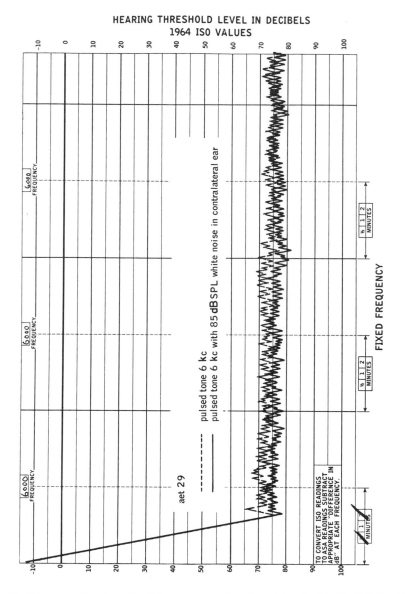

Fig. 11. Bekesy audiometry: Fixed frequency tracings in quiet and with 85-dB SPL white noise in the contralateral ear; subject aged 29.

This would tend to lower the signal-to-noise ratio and consequently produce the paradoxical effect of high levels of externally introduced noise having relatively less impact on the hearing threshold.

Although further experimental and theoretical inquiry is obviously

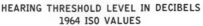

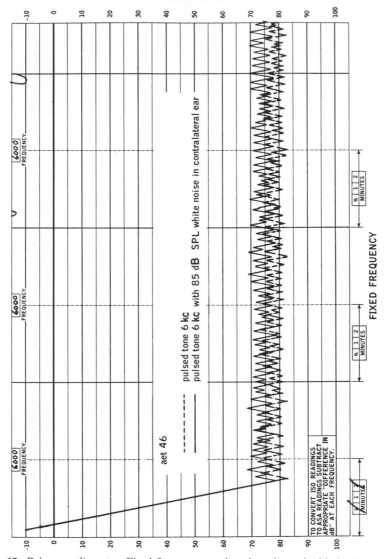

Fig. 12. Bekesy audiometry: Fixed frequency tracings in quiet and with 85-dB SPL white noise in the contralateral ear; subject aged 46.

needed, it is perhaps possible to view these unexpected findings in the light of the suggestion that amplification of ambient sensory inflow may, in the case of older adults, increase the "gain" of the mechanisms upon which the high-information signal impinges (Brebner and Szafran, 1961). The increase in gain might be regarded as corresponding to a higher level of "vigilance" or "arousal." On the other hand, since the threshold resistance data for audiometry and those for tachistoscopic recognition are inter-correlated at a quite impressive level of statistical reliability ($r = .44$, $p < .001$), the alternative hypothesis, which could be considered in this context, is that an important change of "strategy" in detecting distorted signals may occur as a cumulative effect of prolonged experience, and that this change can be relatively immune to the adverse effects of aging in selected individuals.

F. Rate of Gain of Information

The evidence summarized in Table II and Fig. 13 ($N = 282$) makes it abundantly clear that the estimates of rate of gain of information in the baseline condition are not related to age, and that therefore to this extent the traditional association between advanced age and slowing of decision has to be challenged. It will be seen that regression equations were calculated separately for each of the principal age decades, and that although the slope constant shows some unimpressive tendency to increase with age, basically the regression lines resemble each other and are displaced upward,

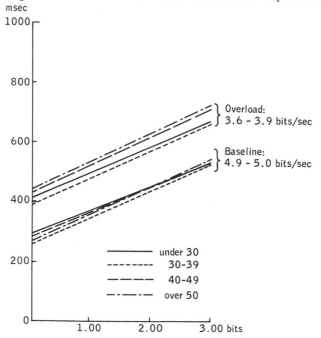

Fig. 13. Rate of gain of information: Mean response latency at different choice levels in the basic and overload conditions plotted for the principal age decades.

TABLE II

STUDY OF SERIAL CHOICE RTs: REGRESSION ANALYSIS OF
INDIVIDUAL PERFORMANCE RECORDS FOR FOUR AGE GROUPS[a] $(RT = a + b \log_2 n)$

	Condition	
Age group	Baseline	Overload
20–29 Mean age = 27.6 N = 29	$RT = .294 + .078 \log_2 n$ $t(b) = 42.25^b$ $R = 4.87$ bits/sec s.d.$(R) = 0.49$ bits/sec	$RT = .416 + .083 \log_2 n$ $t(b) = 23.24^b$ $R = 3.82$ bits/sec s.d.$(R) = 0.59$ bits/sec
30–39 Mean age = 34.8 N = 115	$RT = .270 + .083 \log_2 n$ $t(b) = 97.07^b$ $R = 5.01$ bits/sec s.d.$(R) = 0.51$ bits/sec	$RT = .393 + .087 \log_2 n$ $t(b) = 49.37^b$ $R = 3.91$ bits/sec s.d.$(R) = 0.55$ bits/sec
40–49 Mean age = 44.6 N = 104	$RT = .290 + .080 \log_2 n$ $t(b) = 93.63^b$ $R = 4.87$ bits/sec s.d.$(R) = 0.45$ bits/sec	$RT = .437 + .090 \log_2 n$ $t(b) = 43.23^b$ $R = 3.61$ bits/sec s.d.$(R) = 0.48$ bits/sec
50–60 Mean age = 54.9 N = 34	$RT = .271 + .085 \log_2 n$ $t(b) = 58.63^b$ $R = 4.89$ bits/sec s.d.$(R) = 0.42$ bits/sec	$RT = .446 + .089 \log_2 n$ $t(b) = 22.80^b$ $R = 3.55$ bits/sec s.d.$(R) = 0.37$ bits/sec

	Correlation coefficient (r)		
Comparison	Baseline	Overload	$\Delta = $ (Baseline − Overload)
With age			
Intercept constant (a)	.03	.20 ^{b}	.16 ^{c}
Slope constant (b)	.07	.02	.09
R	− .05	− .23^b	.21^b
Between tasks			
R: Baseline × Overload			$r = .68^b$
Overload × Subtask M			$r = .90^b$
Overload × Subtask DF			$r = .86^b$
Subtask M × Subtask DF			$r = .73^b$

[a]Key: N. number of subjects; RT, response time; $t(b)$, t test on the slope constant; R. rate of gain of information; s.d.(R), standard deviation of the rate.

[b]Significant at 0.1% level or better.

[c]Significant at 1% level.

changing the intercept constant. This important feature is brought out more clearly in the results for the overload conditions, which, however, also reveal a small but consistent negative correlation with age. Another characteristic of the data is the absence of any clear-cut distinction between younger and older subjects with regard to the effects of practice, as indicated in Fig. 14. It seems unlikely that these trends could be attributed to chance effects arising from examination of too limited a number of subjects in the lowest and highest age ranges, though of course this possibility cannot be entirely ignored.

Attention has been drawn (A. T. Welford, 1961) to an important conflict of evidence relative to the formula for choice reactions: $RT = a + b \log_2 n$, in the sense that the slowing of response with age is sometimes reported as an increase in the constant a and at other times as a rise in b. Welford suggests that the effective duration of signals may determine the outcome, producing an increase with age in the intercept when signals are brief, but an increase of the slope when they are long. In the light of the data which have been adduced here, Welford's attempt to resolve the contradictory results on choice and discrimination times must be regarded as inadequate.

On the average, the amount of error made in the primary and subsidiary tasks—of the order of 5% and 15%, respectively—is small enough to be considered as experimentally rather trivial, and thus for practical purposes

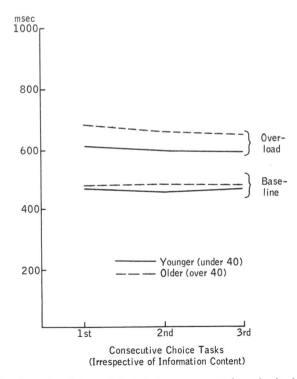

Fig. 14. Effects of practice (balanced design): Mean response latencies in the first, second, and third task, irrespective of information content, plotted for younger and older subjects.

it may well be disregarded. Only in the short-term memory subsidiary task could any suggestion of the possibility of an increase in error with age be entertained ($r = .14$; almost attaining the $p < .05$). Bearing this in mind, it can perhaps be concluded that older pilots are likely to be relatively more susceptible than younger ones to the effects of information overload if this involves short-term recall when some other activity intervenes during the period of retention. Yet the inference of a reduced reserve capacity is not really forced upon us by this evidence, for there arises the conceptual problem of whether a difference of the order of 0.30 bits/sec in the rate of gain of information can logically be regarded as an appropriate measure of loss.

These general trends are reflected in the pattern of results, for a higher degree of choice than that employed in the main study, of an experiment in which, regrettably, only a limited number of subjects have so far been tested. For some 30 pilots ranging in age from 28 to 48, the only differences approaching, but not quite reaching, an acceptable level of statistical significance are with respect to the initial and total rate under conditions of information overload; in line with the results of Crossman and Szafran (1956), the incremental rate remains essentially unaltered.

It is encouraging to find that the overall reliability of the procedure of estimating the rates of gain of information appears to be reasonably good. For 36 subjects (mean age 38) retested after an interval of approximately one year, the correlation coefficients for the baseline and overload conditions are of the order of $r = .70$ ($p < .001$) and $r = .50$ ($p < .01$), respectively. Sixteen of these subjects (mean age 36) have recently been examined for the third time, and the correlation coefficients between the second- and third-year results are of the order of $r = .70$ ($p < .001$) for the baseline and $r = .80$ ($p < .001$) for the overload conditions. Since this group of pilots constitutes the nucleus of a longitudinal study, it will be imperative to check further whether these preliminary indications are not misleading.

The data on the possible relationship between reserve channel capacity and threshold resistance are somewhat more complicated; indeed, there can be much room for debate on the extent of this relationship. Preliminary analysis suggests that such trends as can be discerned are only apparent in the overload conditions ($r = .20$, $p < .05$) and that the baseline rate of gain of information is not, on the present evidence, related to sensory perception indices under conditions of reduced signal-to-noise ratio.

The interpretation of these findings is necessarily speculative. It is clear, however, that they appear to support the conclusion of Shock (1967) that age differences in psychological and physiological tests may be more revealing when observed under conditions of stress than under baseline or resting conditions. It is equally clear that, insofar as skill proficiency can ever be evaluated outside the flying situation itself, the routine aspects of the professional pilot's skill are unlikely to be seriously affected by aging over the usual span of normal working life.

G.   Psychological Refractory Phase and Information Content

For the sake of completeness, mention should be made of data on central refractoriness available for a small group of subjects ($N = 28$), ranging in age from the late twenties to the late forties.

The concept of psychological refractory phase refers to that increase in response latency which can be observed when subjects are required to respond to a signal closely following another. The operative term is borrowed from physiology, the intended analogy being with changes in threshold of neurons following the propagation of nerve impulses, where the recovery is divisible into an absolute and a relative phase. It has been argued by A. T. Welford (1952) that the slowing of response to the second of two successive signals is due not to a temporary reduction of sensitivity in the central mechanisms, but rather to the feature that "no two central organizing times can overlap" (p. 3). Some experiments have suggested that the analogy with physiological refractoriness may, however, be more exact than assumed by this view (Brebner and Szafran, 1961). Apparently in some cases it is possible to distinguish between an "absolute phase," in which signal analysis may be presumed to be held up until the central processes already begun have ended, and a "relative phase," during which the speed of decision is lowered, the duration of each phase being in part a function of signal probability. This distinction, if valid, is of some interest in relation to the question of refractory phase in sequential performance when the number of choices varies. Comparatively little has been done in the present study on this particular problem as yet, but it seems evident from an analysis of response times to the second signal (R_2) at the different intervals between successive signals ($S_1 - S_2$), summarized in Figs. 15 and 16 and in Table III, that what can be inferred from the general shape of the curves points to a change in only the first component up to the level of 1–2 bits. With further increase in input information, both components of the refractory phase appear to be affected. A fuller evaluation of these trends would, however, require consideration of a much wider spectrum of data, which regrettably are not at present available.

As far as the possibility of an increase with age in central refractoriness is concerned (A. T. Welford, 1952; Broadbent, 1958), it is only at the 100 msec interval that any presumptive evidence of a longer sampling time for incoming information can be discerned ($r = -.15$; on a one-tailed test, $p < .05$). Nevertheless, the possibility is worth bearing in mind because of its relevance for the theory of an increase with age in the level of random

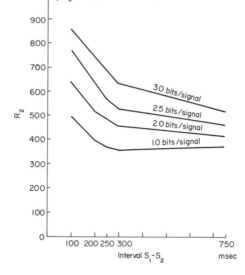

Fig. 15. Central refractoriness and information content: Mean values of R_2 at different intervals (S_1-S_2).

fluctuations in nerve-impulse frequency. The extended duration over which information could be integrated would increase the signal-to-noise ratio and thus allow the input to be more easily distinguished from the system noise (Gregory, 1957). A strategy of this kind, if adopted by the brain, might conceivably improve the selective responsiveness of central mechanisms to high-information signals.

H.   Possible Relationship between Psychological and Physiological Data

As reported at length elsewhere (Szafran, 1963, 1965a, b, c, 1966a, c), the data on the rate of gain of information under conditions of task overload appear to be related to the cardiopulmonary status of the pilots, who—needless to say—are all in perfect health from the clinical standpoint. On the other hand, no such pattern has so far been detected in the baseline rate of gain of information vis-à-vis the relevant physiological indices. To the extent that the slope constant in the formula for choice reaction time tends to covary with postexercise measures of cardiac output ($r = -.26, p < .01$), the present evidence suggests that those earlier investigations which reported slowing of response with age as an increase in the slope must have included, no doubt inadvertently, subclinical cases of cardiovascular disorder.

As already mentioned, even though the slowing with age observed in the

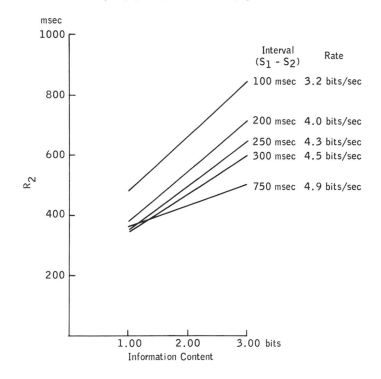

Fig. 16. Central refractoriness and rate of gain of information as estimated from mean response latency at five intervals $(S_1 - S_2)$.

TABLE III

CENTRAL REFRACTORINESS AND RATE OF GAIN OF INFORMATION (R): t TEST ON THE
DIFFERENCES IN R_2 BETWEEN FIVE INTERVALS $S_1 - S_2$ $(RT = a + b \log_2 n)$

Comparison of regressions for different intervals (msec)	p Values		
	Intercept constant	Slope constant	R
100 vs. 200	.001	NS[a]	.001
100 vs. 250	.001	.01	.001
100 vs. 300	.001	.001	.001
100 vs. 750	NS[a]	.001	.001
200 vs. 250	NS[a]	NS[a]	NS[a]
200 vs. 300	NS[a]	.001	.01
200 vs. 750	.001	.001	.01
250 vs. 300	NS[a]	.05	NS[a]
250 vs. 750	.001	.001	.001
300 vs. 750	.001	.001	.01

[a]Not significant.

face of additional information challenge is formally equivalent to a somewhat lower channel capacity, such slowing does not unequivocally indicate a reduced reserve capacity, e.g., for adequate responses to sudden emergencies. It may mean that the forms of code transformations of the information entering the central nervous system are adjusted to the characteristics of the available channel according to the nature of prevailing input and the weight assigned to other inputs (Fano, 1961). At these high neural levels, the information transfer could be taking place in terms of detection of abrupt gradients between presence or absence of activity in any particular channel, rather than by the detection of maxima (Allanson and Whitfield, 1956). Such a process would have the advantage of being able to operate efficiently in a noisy system, and there is some direct neurophysiological evidence that neurons (in, e.g., the auditory system) may indeed have the properties required by the theory (Whitfield, 1965).

A more detailed interpretation of these findings is far from easy and further intensive studies would be desirable, particularly on the effects of partial hypoxia. However, it is difficult to dismiss the possibility that the agreement between the findings from psychological and cardiovascular tests—and the intriguing and no doubt complex relationship which it suggests—might imply that the analytical operations performed by the brain in a high-grade skill are more likely to depend on the efficiency of the lung-heart system than upon age as such. Although it would not be profitable at present to attempt to formulate a theory in strictly physiological terms, and therefore the hypothesis has to be regarded as speculative and sketchy, this interpretation has nevertheless the advantage of linking the psychological and physiological data accumulated in a number of studies (e.g., Birren, Butler, Greenhouse, Sokoloff, & Yarrow, 1963; Obrist, 1965; Spieth, 1965), including the present one. If the idea that neural noise within the central nervous system increases with age is essentially correct, it does not seem unreasonable to suppose that a reduced rate of cerebral blood flow may contribute to the hypothetical random activity in brain cells (Szafran, 1963, 1965a, b, c).

Some qualified support for this contention can be found in the studies of Obrist (1965), who reports that an important factor underlying EEG changes with age is a reduction of cerebral oxygen uptake. There are reasons to believe that the oxygen uptake probably parallels the cardiac output, although much of this relationship is inadequately understood at present. Careful studies by Luft *et al.* (1963) suggest that during exercise maximum oxygen intake may be related to gross body weight and fat-free weight as estimated by hydrostatic weighing. In a recent paper Finkelstein and Luft (1966) report that in some 20 pilots examined annually over five years there was an increase in work capacity related to these factors. They ascribe the improvement in cardiorespiratory competence, despite the increasing age, to a stringent physical exercise regimen maintained by the subjects. Analyzing the cross-sectional data for the pilots participating in the Lovelace Study. Luft (personal communication) finds that fat-free weight does not change significantly with age, thus throwing considerable doubt on the conventional assumption that active tissues are bound to be replaced by inactive fat depots as the organism ages. A final point of interest, in view of the possible relationship between high serum cholesterol levels and coronary heart disease, is that Steinbach (1964) found no evidence of any significant rise with age in cholesterol levels among fishermen, in contrast to the data for older industrial workers. A related report by Rosen and Olin (1965) reveals a much less marked hearing loss with age in certain African populations which, by comparison with Western countries, have typically lower cholesterol levels as well as lower incidence of coronary heart disease.

V. Implications for Gerontological Research

In conclusion, an oblique and partial answer to the question of the broader implications of these interim findings may be in place. As mentioned at the outset, the author is aware of the limitations of his evidence and recognizes that no fully satisfactory discussion can be offered at this stage of the work. Nonetheless, the analysis of the major trends reported here, as far as it goes, does seem to raise at least one point of the utmost importance, namely, that it would be rash to conclude that the capacity for discrimination and choice, when examined within the overlearned repertoire of adult professional life, need necessarily decline with advancing age (Szafran, 1963, 1964).

Certain features of sensory perception commonly investigated in studies of aging appear, in the light of the present material, unremarkable. Thus, for example, even though the amplitude of accommodation is reduced in later adulthood, and in spite of the fact that less and less light reaches the retina, we may question the justification for inferring from variations in ocular refraction or pupil diameter any "law of physiological aging" (Bernstein and Bernstein, 1945) governing visual performance. It would appear from the data adduced here that it might be more pertinent to reflect on how effective the increased thresholds are in unfavorable circumstances, in which case we need not necessarily be pessimistic. As Rartlett (1943, p. 423) has astutely observed: "It is possible for all of the peripheral mechanisms to reach a high degree of efficiency and at the same time to find that when these mechanisms have to work in their full setting of central nervous function the result is disappointing and inaccurate. Conversely, it is possible for the peripheral factors involved to be below normal in efficiency and still for the full machinery of perception to work accurately and well." There can be little doubt that Bartlett's prediction has been sustained and amplified by nearly all modern investigations of sensory perception in which energy considerations are supplemented by those of information.

Bartlett (1951, 1962) goes on to argue, after reviewing a number of recent studies of high-grade skill, that under a wide range of different forms of stress, as in conditions of fatigue and organically based age changes, the central nervous system is able to maintain the very high efficiency of its integrative action. The present findings, together with other cases in the literature, conclusively demonstrate that many of the characteristics alleged-ly suggestive of "relative functional loss" are not a neccessary feature of the performance of a professionally successful and healthy middle-aged or older adult. It is of course only a surmise, but hopefully not an overstatement, that in sketching the "aging profile" of capacities from a physiological and psychological standpoint, considerations of reserve channel capacity and threshold resistance may eventually introduce important qualifications to the doctrine of wear-and-tear, a doctrine which appears to be stronger than the facts.

For the time being, however, this broad question has to remain a con-troversial issue on which more experimental detail would be welcome. At least in the case of professional pilots, their impressive ability to guard against the very subtle shift with the passage of time in the direction of "chronic fatigue" is probably a combination of a specific capacity to adapt rapidly to changing requirements and conditions and of a general willingness to plan the effort so as to maximize the likelihood of sustained performance in the skills that provide their *raison d'être* (Bartlett, 1947, 1962; Hick, 1951; Birren, 1964; Szafran, 1965c, 1966b). In some ways it is unfortunate that the theory of the human operator of control systems is of only limited value in handling a quality of this kind, for it undoubtedly deserves to be taken fully into account when speculating about the possible effects of aging on professional flying. The older pilot, like other employees, is com-monly defined as one who approaches a conventionally fixed age limit, a practice that may be totally misleading; how misleading this convention occasionally proves to be can be judged from those recurrent instances when it leads otherwise sensible people to paint a depressing picture of "premature aging in pilots at the age of 40 or 50" in the popular press (e.g., Eaby, 1964, p. 181). The present study makes it possible to argue that at least in this profession, age per se could not necessarily be equated with decline, nor should it be considered a sufficient reason for retirement. In suggesting these conclusions, however, it must be recognized that, as always, there is room for other views. Only the exigencies of a limited presentation compel the author to appear dogmatic.

A mounting body of opinion has it that perhaps too much emphasis has been placed in the past on the various disadvantages of later life, and too little effort made by investigators to look for positive aspects of aging. The purpose of this paper is to belabor this very point, for it would seem to follow from the experimental data adduced here that the difficulties which arise about "unscrambling" the effects of aging and those of minimal pathology should not prevent gerontologists from attempting to come to terms with the question of what is normal in studies of aging. Of course, investigations of aging which would be entirely free of pathology are to some extent imaginary. Much of the relevant literature is scattered through so many journals, serving such a variety of interests, that it is hardly surprising to find even highly qualified experts complaining about "too little being known, and too much being written" (Comfort, 1961; Post, 1965, p. 1).

The nature and magnitude of age changes must be understood more clearly before the empirical observations, many of them undoubtedly selected, are allowed to become accepted as established facts. Otherwise all discussion about "loss of capacity" in later adulthood is likely to arrive at that puzzling junction of biology and semantics where the terms become too elastic to remain meaningful.

ACKNOWLEDGMENTS

The preparation of this paper as well as the investigation reported therein were supported by the United States Public Health Service Research Grant No. HD-0518 from the National Institutes of Health. The late Dr. W. R. Lovelace, II—a pioneer in aerospace medicine who lost his life in a light plane crash in 1965—has been closely associated with the work reported herein. Thanks are also due to Prof. J. E. Birren, Prof. F. Bourliere, Prof. E. R. F. W. Crossman, Prof. R. L. Gregory, Prof. H. Kay, Prof. R. Melzack, Dr. J. H. Price and Dr. C. S. White for constructive criticism; to Dr. T. W. Norris for advice on audiometry; to Dr. N. T. Welford and E. E. Fletcher for help with the instrumentation; to A. G. Pavlos, V. Bogo, Mrs. J. Massey, Miss C. Baca, and Mrs. J. Hicks for assistance in the testing of subjects; to Prof. V. R. Cane for advice on statistical problems; to J. Paden, Mrs. B. Sklower and Mrs. M. Elrick for help with the computer analysis of the data; and to Mrs. A. Adams for the secretarial work.

REFERENCES

Allanson, J. T., & Whitfield, I. C. The cochlear nucleus and its relation to theories of hearing. In C. Cherry (Ed.), *Information theory*, London & Washington, D. C.: Butterworth, 1956.

Barlow, H. B. Retinal noise and absolute threshold. *J. opt. Soc. Amer.*, 1956, 46, 634.

Bartlett, F. C. Current problems in visual function and visual perception. *Proc. physical Soc.*, 1943, 55, 417.

Bartlett, F. C. The measurement of human skill. *Brit. med. J.*, 1947, 1, 835 and 877.

Bartlett, F. C. The bearing of experimental psychology upon human skilled performance. *Brit. J. industr. Med.*, 1951, 8, 209.

Bartlett, F. C. The outlook for flying personnel research. In A. B. Barbour and H. E. Whittingham (Eds.), *Human problems of supersonic and hypersonic flight*. New York Pergamon 1962.

Bekesy, G. von. A new audiometer, *Acta Oto-laryngol.*, 1947, 35, 411.

Bernstein, F., & Bernstein, M. Law of physiologic aging as derived from long range data on refraction of human eye. *Arch. Ophth.*, 1945, **34**, 378.

Birren, J. E. *The psychology of aging.* Englewood Cliffs, N. J.: Prentice-Hall, 1964.

Birren, J. E., Butler, R. N., Greenhouse, S. W., Sokoloff, L., & Yarrow, M. R. *Human aging.* Washington, D. C.: U. S. Dept. Health, Educ. & Welfare, 1963.

Bragg, V. C., & Greene, J. W. Speech discrimination in senior naval aviators. *U. S. Nav. School Aviat. Med. Res. Rept.*, August, 1963.

Brebner, J., & Szafran, J. A study of the psychological refractory phase in relation to ageing. *Gerontologia*, 1961, **5**, 241.

Broadbent, D. E. *Perception and communication.* New York: Macmillan (Pergamon), 1958.

Broadbent, D. E., & Gregory, M. Division of attention and the decision theory of signal detection. *Proc. roy. Soc. B*, 1963, **158**, 222.

Bruckner, R. Uber Methoden longitudinaler Alternsforschung am Auge. *Ophthalmologica*, 1959, **138**, 59.

Burns, W., & Hinchcliffe, R. Comparison of the auditory threshold as measured by individual pure tone and by Bekesy audiometry. *J. acoust. Soc. Amer.*, 1957, **29**, 1274.

Cherry, C. *On human communication.* New York: Wiley, 1957.

Comfort, A. The position of fundamental age studies. *Amer. Heart J.*, 1961, **62**, 293.

Corso, J. F. Effects of testing methods on hearing thresholds. *A. M. A. Arch. Otolaryngol.*, 1956, **63**, 78.

Craik, K. J. W. Instruments and methods for measuring sensory events. *J. sci. Instrum.*, 1940, **18**, 1.

Craik, K. J. W. Theory of the human operator in control systems. *Brit. J. Psychol.*, 1947, **38**, 56, 142.

Crossman, E. R. F. W. The measurement of discriminability. *Quart. J. exp. Psychol.*, 1955, **7**, 176.

Crossman, E. R. F. W. Information processes in human skill. *Brit. med. Bull.*, 1964, **20**, 32.

Crossman, E. R. F. W., & Szafran, J. Changes with age in the speed of information intake and discrimination. *Experientia (Suppl.)*, 1956, **4**, 128.

Crowe, S. J., Guild, S. R., & Polvogt, L. M. Observations on the pathology of high tone deafness. *Bull. Johns Hopkins Hosp.*, 1934, **55**, 315.

Duane, A. Studies in monocular and binocular accommodation with their clinical application. *Amer. J. Ophth.*, 1922, **5**, 865.

Eaby, P. Are pilots too old at 50? *Airways Intern.*, 1964 (July-August).

Fankhauser, F., & Schmidt, T. Die Untersuchung der Funktionen des dunkeladaptierten Auges mit dem Adaptometer Goldmann-Weekers. *Ophthalmologica*, 1957, **133**, 264.

Fano, R. M. *Transmission of information.* New York: Wiley, 1961.

Finkelstein, S., and Luft, U. C. Five-year study of physical competence. (Abstract.) *Aerospace Med.*, 1966, **37**, 276.

Fletcher, H. Auditory patterns. *Rev. mod. Phys.*, 1940, **12**, 47.

Gregory, R. L. An experimental treatment of vision as an information source and noisy channel. In C. Cherry (Ed.), *Information theory.* London & Washington, D. C: Butterworth, 1956.

Gregory, R. L. Increase in "neurological noise" as a factor in ageing. *Proc. 4th int. Congr. Geront., Merano*, 1957, **1**, 314.

Harbert, F., & Young, I. M. Threshold auditory adaptation. *J. aud. Res.*, 1962, **2**, 229.

Hick, W. E. Man as an element in a control system. *Research*, 1951, **4**, 112.

Hick, W. E. On the rate of gain of information. *Quart. J. exp. Psychol.*, 1952, **4**, 11.

Hirsch, I. J. Bekesy's audiometer. *J. acoust. Soc. Amer.*, 1962, **34**, 1333.

Jerger, J. Hearing tests in otologic diagnosis. *J. Amer. speech & hear. Assoc.*, 1962, **4**, 139.

Julesz, B. Binocular depth perception and pattern recognition. In C. Cherry (Ed.), *Information theory.* London & Washington, D. C.: Butterworth, 1961.

Kay, H., & Szafran, J. Motor performance. In G. Humphrey, (Ed.), *Psychology through experiment*. London: Methuen, 1963.

Klensch, von H. Der Informationcharakter der modernen Ballistographie. *Elektromedizin* 1961, **6**, 104.

Landis, C., & Hamwi, V. Critical flicker frequency, age and intelligence. *Amer. J. Psychol.*, 1956, **69**, 459.

Lee, B. S. Effects of delayed speech feed-back. *J. acoust. Soc. Amer.*, 1950, **22**, 824.

Luft. U. C. Early detection of deteriorative trends in pulmonary function. In W. L. Marxer and G. R. Cowgill (Eds.). *The art of preventive medicine*. Springfield. Ill.: Charles C. Thomas, 1967.

Luft, U. C., Cardus, D., Lin, T. P. K., Anderson, E. C., & Howarth, J. L. Physical performance in relation to body size and composition. *Ann. N. Y. Acad. Sci.*, 1963, **110**, 795.

McFarland, R. A., & Fisher, M. B. Alterations in dark-adaptation as a function of age. *J. Geront.*, 1955, **10**, 424.

McFarland, R. A., & O'Doherty, B. M. Work and occupational skills. In J. E. Birren (Ed.), *Handbook of ageing and the individual*. Chicago, Ill: Univer. of Chicago Press, 1959.

McFarland, R. A., Warren, A. B., & Karis, C. Alterations in critical flicker frequency as a function of age and light-dark ratio. *J. exp. Psychol.*, 1958, **56**, 529.

National Health Survey. *Hearing levels of adults by age and sex, U. S. 1960–1962*. Washington, D. C.: U. S. Dept. Health, Educ. & Welfare, 1965.

Obrist, W. D. Electroencephalographic approach to age changes in response speed. In A. T. Welford and J. E. Birren (Eds.), *Behavior, aging and the nervous system*. Springfield, Ill.: Charles C Thomas, 1965.

Palva, T. Recruitment tests at low sensation levels. *Laryngoscope*, 1956, **66**, 1519.

Post, F. *The clinical psychiatry of late life*. New York: Macmillan (Pergamon), 1965.

Poulton, E. C. Measuring the order of difficulty of visual-motor tasks. *Ergonomics*, 1958, **1**, 234.

Rambo, V. C., & Sangal, S. P. A study of the accommodation of the people of India. *Amer. J. Ophthal.*, 1960, **49**, 993.

Rose, A. The sensitivity performance of the human eye as an absolute scale. *J. opt. Soc. Amer.*, 1948, **38**, 196.

Rosen, S., & Olin, P. Hearing loss and coronary heart disease. *Arch. Otolaryng.*, 1965, **82**, 236.

Rushton, W. A. H. Blue light and the regeneration of human rhodopsin in situ. *J. gen. Physiol*, 1957, **41**, 419.

Schouten, J. F., Kalsbeek, J. W. H., & Leopold, F. F. On the evaluation of mental and perceptual load. *Ergonomics*, 1962, **5**, 251.

Schreuder, O. B. Medical aspects of aircraft pilot fatigue with general reference to the commercial jet pilot. *Aerospace Med.*, 1966, **37**, (No. 4, Sect. II), 31.

Shock, N. W. The beginning of deterioration. In W. I., Marxer and G. R. Cowgill (Eds.). *The art of preventive medicine*. Springfield. Ill.: Charles C. Thomas. 1967.

Schuknecht, H. F. Presbycusis. *Laryngoscope*, 1955, **65**, 402.

Spieth, W. Slowness of task performance and cardiovascular diseases. In A. T. Welford and J. E. Birren, (Eds.), *Behavior, aging and the nervous system*. Sprinffield, Ill.: Charles C Thomas, 1965.

Steinbach, M. The normal in cardiovascular diseases. *Lancet*, 1964, **2**, 116.

Szafran, J. Age differences in choice reaction time and cardiovascular status among pilots. *Nature*, 1963, **200**, 904.

Szafran, J. Prospects in psychological research on ageing. In P. From Hansen (Ed.), *Age with a future*. Copenhagen: Munksgaard, 1964.

Szafran, J. Decision processes and ageing. In A. T. Welford and J. E. Birren (Eds.), *Behavior, aging and the nervous system*. Springfield, Ill.: Charles C Thomas, 1965. (a)

Szafran, J. Age differences in sequential decisions and cardiovascular status among pilots. *Aerospace Med.*, 1965, **36**, 303. (b)

Szafran, J. Some limitations of the human operator of control systems to process information. *Proc. XVth int. astronaut. Congr.*, Warsaw and Paris, 1965, **4**, 207. (c)

Szafran, J. Age, cardiac output and choice reaction time. *Nature*, 1966, **209**, 836. (a)

Szafran, J. Limitations and reliability of the human operator of control systems to process information. *Aerospace Med.*, 1966, **37**, 239. (b)

Szafran, J. Age differences in the rate of gain of information, signal detection strategy and cardiovascular status among pilots. *Gerontologia*, 1966, **12**, 6. (c)

Tanner, W. P., & Swets, J. A. A decision-making theory of visual detection. *Psychol. Rev.*, 1954, **61**, 401.

Weale, R. A. *The ageing eye.* London: H. K. Lewis, 1963.

Welford, A. T. The psychological refractory period and the timing of high-speed performance. *Brit. J. Psychol.*, 1952, **43**, 2.

Welford, A. T. *Ageing and human skill.* London & New York: Oxford Univer. Press, 1958.

Welford, A. T. Age changes in the times taken by choice, discrimination and the control of movement. *Gerontologia*, 1961, **5**, 129.

Welford, N. T. An electronic digital recording machine—the Setar. *J. sci. Instrum.*, 1952, **29**, 1.

Whitfield, I. C. "Edges" in auditory information processing. *Proc. XXIIIrd int. Congr. physiol. Sci.*, Tokyo, 1965, **1**, 245.

Young, J. Z. *A model of the brain.* London & New York: Oxford Univer. Press, 1964.

Zangwill, O. L. Speech. In J. Field *et al.* (Eds.), *Handbook of physiology*, Sec. 1, Vol. 3. Washington, D. C.: Amer. Physiol. Soc., 1960.

Age and the Use of Structure in Transmitted Information

PATRICK RABBITT

Medical Research Council

Applied Psychology Research Unit, Cambridge,

England

I.   Introduction

It is notorious that old people process information more slowly than the young, but the implications of this fact for models of degenerative performance changes are still obscure. The purpose of this review is to suggest that we are now in a position to measure the *efficiency* with which old people process information, using somewhat more complex criteria than the speed and accuracy with which they perform tasks. In particular it will be suggested that criteria for estimating the efficiency of performance may conveniently be borrowed from computer engineering. It is our ambition to persuade the reader that a comparison between senescent humans and obsolescent computers is more than merely a whimsical analogy.

There are a number of reasons why one computer may be faster than another, but three in particular seem to offer schemes in terms of which recent evidence of age changes in performance may be classified:

1. A computer may be slow simply because its component switchery is slow. Thus, each operation that it performs will be delayed by some constant

t, and a sequence of N operations will be delayed by some multiplicative function $N(t)$, relative to some other faster machine.

2. A computer may reduce a given set of data to a given solution either rapidly or slowly, depending on the efficiency with which it is programmed for a task. A fast program will reduce the number of operations that the machine must perform to a minimum. A slow program will perform superfluous operations, and so waste time.

3. The speed of a computer may be a direct function of its size. This is not merely because the components of large (and expensive) machines tend to be fast, but because large machines have the capacity to carry out operations of considerable complexity "in parallel" rather than "in series."

A relatively small machine may have to be programmed to break down a complex calculation into a number of discrete steps, each step representing a quantum limit to the amount of information upon which it can simultaneously effect a transformation. A large machine can operate in terms of larger informational quanta, thus performing complex calculations more economically.

Let us consider whether some experimental evidence of psychomotor slowing with advancing age can be classified in terms of these three points.

II. Sequential Redundancy

The classic type of experiment made to assess Ss' ability to use sequential redundancy is a choice-response task in which the various signals occur with unequal frequencies (Hyman, 1953). In such tasks young Ss soon learn to estimate the relative frequencies of the signals and are able to use this information to respond faster to the frequent than to the rare events. A direct comparison of the efficiency with which young and old recognize and use sequential redundancy is reported by Griew (1962). His Ss were given continuous-performance two-choice tasks in which one signal (and response) was more frequent than the other. Both age groups learned to respond faster to the relatively frequent signal, but the old Ss appeared to detect the frequency bias earlier than the young. The absolute difference in reaction time (RT) to rare and to frequent signals was also larger for the old group. Griew concludes that old people detect and use sequential bias better than their juniors.

Unfortunately this result alone does not establish the proposition. It is known that Ss responding to sequences of signals are able to respond much faster when the same signal is repeated than when one signal is followed by another to which a different response is appropriate (Bertelson, 1961). In Griew's task repetitions of the biased signal would naturally be more frequent than repetitions of the rare signal. It is therefore not clear whether Griew's result implies a change, with age, in the detection of signal frequency or in the response-repetition effect. Recent work with young Ss illustrates a technique by which this important distinction may be easily made (Leonard, Newman, & Carpenter, 1966).

Also crucial to a distinction between repetition and frequency effects would be a demonstration that the old recognize and use the conditional probability of one signal and response given another. An experiment by Rabbitt and Rogers (1965) provides evidence on this question. Here old and young Ss responded to sequences of signals on each of three neon lamps, A, B, and C. The illumination of each lamp required the S to make a different response. Any response to lamp A might be followed by a signal on either lamp B or lamp C with equal probability. Responses to either B or C, however, were invariably followed by the ignition of lamp A. The data thus allowed the RTs of old and young Ss to be compared on trials when they responded to completely predictable signals (on A) and when they responded to unpredictable signals (on B or C). Mean RTs from two different versions of this task are given in Table I.

It can be seen from Table I that both groups responded faster to predictable than to unpredictable signals, but there is no suggestion that either group benefited more than the other from the redundancy implicit in the task.

In sum, no clear demonstration of an age-related advantage or disadvantage in the use of sequential redundancy emerges from the data. In the light of Griew's (1962) results, the possibility of age differences in the magnitude of response-repetition effects urgently requires to be examined.

III. Discrete-Response Tasks: The Conditional Probability of One Signal Given One Other

Sequential redundancy may be introduced into discrete-response tasks by varying the amount of information conveyed by a foresignal about the reaction signal that is to follow it. Foresignals can be used to convey two different types of information: they may allow the S to predict the moment in time when the reaction signal will occur, and they may inform him which of a set of possible signals he is to expect. Age comparisons have been made in both contexts.

A. Time Information

When foresignals only convey information about the moment of arrival of the reaction signal, the experimental results cannot simply be evaluated in terms of a recognition of the transitional probability of one event, given

TABLE I

MEAN RESPONSE TIMES FOR TRANSITIONS BETWEEN CONTACT SWITCHES

	Mean response time (msec)							
	Condition 1				Condition 2			
Transition:	A → B	A → C	B → A	C → A	A → B	A → C	B → A	C → A
Young group	485	478	469	469	425	575	415	499
	$\sigma = 35$	$\sigma = 47$	$\sigma = 41$	$\sigma = 40$	$\sigma = 44$	$\sigma = 40$	$\sigma = 38$	$\sigma = 41$
Old group	625	623	601	594	605	699	602	635
	$\sigma = 81$	$\sigma = 82$	$\sigma = 64$	$\sigma = 67$	$\sigma = 100$	$\sigma = 76$	$\sigma = 60$	$\sigma = 61$

another. Relevant also are factors such as the ability of the S to estimate accurately various intervals of time, and assumptions about the foresignal duration at which his condition of preparation for the reaction signal reaches some asymptotic level. Nevertheless, even when a wide range of foreperiod durations are compared, it appears that old Ss benefit less from the use of regular foresignals than the young. Indeed, it has been questioned whether regular foresignals are of any use whatever to old Ss (Talland, 1965).

An important variation in this experimental situation occurs when two or more different foreperiods are used, at random, during the same experimental run. In this case the S's estimate of the probable duration of a foreperiod is based upon the duration in the trial immediately preceding (Botwinick, Brinley, & Birren, 1957; Zahn and Rosenthal, 1966). Thus, Ss are "caught napping" when a trial with a short foreperiod follows a trial in which a relatively long foreperiod is used. Botwinick et al. (1957) have shown in this situation that the relative slowing on "unexpected" foreperiods is greater for old than for young Ss. We thus have the paradox that old Ss appear to benefit less than the young when foresignals are predictable, but are relatively slower when their expectancies are disconfirmed in an irregular foreperiod task. In sum there seems to be little evidence that old Ss benefit from foresignals in any situation (Talland, 1965), whereas there is evidence that their responses are often slower because they form false expectancies (Botwinick et al., 1957). Two paradoxes in these data require notice because they reappear in evidence discussed later.

First, it appears that old Ss do attend to foresignals, and form expectancies as a result. Nevertheless, when the expectancies are correct, their responses are not facilitated, whereas if their expectancies are false, they are relatively more slowed than the young.

Second, old Ss would have faster mean RTs if they could ignore the foresignals presented to them altogether. They are apparently not able to do this.

B.   Use of Partial Advance Information from Foresignals

The "information value" of an expectancy to a S may be quantified in a task in which a choice of foresignals instructs the S that a coming response signal will be from one or other subset of possible signals on a display. In such situations the foresignal has been regarded as conveying "partial advance information" to the S (Leonard, 1958). An age comparison in a task of this type is reported by Rabbitt (1964b). Here Ss had to select the appropriate one of four possible responses, each made to one of four different sets of two signals. Two such sets were letters of the alphabet and two were decimal digits. Each signal from the display was preceded by a foresignal. In separate experimental runs foresignals occurred at constant intervals of 0.2 sec, 0.5 sec, 1.0 sec, and 1.5 sec before the onset of the reaction signal. Two types of foresignal were used in different experimental conditions. In one condition the foresignal was always a flash of light, conveying only time information. In the comparison condition a foresignal on any trial might be either the letter F or the letter L preceding the reaction signal (letter or digit) and lasting for the foresignal duration specified for the experimental run in question. Presentations of the letter F were followed by a digit and presentations of the letter L by a letter. Thus the foresignal not only conveyed information as to when the reaction signal would appear, but also potentially reduced the S's uncertainty about which response he would have to make by 1 bit of information (i.e., to two possibilities out of four).

On very rare occasions, these informative foresignals were made deliberately false (so that F preceded a letter, or L a digit). This was explained to Ss as a rare, intermittent apparatus fault that they must nevertheless overcome by responding as fast as they possibly could.

The RTs of young Ss were significantly faster when they were given partial advance information than when the foresignal was simply a flash of light. Old Ss did not respond faster when partial advance information was given at any foreperiod duration. This was not because they ignored the foresignals, or because they could not identify the letters L or F at the foresignal durations used. This was known because when advance information was deliberately falsified, both young and old Ss took longer to respond to the reaction signal. Indeed, false advance information slowed the RTs of the old group significantly more than those of the young. Thus again we find the paradoxes encountered in data by Botwinick *et al.* (1957). The old Ss do not benefit from the correct advance information, but are relatively more affected when this information is disconfirmed. Further, although the old Ss are never helped, and are sometimes hindered, by attention to the foresignals, they are apparently not able to ignore them.

Since the old clearly form expectancies, but do not respond faster in consequence of them, we must assume that a correct expectancy does not reduce the amount of information which they process in order to identify the signal to which they respond. They appear to check their expectancy very thoroughly against the signal before they commit themselves to a response. When there is a discrepancy between their expectations and the actual signal, we may suppose that they pause to analyze the aberrant situation. In brief, unlike the young, they appear to adopt an unconfident strategy which leads them to process redundant information.

IV. Attention to Redundant Signals in Serial Tasks

Support for this hypothesis would be a demonstration that, in a serial choice-response task, old people attend to signals that the young (to their advantage) learn to ignore. In such a task the young would suffer relatively more than the old from the introduction of rare contingencies when normally redundant signals become crucial (i.e., when the signals abruptly cease to be redundant). An experiment by Rabbitt and Birren (1967) was designed to test this.

Groups of old and young Ss performed a choice-response task in which runs of repetitive signals requiring completely predictable sequences of responses were rarely interrupted at unpredictable intervals by random discontinuities. At each of these discontinuities a repetitive sequence was terminated by a new (interruptive) signal that had to be answered before another repetitive sequence commenced.

Old Ss, as usual, were much slower than the young and made many more errors during the performance of the repetitive sequences, so that their overall accuracy was significantly lower. A subclass of errors occurred because Ss frequently persisted in a repetitive sequence after it had terminated, giving place to an interruptive signal ("continuation errors"). Such errors were associated with fast and accurate performance on repetitive sequences, and were significantly more common in the young than in the old group. Other details of performance in these tasks supported the simple hypothesis that the fast young Ss ran off sequences of repetitive responses very accurately, while paying only intermittent attention to the display. Since they did not identify each signal in turn, we may suppose that they economized on the information they transmitted and could respond faster partly for this reason. This strategy had the liability that they usually made one or two continuation errors before they noticed that a repetitive sequence had given place to an interruptive signal. In contrast, although old Ss were aware that repetitive sequences were completely predictable, they appeared to pause to analyze each signal from the display in turn before responding to it. Their caution was of limited value, since they were less accurate then the young. However, they observed repetitive signals as soon as they occurred, and so made few continuation errors.

The point is again made that the old fail to make use of redundancy implicit in choice-response tasks. They may in consequence be slower than the young, but this appears to be as much a question of the *efficiency* with which they process information as of the *speed* with which their decision can be made.

V. Redundancy in Discriminations between Complex Stimuli

We have so far considered tasks in which redundancy was implicit in the fact that events occurred in determinate sequences or with fixed conditional probabilities that Ss might learn to use. As is well known (Attneave, 1957; Garner, 1962), the same concept may be applied to discriminations between complex stimuli, which may be distinguished from each other by the presence or absence of any one of a number of attributes. Thus we may discriminate cats from goldfish in terms of a number of valid criteria. However, if we are sure that the universe of objects with which we are concerned contains *only* goldfish and cats, only one of the many possible criteria are necessary (e.g., the cats are furry). Indeed, it would be highly inefficient to consider all the possible criteria, since we should then be processing information redundant to the discrimination required. Two different kinds of experiments have shown that old people are at a disadvantage compared to the young when they are required to discriminate between classes of complex symbols (Rabbitt, 1964a, 1965a,b). Further evidence suggests that possibly the reason for this disadvantage is that the old fail to ignore redundant or misleading attributes of complex stimuli (Rabbitt, 1966).

Rabbitt (1964a) compared the performance of young and old Ss on a choice-response task during which they were required to discriminate between classes of stimuli rather than between single signals. The stimuli were letters of the alphabet or decimal digits, printed one on each card of a pack. Packs of symbols were classified by being sorted into two or four bins, according to arbitrary schemes in which Ss were instructed and practiced. Eight different packs were made up to vary independently the number of different letters and digits that Ss had to classify in this way, as well as the number of classes into which they had to separate them. Four of these packs were designed to be sorted into two classes (bins). One of the packs was made up of equal numbers of two symbols, each of which represented a "class" of one item. The other packs required the S to discriminate between two classes of two items, four items, and eight items each. Similarly in the four-class (bin) task Ss discriminated between four classes, each comprising one, two, four, or eight items. The times taken by Ss to sort each of these various packs of cards thus allowed independent estimates of the effects on RT of variations in the number of classes into which populations of stimuli were discriminated and of variations in the number of stimuli in each such class. It emerged that for the young Ss variations in the number of stimuli within each response class had relatively little effect on choice RT, as was the case in other experiments (Rabbitt, 1959; Broadbent & Gregory, 1962; Pollack, 1963). The choice RTs of the old Ss were, however, significantly more affected by variations in stimulus entropy than were those of the young. It appears that old Ss found it more difficult to learn and to respond to classes of signals than did their juniors.

A special case of stimulus classification occurs in visual search, where Ss may have to locate members of a class of "relevant" items that are embedded among other items irrelevant to decisions which they have to make. The relative difficulty experienced by old people in discriminating between classes of stimuli suggested that they might also be at a disadvantage in distinguishing relevant from irrelevant items in visual search. Rabbitt (1965a) and Talland (1966) have found this to be so.

As we saw earlier, the classification of complex stimuli may be optimized if some single characteristic is shared by all members of one class, but is absent in all items from which this class must be discriminated. Where no single identifying attribute (cue) exists, it may be necessary to test for the presence or absence of several cues before a decision is possible. In such cases many different cue systems may allow efficient discrimination, but some may be better than others because they require the S to test for the presence or absence of fewer and more reliable cues. If we suppose that the checking of each cue takes up time (or channel capacity, or both), discriminations between classes of stimuli will take longer if Ss consider irrelevant or misleading (redundant) cues than if they test for only a minimum critical set of discriminating features. Following this argument, it was possible that old Ss took longer than the young to discriminate between classes of complex items because they could less efficiently learn and use optimal nonredundant cue systems; in other words, that old people took longer to discriminate between classes of items because they considered more than the minimum number of cues necessary to make an identification.

This hypothesis implies that Ss improve their performance at stimulus classification with practice partly because they learn and use an optimal cue system. It follows that one of the difficulties encountered on transfer from one classification task to another is likely to be that a learned optimal cue system is inappropriate for a new set of discriminations. Thus, decrement in performance on such a transfer at any point in practice will be an index of the extent to which improvement, up to that point in practice, has been due to mastery of a specific cue system. The extent of such improvement will indicate differences in the relative complexities of the cue system used early and that used late in practice.

Rabbitt (1964b, 1967) used this technique to show that the complexity of the cue systems used to discriminate between relevant and irrelevant letters in visual search was (early in practice) directly proportional to the number of letters in the relevant set. The same technique has been used to show (Rabbitt, 1964a, 1966) that old Ss, early in practice, use a more complex cue system to discriminate relevant from irrelevant letters than do the young.

It is, of course, not likely that the only reason why old people are relatively slow at stimulus classification and visual search is their apparent failure to make use of stimulus redundancy. However, it seems safe to assume that this is at least a contributing factor. The results of these experiments can therefore again be interpreted in a manner consistent with the general theme of this review—the ability to recognize and use structure in transmitted information declines with age.

VI. Concept Formation

The separation of critical from incidental attributes of complex stimuli has long been a theme for "concept-formation" studies, in which Ss are required to derive rules of classification from presented instances of complex patterns, or to use derived schemes of classification to aid their learning by reducing the number of stimulus attributes that they need to consider. In contrast to recent work in the field of general experimental psychology, investigations of age changes in concept-formation tasks are curiously rare. In general, the evidence is consistent with a statement that the heuristics employed by old people in problem solving and concept formation involve redundant operations, or the needless repetition of necessary operations. Failures in two different aspects of performance seem to be involved. First, it has been suggested that the strategies used by the old were made less systematic by their inability to remember when they had disconfirmed invalid hypotheses, or to meaningfully relate experience gathered over successive trials. Second, there is evidence that old subjects fail to extract from available data rules of classification that may simplify a task (in other words, to select between critical and incidental aspects of complex situations, so as to improve their learning). An experiment by Rabbitt (1964c) was designed to demonstrate the latter point.

Attneave (1955, 1957) and Fitts, Weinstein, Rappaport, Anderson, and Leonard (1956) have shown that Ss learning to identify patterns in paired-associate tasks show considerable selectivity in considering only cues that discriminate between the subsets of items with which they are concerned. Other cues are eliminated from consideration as being misleading, or redundant to the discriminations required. For any given ensemble of patterns there may be a single optimal set of cues having minimum redundancy, or a number of such sets, all representing equally efficient means of classification. Sets of patterns may be constructed so as to offer hierarchical systems of classification, so that at least two different cues may be necessary in order to completely identify each pattern: the first cue specifying a subset of which the pattern is a member and the second identifying the pattern within such a subset. Ss optimizing their coding system by learning such conditional cues may be considered to be mastering rules for classification of an ensemble of patterns. Since relevant cues cannot be recognized, nor redundant cues ignored, until the S has some knowledge of the set of patterns as a whole, progress toward mastery of optimal rules of classification will be reflected in the various types of confusions made early in learning.

Rabbitt (1964c) compared the progress made by groups of young and old Ss in learning such a group of patterns. It emerged that, early in practice, the young made systematic confusions between patterns that might have been predicted from the optimal rules of classification. (That is, patterns were chiefly confused with other patterns in the same logical class.) Old Ss showed a significantly lower incidence of systematic confusions during learning. It appeared that they, unlike the young, were not making use of the structure implicit in the situation in order to simplify the task.

VII. Short-Term Memory

It is intuitively reasonable that lists of items should be more easily remembered if they have some order or structure that can be recognized and used than if they offer no pattern that can be grasped. This point has been formally made many times, and the presence of many different types of sequential structure has been shown to increase short-term memory span (Aborn & Rubenstein, 1952; Baddeley, Conrad, & Hull, 1965). In the terminology we have been using, it is now recognized as a truism that short-term memory span varies directly with sequential redundancy in lists of items presented for retention.

A type of structure that Ss can recognize and use with particular ease is that implicit in language. Thus Miller and Selfridge (1950) have shown that the same lists of words are better remembered if they are presented as grammatical English sentences then if they are presented as random strings. The types of comparison that we have discussed make it a natural question whether old people can recognize and use linguistic redundancy as efficiently as their juniors, and if so, whether they can also make use of such redundancy to aid their short-term retention of material presented to them.

Elsewhere in this volume Dr. F. I. M. Craik describes experiments that directly raise these points. Craik wished to test whether old people recognized redundancy in English text as efficiently as the young. A common demonstration that language is redundant requires Ss to guess, in turn, each successive word in some predetermined sentence once they have been given the first word or phrase.

As they progress through the sentence, the accumulation of context renders the task progressively easier, and many words are completely predictable once their predecessors have been established. Craik recorded the times taken by groups of old and young Ss to guess their way though the sentence, "There is a big house on top of the hill." Old Ss took significantly longer and required more guesses to complete the task.

This result opens many interesting lines of speculation about the ways in which the use of language may change with advancing age. Investigations in which such factors as word frequency, type-token ratios, and grammatical structure are systematically varied may be expected to allow us to interpret this result. A crucial point is whether the guesses of the old Ss represented sensible alternatives consistent with the context they achieved at any point, or whether they represented random selections of inappropriate words and phrases. We would also like to know such details as whether the old guess in terms of single words or entire phrases, whether they use relatively high- or low-frequency words in their responses, and what types of grammatical transform they seem most ready to predict. Meanwhile, in association with two other results described by Craik, this datum is consistent with the generalization that the old make less efficient use of linguistic redundancy than the young.

In a further experiment Craik compared the performance of Ss over the age range 20–80 who were required to remember lists of three different types of verbal material: random lists of color names; scrambled proverbs; and plain text. All Ss, as expected, recalled the English text better than unstructured lists of color names, but this improvement was relatively smaller for the old than for the young groups. In a second experiment Craik compared Ss' ability to recall lists of words derived by Miller and Selfridge (1950) as first- to fifth-order statistical approximation to English text. As in all earlier investigations, recall improved with the degree to which the material approximated to text, and recall of plain text was better than for approximations. Once again, however, the improvement in recall with increasing redundancy was relatively smaller for the old than for the young.

The interpretation of these effects will depend on the model for short-term memory processes that we finally adopt. At present, selection between a number of viable alternatives is still not possible. In view of the small magnitude of the interactions between the effects of age and the effects of redundancy, the effects of experimental variables, such as practice, the rate at which the material is presented, and the rate at which Ss can rehearse and recall it, may all turn out to be of crucial importance. Craik's discussion represents a useful advance in the sophistication of attack on problems of age-related decrements in short-term memory. In the context of the present review his data may be cited as reflecting a more general point, in that they are again consistent with the view that the old fail to recognize, or to use, sequential structure in stimulus material as efficiently as the young.

VIII. Further Work

The nature of the experimental evidence reviewed has made it necessary to discuss the concepts of redundancy and structure in terms of a rather loose functional analogy. Readers accustomed to more rigorous mathematical treatments (Shannon & Weaver, 1949; Quastler, 1955; Garner, 1962) will at once recognize that experiments crucial to the point of this review have not yet been made. Some acknowledgement of this fact is due.

Miller (1956) bases a discussion of information transmission by the human operator on the results of a series of studies in which Ss were required to make absolute discriminations among members of a set of stimuli. The maximum number of stimuli between which the S can discriminate in this way is known as his absolute judgment span, and provides an estimate of the amount of information that he can transmit about a given stimulus population. Miller concluded from his review of the evidence that where stimuli differed from each other in terms of a single sensory "dimension" (e.g., salinity, sweetness, pitch, loudness, or color saturation) highly practiced young Ss can reliably discriminate between only 5–9 stimulus states, thus transmitting only 2.3–3.2 bits of information. The choice of any sensory modality or of any dimension of sensitivity of a sensory modality seemed to have little effect on this limitation.

Cases in which Ss make absolute judgments about stimuli which differ in terms of more than one sensory dimension are of considerable theoretical interest. If information transmission is independent for each of several dimensions, the maximum information transmitted about a multidimensional stimulus should be equal to the simple sum of the maximum transmitted for each component dimension in isolation. In fact this does not happen

(Klemmer & Frick, 1953; Pollack & Ficks, 1954). Although the amount of information transmitted increases with the number of dimensions of difference between stimuli, the total transmitted is much less than would be predicted from a model assuming independence of transmission for each dimension.

In calculating the amount of information transmitted for discriminations between complex stimuli, we may discuss the uncertainty of the state of each of these dimensions contingent upon the states of the others. The degree of correlation between the various possible states of component dimensions may, of course, vary from 0 to 1. In the latter case, the state of any one dimension completely specifies the states of all others. In intermediate cases, knowledge of the state of one or other dimension reduces our uncertainty about the state of others. Taking all possible interrelationships into consideration, we can estimate the mean contingent uncertainty for a given situation. In this case an estimate of mean contingent uncertainty for a given set of dimensions will also serve as an estimate of redundancy for a given task. The theoretical improvement in information transmission resulting from any variation in redundancy may then be compared with the actual improvement observed in a given task. In this way we can obtain a direct estimate of the extent to which Ss are able to recognise and use structure in stimulus material to improve their information transmission.

The mathematics necessary for the discussions of bivariate and multivariate contingent uncertainty are elegantly presented by Garner (1962). Experiments by Ericksen and Hake (1955) and by others have already provided estimates for the degree to which young Ss can use redundancy in this way. The implications of these techniques for the argument of the present review are direct and obvious: First, as we have seen, the amount of information transmitted in absolute-judgement tasks is known to increase with the number of dimensions along which stimuli differ. Functions obtained for young people suggest that this is an asymptotic improvement and that performance may actually deteriorate when the number of dimensions of difference exceeds some optimum limit (Garner, 1962). It is likely that comparison data from old Ss will reveal that the improvement of transmission with stimulus dimensionality is less marked for the old than for the young and that, as stimulus complexity increases, a point is sooner reached for the old than for the young at which information transmission is impaired rather than improved.

More important, once the nature of these functions has been ascertained for complex stimuli with uncorrelated dimensions of difference, the relative effects of redundancy on information transmission by old and young Ss can be directly ascertained by testing the effects of various levels of correlation between stimulus dimensions.

IX. Conclusion

As we have seen, the trend of evidence from a number of different tasks suggests that the old are inefficient, rather than merely slow, at transmitting received information. They are unable to ignore irrelevant information in visual search (Rabbitt, 1962, 1965a,b). They do not ignore foresignals, which apparently never help them and often distract them (Botwinick *et. al.*, 1957; Rabbitt, 1964b; Talland, 1965). They process information from redundant signal sources (Rabbitt & Birren, 1967). In pattern learning they fail to abstract economical rules of classification, and so to reduce the range of information which they have to remember (Rabbit, 1964a). Their performance on short-term memory tasks is relatively little improved by the presence of structure in the material which they are required to recall (Craik, this volume).

We may now consider the analogies drawn between obsolescent computers and aged human beings: our first analogy is clearly of only limited utility. With advancing age the human central nervous system may indeed perform any given sequence of operations more slowly. Much evidence from age-related changes in performance in psychomotor tasks suggests that this is so (Welford, 1958; Birren, 1955). The evidence considered earlier, however, forces us to recognize that the old also process information inefficiently. In other words, in terms of the second analogy suggested, the old behave like computers that have been inefficiently programmed rather than simply like computers in which each successive operation is lagged by a time constant. Judged from the point of view of youthful performance, the old appear to carry out more operations than are optimal to perform a wide variety of tasks. Such a statement can have at least two theoretical implications, which need to be distinguished.

First, we may consider the behavior of the old as a precaution against their failing capacities. On such a hypothesis old *S*s would be supposed to consider redundant information because they wish to reduce to a minimum the possibility that they will make errors. This argument has considerable face validity in the particular experimental situations we have discussed. For example, it might be suggested that the old attend to foresignals, as the young do, but unlike the young they do not allow their recognition of the foresignal to reduce the time they spend verifying each reaction signal to which they respond. In a study by Rabbitt (1964b) foresignals were sometimes (though very rarely) false; similarly, in Botwinick *et al.* (1957) expectancies based on foresignals could often be misleading. Talland and Cairnie (1961) gave their *S*s very little practice on a bewildering variety of successively tested foresignal conditions. In all these cases the old might simply have been displaying more caution than the young, in view of real uncertainties as to the informational value of foresignals. Similarly, in an experiment by Rabbitt and Birren (1967) old *S*s *did* benefit from more continuous monitoring of a largely redundant visual display—they made fewer continuation errors than the young. It is true that, in spite of this continuous monitoring, the old *S*s made more errors in total than the young, but we have no means of assessing what their performance would have been had they adopted any less cautious approach to the display.

The generalization that the old compensate by increased caution for real or imagined decrements in performance has been thematic in the literature for some time. The advent of mathematical models for evaluating the levels of confidence with which operations are conducted (Swets, Tanner & Birdsall, 1961) now gives some hope of a quantitative framework for the relation of disconnected observations. Suggestions that signal-detection theory might be applied to age comparisons in discriminations between complex stimuli were made some time ago (Rabbitt, 1962, pp. 6.12–6.15) and a formal consideration of some implications of this metric for studies of aging is now available (Welford, 1962). Experimental investigations are already appearing (Talland, 1966) and further studies will, no doubt, allow a clear statement of what the apparent caution of old *S*s really implies. For the moment it is unwise not to recognize another line of argument equally supported by the data we have considered.

Irrespective of the confidence with which they make perceptual judgments, the failure of the old to use redundancy or to ignore irrelevant information may itself be a symptom of diminished capacity. It is known that young *S*s can efficiently select between relevant and irrelevant aspects of complex stimuli so as to base their perceptual discriminations upon some minimum necessary range of cues (Attneave, 1955, 1957; Fitts *et al.*, 1956; Rabbitt, 1964a). Naturally such "optimal" cues are not self-evident for any given subset of items, but must be recognized and learned. In order to abstract this optimum range of cues it is necessary to store, and to subsequently test against other perceived stimuli, as large a range of stimulus attributes as possible. The type of process we may envisage is logically similar to techniques of autocorrelation used in computers of average transience. Cumulative recordings of successive samples of input allow recurrent critical features to be discriminated from incidental (and therefore transiently occurring) characteristics (i.e., from random noise). The point to be emphasized is that this technique for separation of signal from noise will be sensitive in proportion as the computer can store in some analog form *all* variations in successive input samples. The efficiency of the process of selection and abstraction of critical input features will depend on the "fineness of the grain" with which these analogs of input states can be made. Any reduction in the amount of information that the system can record and store for its successive comparisons will diminish the efficiency of selection.

There is thus considerable point to the third and final analogy proposed between computers and human beings: The efficiency of both types of systems will depend on the amount of information that can be processed at a single sample in a given unit of time. We might therefore hypothesize not only that old people process redundant information because they are cautious, but that they process redundant information because the highly selective information handling of the young is only possible because of their greater information-handling *capacity*.

It remains to justify the use of analogies drawn from computer engineering as explanatory constructs. Two objections may be raised. First, since problems of redundancy and structure in transmitted information have been treated with some rigor (e.g., by Garner, 1962), purists may regard the present attempt to paraphrase these insights in functional terms as a debasement of a good mathematical currency. It may also, rightly, be objected that if we *must* have functional rather than mathematical models for our data, they need not be of this kind. That computer engineering is a developed science with a rich and precise terminology represents a danger as well as an advantage. We may waste time attempting to justify attactive theoretical constructs, derived from the vocabulary we borrow, that may have little to do with the data we hope to explain.

Both these arguments must, in the long run, be admitted and remembered as disciplines to our thinking. However, we cannot escape the fact that in gerontological studies we are obliged to consider relationships between data from many different fields. Performance data and behavioral evidence are often of little interest in the abstract, unless they can be related to biochemical, neuropathological, social, or psychiatric observations. It is less meaningful in this dicipline than in others to dissect out particular aspects of performance and study them in isolation. Apart from their frustrating but necessary complexity, it may be further argued that the kinds of models that we must seek to achieve in gerontology are very different from those that are useful in general experimental psychology. Eventually we must seek to describe a complex process, long drawn out in time, representing the adaptation of central nervous system function to degenerative changes that can occur in many different temporal orders and that may vary in their severity and mutual impact. This is quite unlike the type of model that describes an optimum "steady state" of performance in normal young adult Ss. Our models must be capable of incorporating a very great deal of physiological evidence, and there is an urgent need for such models to replace those currently used.

The distant rapprochement between neurophysiological and behavioral data is a well-established cliché in psychological thinking. In most branches of experimental psychology this goal is so comfortably distant as to be irrelevant to the strategy of current research. Gerontologists, even now, cannot evade these issues, and functional models, even if they are premature, are essential conceptual aids. Since we must have them, an obvious terminology is one that is becoming increasingly popular in both neurophysiology and experimental psychology. If we are forced to live on unwanted territory between these two cultures, it is an advantage to have a language that is comprehensible in both. In adopting "computerese" as a lingua franca we may be forced to repeatedly discover, and to remark aloud, that terms popular in both disciplines (e.g., channel, message) have separate and inconsistent usages in each. We must accept this, and our other social responsibilities, with what dignity we can muster.

ACKNOWLEDGMENT

The author is most grateful to Dr. F. I. M. Craik for an opportunity to read a draft of his chapter before publication.

REFERENCES

Aborn, M., & Rubenstein, H. Information theory and immediate recall. *J. exp. Psychol.*, 1952, **44**, 260–266.

Attneave, F. Symmetry, information and memory for patterns. *Amer. J. Psychol.*, 1955, **68**, 209–22.

Attneave, F. Transfer of experience with a class-schema for identification-learning of patterns and shapes. *J. exp. Psychol.*, 1957, **54**, 81–8.

Baddeley, A. D., Conrad, R., & Hull A. J. Predictability and immediate memory for consonant sequences. *Quart. J. exp. Psychol.*, 1965, **17**, 175–177.

Bertelson, P. Sequential redundancy and speed in a serial two-choice responding task *Quart. J. exp. Psychol.*, 1961, **12**, 90–102.

Birren, J. E. Age-differences to startle reaction-time of the rat to noise and electronic shock. *J. Geront.*, 1955, **10**, 437–40.

Birren, J. E. Principles of research on aging. In J. E. Birren (Ed.), *Handbook of aging and the individual.* Chicago, Ill.: Univer. of Chicago Press, Pp. 3–42.

Botwinick, J., & Brinley, J. F. Analysis of set in relation to reaction time. *J. exp. Psychol.*, 1962, **63**, 568–574.

Botwinick, J., Brinley, J. F., & Birren, J. E. Set in relation to age. *J. Geront.*, 1957, **12**, 300–305.

Broadbent, D. E., & Gregory M. L. Human responses to classes of stimuli. *Nature*, 1962, **193**, 1313.

Ericksen, C. W., & Hake, H. W. Multidimensional stimulus differences and accuracy of discrimination. *J. exp. Psychol.*, 1955, **50**, 153–160.

Fitts, P. M., Weinstein, M., Rappaport, M., Anderson, N., & Leonard, J. A. Stimulus correlates of visual pattern recognition. *J. exp. Psychol.*, 1956, 51, 1–11.

Garner, W. R. *Uncertainty and structure as psychological concepts.* New York: Wiley, 1962.

Griew, S. Learning of statistical structure. A preliminary study in relation to age. In C. Tibbets & W. Donahue (Eds.), *Social and psychological aspects of ageing.* New York: Columbia Univer. Press, 1962. Pp. 124–126.

Hyman, R. Stimulus information as a determinant of reaction-time. *J. exp. Psychol.*, 1953, **45**, 188–196.

Klemmer, E. T., & Frick, F. C. Assimilation of information from dot and matrix patterns. *J. exp. Psychol.*, 1953, **45**, 15–19.

Leonard, J. A. Partial advance information in a choice reaction task. *Brit. J. Psychol.*, 1958, **49**, 89–94.

Leonard, J. A., Newman, R. C., & Carpenter, A. On the handling of heavy bias in a self-paced task. *Quart. J. exp. Psychol.*, 1966, **18**, 130–141.

Miller, G. A. The magical number seven, plus or minus two. *Psychol. Rev.*, 1956, **63**, 81–97.

Miller, G. A., & Selfridge, J. A. Verbal context and the recall of meaningful material. *Amer. J. Psychol.*, 1950, **63**, 176–185.

Pollack, I. Speed of classification of words into superordinate categories. *J. verb. learn. verb. Behav.*, 1963, **2**, 159–165.

Pollack, I., & Ficks, L. Information of elementary multidimensional auditory displays. *J. acoust. Soc. Amer.*, 1954, **31**, 7–8.

Quastler, H. (Ed.) *Information theory in psychology: problems and methods.* New York: Free Press, 1955.

Rabbitt, P. M. A. Perceptual discrimination and the choice of responses. Unpublished doctoral thesis, Univer. of Cambridge, 1962.

Rabbitt, P. M. A. Ignoring irrelevant information. *Brit. J. Psychol.*, 1964, **55**, 403–414. (a)

Rabbitt, P. M. A. Set and Age in a choice-response task. *J. Geront.*, 1964, **19**, 301–306. (b)

Rabbitt, P. M. A. Grouping of stimuli in pattern-recognition as a function of age. *Quart. J. exp. Psychol.*, 1964, 16, 172–176. (c)

Rabbitt, P. M. A. An Age-decrement in the ability to ignore irrelevant information. *J. Geront.*, 1965, **20**, 233–238. (a)

Rabbitt, P. M. A. Age and discrimination between complex stimuli. In A. T. Welford & J. E. Birren (Eds.), *Behaviour, aging and the nervous system.* Springfield, Ill.: Charles Thomas, 1965. Pp. 35–53. (b)

Rabbitt, P. M. A. Age-effects in ignoring redundancy. Paper read at 7th int. Congr. Geront., Vienna, 1966.

Rabbitt, P. M. A. Effects of independent variations in stimulus and response probability, *Nature*, 1959, **183**, 1212.

Rabbitt, P. M. A. Learning to ignore irrelevant information. *Amer. J. Psychol.*, 1967, **80**, 1–13.

Rabbitt, P. M. A., & Birren, J. E. Age and responses to sequences of repetitive and interruptive signals. *J. Geront.*, 1967, **22**, 143–150.

Rabbitt, P. M. A., & Rogers, M. Age and Choice between responses in a self-paced repetitive task. *Ergonomics*, 1965, **8**, 435–444.

Shannon, C. E., & Weaver. *The mathematical theory of communication.* Urbana, Ill.: Univer. of Illinois Press, 1949.

Swets, J. A., Tanner, W. P., & Birdsall, T. G. Decision processes in perception. *Psychol. Rev.*, 1961, 68, 301–340.

Talland, G. A. Initiation of response, and reaction time in ageing, and with brain damage. In A. T. Welford and J. E. Birren (Eds.), *Behaviour, ageing and the nervous system.* Springfield, Ill.: Charles C. Thomas, 1965. Pp. 526–561.

Talland, G. A. Continuous performance changes with age in signal detection. Paper presented at 7th int. Congr. Geront., Vienna, 1966.

Talland, G. A., & Cairnie, J. Ageing effects on simple disjunctive and alerted finger reaction-time. *J. Geront.*, 1961, **16**, 370–374.

Welford, A. T. *Ageing and human skills.* London & New York: Oxford Univer. Press, 1958. (For the Nuffield Foundation.)

Welford, A. T. Arousal, channel capacity and decision. *Nature*, 1962, **194**, 365–366.

Zahn, T. P., & Rosenthal D. Simple reaction time as a function of the relative frequency of the preparatory interval. *J. exp. Psychol.*, 1966, **72**, 15–19.

Age and the Span of Immediate Recall*

GEORGE A. TALLAND

Harvard University Medical School
Massachusetts General Hospital
Boston, Massachusetts

I. Introduction: Learning, Memory, and the Attention Span

A. Age and Memory

Old people are notorious for remembering long past events in minute detail, and also for their propensity to forget recent experiences and novel information. Some of those old memories may not be quite accurate, others may be so vivid because they have been revived many times over the

*This research was carried out with the help of a research career development grant (HD 15418) and a research project grant (HD 00340) from the National Institutes of Health, United States Public Health Service. Several of the experiments were conducted in conjunction with the normative aging research of the Veterans Administration Clinic, Boston, Massachusetts.

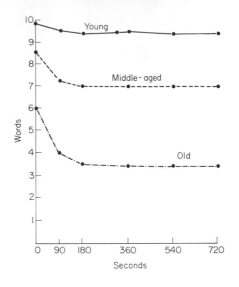

Fig. 1. Forgetting curves of meaningful CVC words in repeated recall. Young men ($N=20$) aged 20–25; middle-aged men and women ($N=40$), aged 47–62 (mean 58); old men ($N=20$), aged 77–89 (mean 81).

years, but there is no reason to doubt that the ability to retain new information in a readily accessible state deteriorates with age. This decline can
be attributed to an impairment of the mechanisms active in either the
acquisition or the retention of new information, and there is experimental
evidence to support both explanations. Indeed, it seems quite probable that
efficiency declines with age in all the processes that are involved in memory
function, in recall and recognition as well as in the initial acquisition of
information and whatever mechanisms subserve the storage of information.

A series of experiments in paired-associate learning has demonstrated
a deficit in middle age, and a still greater loss in old age, in verbal learning
ability (Ruch, 1934; Gilbert, 1935, 1941; Korchin & Basowitz, 1957; Gladis
& Braun, 1958; Wimer, 1960; Canestrari, 1963; Arenberg, 1965). A study
by Hulicka and Weiss (1965) is notable for showing that the difference
between old and young may be restricted to the efficiency with which
each establishes new associations and that, if older Ss are allowed enough
trials or time to reach the same criterion of initial learning as the young,
retention does not vary with age. This view is also borne out by Talland's
(1966) experiments with repeated free recall of meaningful and meaningless consonant-vowel-consonant (CVC) words, as illustrated in Figs. 1
and 2. Recall immediately after the 3-min. period of learning is at a
lower level with each successive age group, but the shapes of the forgetting
curves are quite similar, except for the youngest group's almost perfect
retention of natural words.

There is thus strong, though not undisputed, experimental evidence that the capacity to acquire new verbal information deteriorates with age more powerfully than the other mechanisms of memory function. In operational terms, immediate recall or short-term rentention (STR) declines most steadily with advancing years. This trend is so strongly marked that Welford (1962) attributed the performance decrement with age in seemingly quite unrelated skills and problem-solving tasks to this source. Experiments probing STR are therefore particularly germane to gerontological research, and in fact have been used by a number of investigators for this purpose.

B.   What is Tested in Immediate Recall?

Experiments with paired associates are typically used to test learning. Lists of arbitrary couplings of verbal items are presented to the S repeatedly or for some time so that he can learn them to a criterion of mastery. The experiments differ in the criterion imposed, as well as in content and procedure. Variations in all these experimental conditions make for different functional relationships between performance and chronological age. Comparisons between very old persons and those in the prime of life, of course, show the former at a disadvantage in tests of virtually any cognitive function. It does not follow, though, that such differences represent an advanced stage in a progressive change over the adult decades. Results of tests of verbal learning, and more especially of STR, offer a

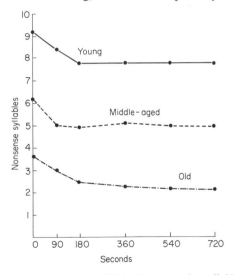

Fig. 2. Forgetting curves of CVC nonsense syllables in repeated recall. Young men (N=20) aged 20–25; middle-aged men and women (N=40), aged 47–62 (mean 58); old men (N=20) aged 77–89 (mean 81).

wide variety of curves, including examples of relative stability as well as of declining proficiency, over the span of maturity. Differences between these curves throw light on the mechanisms that deteriorate with advancing age and that should be considered as distinct components of the complex functions involved in learning and memory.

The procedure most widely used to test STR entails the single presentation of a message, and immediate testing of its recall or recognition. The messages may consist of grammatically correct and meaningful sentences, but usually they are arbitrarily assembled strings of discrete items (digits, letters, nonsense syllables, or natural words) or, less commonly, pairs of such items in any combination. The material is deliberately constructed so as to minimize the S's opportunity to use his previous experience or tactical skills in its organization for retention (Posner, 1965). This would seem to be a device designed to penalize older people, although in view of their inefficiency in applying one kind of organizing tactics, namely, the formation of mediators (Hulicka & Grossman, 1976; Chapter by Canestrari in this volume), STR experiments may not favor the young for this reason.

More serious is the objection to STR techniques on the ground that they are quite remote from instances of learning and remembering in real-life situations. This criticism applies particularly to tests of serial recall, in which the material to be memorized consists of extremely familiar items (e.g., digits) and all that has to be learned is their sequential arrangement. The argument advanced for extrapolations from STR experiments to memory processes that are more familiar from life situations is based chiefly on observations (Melton, 1963; Postman, 1964) of close parallels between the slopes of forgetting curves and between certain characteristic types of failures in these experiments and in long-term memory (LTM). These parallels, however, may be superficial and may but reflect that there are only so many ways in which information can be forgotten or misremembered.

Tests of recall employing content as simple, uniform, and overlearned as digits or the letters of the alphabet may indeed depend for successful performance on the execution of certain mental operations that are also necessary for remembering an appointment, the plot of a story, or the latest rule on income tax allowances. Performance in such tests could therefore be used for predictions of performance in life situations, but STR experiments represent a limiting case in learning and serve at most the purpose of determining one boundary of the S's capacity to acquire new information. This is the justification of their inclusion in tests of mental ability. They are not a miniature version of those processes that constitute the feats and failures of human memory.

Only in special circumstances does remembering consist of the exact reproduction of unrelated items, and only rarely would memory be tested immediately after the registration of its content. A combination of these circumstances is still less characteristic of human memory, yet both are present in STR experiments. The inadequacy of standard STR techniques as tests of memory has also been demonstrated empirically. The most widely used procedure to determine STR, the standard digit span, has repeatedly been shown (Wechsler, 1917; Zangwill, 1943; Talland, 1965a), to be within the normal range in severely amnesic Korsakoff patients, who instantly forget all new information and rarely manage to recollect even quite recent personal experiences.

Nevertheless, STR methods do test a component in learning and remembering; they test the S's capacity to transmit information. This applies primarily to incoming information, and to some extent to the recovery of information stored in LTM as well. As Klemmer (1962) has pointed out, man does not transmit information with its physical parameters intact; he does so by recoding and decoding it. One such coding operation is required to transfer a visual message into an acoustic delivery system. By means of appropriate coding operations, information is transmitted through the central nervous system alike in tasks that are completed with the immediate response—manual or verbal—and in those that involve registering information for future availability. Proficiency in various skills depends on the operator's capacity to transmit information, a capacity that can be estimated by suitable tests of STR. Memory may also be determined by this capacity at the stage of registration, but it is neither self evident nor empirically proven that this capacity is always a principal determining factor.

To avoid unwarranted conclusions, the span of STR should be designated as the attention span rather than as a memory span. It is usually referred to as the immediate or short-term memory span, yet it is contrary to customary usage to speak of memory when neither delay nor distraction intervenes between the presentation of some information and its recall or recognition.

II. Experiments with the Stable Item Span

A. Tests of the Word Span

There are more ways than one to determine a person's word span. Since meaningful sentences contain redundancies due to grammatical constraints, strings of disconnected words furnish a truer estimate. These words can be familiar or rarely used, possibly drawn from a foreign language, or indeed artificially constructed; they can be short or long, easy to pronounce or acoustically difficult; they can be uniform in regard to these properties or mixed. Even disregarding the varieties in the attributes of the words, the method of testing allows for several different measures of the span. It can be determined by the number of words correctly reported from a list, with or without allowance for incorrect responses, or set at the length of a list that the S can reliably recite without error or omission. In all such tests of STR the very performance of recall creates conditions in which information is lost.

There is experimental evidence that the amount of information available immediately after receiving a message of several unrelated items is underestimated by the usual tests of free or serial recall (Anderson, 1960; Sperling, 1960; Buschke, 1963). The technique employed to avoid the loss of information that follows from the recitation of a list is to call for the reproduction of only one item from the message presented. Since the S does not know which item will be asked until after completion of the message, he must attempt to retain them all in order to have it available. Judged by correct responses in this type of test, the STR span is longer than it is when measured by free or serial recitation.

Partial recall eliminates forgetting through interference and possible decay that would affect items held in store while the preceding items are spoken or written down; it eliminates a source of forgetting that has been referred to as *destructive readout*. Partial recall does, however, demand mental operations that could result in just as much interference with STR, namely the selection of the appropriate item, that involves scanning and testing for fit. An experiment with the word span was conducted to assess the interference effects of these operations and of alternate procedures for immediate recall.

1.   Method

The purpose of the experiment was to determine any changes that may occur in the word span of healthy, normal people over five consecutive decades of adulthood. Three techniques were used to estimate the word span: free recall; partial, or *selective*, recall; and a method that combined the disadvantages of both these techniques, which will be referred to as *restrictive* recall. The messages presented consisted of unrelated monosyllabic words, all familiar and in frequent use, presented well above the threshold of intelligibility from a recorded tape at the rate of one word per second. For free recall, lists ranged in length from four to thirteen items, all different words. For selective recall, lists of 4, 5, 6, or 7 words were presented in strings that repeated all but one of them in the second part.

Experiments in partial recall raise the problem of indicating the item selected for recall, without dropping a hint at the time of presentation. Several devices have been employed for this purpose, and perhaps none is entirely satisfactory. In the present experiment a method devised by

Yntema and Trask (1963) was used, according to which each item listed in the first half of the string is repeated in a different order in the second half, except for one. The *S*'s task is to report the one unrepeated item; he does not know which it is until the end of the string has been reached, although if he can process information fast enough, he could try to discard each item as it arrives a second time. The same type of string was also used to test restrictive recall, with the instruction that the *S* repeat every word but hold to the end the word that was presented only once. This task gives rise to all the interference from recitation and from the categorizing or other processing operations demanded by selective recall. In addition, it imposes on the *S* the burden of holding in separate store a specially selected item while he is engaged in delivering all the others.

The design of the experiment has been described in a published report (Talland, 1965b), as have the results in some detail. Here they will be summarized, as much for comparison with the results of the other experiments discussed as for the conclusions drawn from them. The *S*s, as in all the experiments reported here, were drawn from a pool of men, screened by various medical examinations, who represented a stratum rather above the population mean in regard to health and intelligence. All had been to high school and held, or had recently retired from, clerical jobs. Two hundred *S*s were tested, forty representing each decade between 20 and 69 years of age.

2.   Results and Discussion

Judged by faultless performance, recall varied with age under the three conditions of testing as shown in Fig. 3. It is apparent that the word span by free recall did not change monotonically with age; indeed, the men in

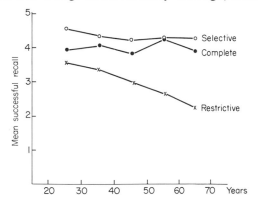

Fig. 3. The word span tested by three different methods. Mean success of recall according to instruction in eight trials compared by age.

the sixth decade reached the highest mean level and the oldest group obtained the same average score as the youngest. In selective recall also, variability among Ss in any one age group was high enough to prevent the slight progressive trend over the early phase of maturity from reaching statistical significance. Only in restrictive recall was there a steady decline with each successive decade, and this effect proved significant ($p < .01$).

Faultless performance in restrictive recall entailed reproducing the entire list and reporting the unrepeated word after all the others. The gradual and significant narrowing of the word span with advancing age, however, was evident even with the alternative and less stringent criteria of (a) complete recall without regard to the postition of the unrepeated word; (b) reporting the unrepeated word last, without regard to the number of other items reproduced from the list; (c) number of items correctly reproduced in any order.

Judged by the number of words reported rather than by complete reproduction of the list, free recall did not change significantly with age with lists of seven words or fewer. With lists of nine words the oldest decade performed significantly less well than the others; with lists of eleven words the significant difference arose between the two oldest and the three younger age groups; with the longest list the dividing line dropped by another decade. Errors by incorrect response were few; they tended to increase with the length of the list, and varied only slightly with the condition of testing or with age. Since each S was tested twice on lists of a given length under each instruction, a measure was available to evaluate his consistency in performing at capacity level. In restrictive recall this index of consistency, as well as the mean level of performance, diminished with advancing age.

Viewed as a measure of transmitting information with minimal transformation, or indeed of STR without regard to hypothetical models of neuropsychological function, the most striking finding of this experiment is the narrow compass of the word span. The messages, it should be stressed, consisted of common, acoustically unambiguous, monosyllabic English words; the rate of presentation was quite comfortable and recall proceeded at the S's chosen pace. Interference spreading from one list to the next, moreover, was excluded by interpolating series of ten tests of reaction time between any two word lists. Nevertheless, the mean span of 200 men fell below four and one half words by partial recall, and barely rose above four words by free recall. Not one of the Ss succeeded in reproducing a list of nine or eleven words, so that the "magical number seven" that Miller (1956) recognised as a modal value of STR in student Ss, here exercised its power by setting an upper limit.

Age would hardly account for the differences between the word span in this experiment and other similar experiments, since our youngest group overlapped in age with the student population, and their mean ages could be but a few years apart. Furthermore, one of the conclusions to be drawn from this experiment is that, tested by free recall, the word span is quite stable between the ages of 20 and 70 years. Neither does the word span by partial recall diminish significantly over that period of five decades, but restrictive recall, as defined in the present experiment, makes for a progressively smaller word span with advancing age, no matter how that span is determined.

It is apparent that the change with age takes place in those machanisms that are called into operation by the instruction for restrictive recall. These mechanisms are in part identical with those operating under instructions for free or selective recall. The one additional demand imposed on the S by restrictive recall is that he hold in reserve a specially defined item while he is reciting the remainder of the list. This requirement increases the difficulty of the task for young as well as for old Ss; yet, when judged by the same criteria of performance, the young men equaled their word span under instructions for restrictive and free recall. Undoubtedly the repeated presentation of the major part of the list compensated for the heavier processing load imposed by the restrictive instruction. This compensatory equation gradually broke down with advancing age.

There is no reason to assume that the advantage of hearing the same word twice diminishes with increasing age; indeed, if there is any reason for supposing that such factors as reduced sensory acuity or fluctuating attention may place older people at a disadvantage in STR experiments, a second chance to hear—and check—a word should be of more use to the older Ss than to the young. Their difficulties, therefore, must stem from the effort to perform simultaneously the two operations of holding an item in a special compartment and of delivering others from a common store of STR. That older people have more difficulty in tests of STR when part of the message must be held over in the course of recall has been demonstrated by Inglis (1965) and Taub and Greiff (1967), using entirely different experimental procedures. Probably the operations of delivering parts of the message and holding another part are not exactly simultaneous, but alternate in rapid succession, as they must if a limited-capacity processing system, as postulated, e.g., by Broadbent (1958), is transacting both operations. A slowing down of the rate at which a S can alternate between two parallel operations is characteristic of advancing age (Botwinick, Brinley & Robbin, 1958; Welford, 1958; Talland, 1959), as is a decrement in performance of two tasks performed simultaneously (Broadbent & Heron, 1962; Talland, 1962).

The exact conditions of this experiment with restrictive recall are, of course, remote from the usual circumstances of learning and remembering. The requirement to hold some portion of the information input apart while processing the remainder, however, is quite common both at the stage of registering information and of its retrieval. To be sure, the operations in these instances are not those of overt recital, but neither is the source of interference the vocal aspect of the response. Sequentially presented information is not always most effectively encoded in the order of its arrival, nor is it necessarily always reproduced in the order of its emergence in memory. The companion who plies you with his reminiscences just as they flow in the amorphous shapes of free association is apt to become a bore. The conversationist or advocate who can save the telling point for the most dramatic moment is more likely to be entertaining or to score a hit. A number of factors determine one's success in conversation or debate, and some people may improve in effectiveness as they grow older and more experienced or more secure, but quite a few become bores.

B.   Tests of the Digit Span

Immediate recall, as tested by the standard digit span, changes but little over the years of maturity. Bromley (1958) found no significant difference between the performances, repeating the strings in forward order, of three groups with mean ages of 27.0, 46.5, and 66.5 years, respectively. Gilbert (1941) ascertained a deficit of 8% at the age of 60 as compared with early maturity, and according to Wechsler's (1955) population norms the digit span drops less than 20% below peak level by the end of the eighth decade; his test, moreover, includes reciting digits backward as well as forward. Reciting a message in reverse creates special problems of transformation; the digit span forward, however, imposes only the constraint of serial recall, and that is almost invariably the easiest way to reproduce a list immediately after presentation. Recitation, of course, creates its own impediments to perfect recall, but these do not change systematically with age, as was apparent, e.g., from the word span tested by free recall. Moreover, the digit span is usually administered in gradual steps of increasing information load, beginning with a fairly short string that is then successively extended by one item. In mental testing, at any rate, the S is not carried many steps past his capacity. This procedure may indeed favor older people, for there is reason to believe (Welford, 1958; Kay, 1959) that their difficulties in STR arise chiefly with messages that exceed their span.

   The span of immediate recall is, as Miller (1956) has shown, about seven digits, allowing for one or two more or less. It is safe to assume that numbers of nine digits exceed the digit span of the average S, and for this reason several experiments testing the STR of nine-place numbers have been conducted in recent years. Specifically, the reason is that Hebb (1961) used this test to demonstrate that a single presentation of a message produces a structural trace that can be cumulative. This conclusion radically challenges the dual-trace model of memory for which Hebb (1948) had, for many years, been the most persuasive spokesman.

Hebb's interpretation of his experiment with the digit span has understandably aroused the interest of some psychologists concerned with the problems of aging, for it promised a clue to that change which manifests itself in a reduced capacity to learn and remember with advancing age. Perhaps it is the capacity to form structural traces in a single trial that diminishes with age, and perhaps this diminution comes about because of an increase in neural "noise" with the cumulative loss of neurons from the brain, an explanation put forward by Crossman and Szafran (1956) and Welford (1958).

Caird (1966), using Hebb's technique, found that his old Ss, free from memory disorder, improved in recall with repeated presentation of the test number. Heron and Craik (1964) followed Hebb's procedure to the extent of presenting the same number in every third position, while all other numbers occurred only once, but these numbers consisted of either five or eight digits. The study comprised three experiments that differed in several respects, and its conclusions regarding the interaction of aging and cumulative learning effects, are contradictory. The authors did, however, report an unpublished experiment by Rabbitt, who presented messages of seven digits according to Hebb's procedure, and observed the cumulative effect in young, but not in middle-aged, men.

1. Method

The experiment to be discussed deviated further still from Hebb's model, though only in some details of design, which were closer to Melton's (1963). As in Hebb's and Melton's experiments, the messages consisted of nine digits and were presented both vocally (as by Hebb) and visually (as by Melton). In addition to messages presented as continuous numbers, there was a vocal and a visual version of the experiment in which the messages were broken up into triplets. All responses were written on separate 3 × 5-inch cards for each trial. The presentation time of the message—whether visual or auditory, continuous or broken into triplets—was uniformly 3 sec; recall began 1 sec after the termination or removal of the message and had to be completed within 9 sec; the next message was presented after an interval of 10 sec.

Each message included every digit except zero, and the fifty-two different messages compiled were divided into four sets, so that within each set a sequence of any two digits occurred no more than twice. The thirteen messages within each set were presented in the following order: a-b-c-d-e-b-e-d-f-d-c-g-f-b-h-i-f-j-k-g-k-l-h-l-m. A second or third listing of a letter represents the first or second repetition of the message, and these occurred at intervals of two, four, or eight places. Within each set, four different lists were compiled so that different numbers (messages) were unrepeated or twice repeated, and each was repeated once with approximately equal frequency. Associations between sets and conditions of presentation and of sequences within sets were balanced across Ss within an age group.

This design called for 16 Ss per group, and these were drawn from the same population as described in Section II, A, although made up of different samples. The order of the four conditions of presentation—auditory-continuous (Ac), auditory triplets (At), visual continuous (Vc), visual triplets (Vt)—was also systematically balanced within each age group, and the group of 25 trials under each of these conditions was separated from the next by some other experiment taking from 12 to 25 min.

2. Results and Discussion

Performance in this experiment, as in that testing word span by free recall, can be evaluated either by the number of digits written down in the correct order or by the number of faultless reports. The latter criterion demands the reproduction of all nine digits in the order of presentation; the former, in this instance, gave credit for every digit written down in the correct order from left to right, but disallowing all entries to the right of the first error or gap. Figures 4–11 illustrate the variation in the digit span with age according to all trials; first, second, and third occurrence; method of presentation, and subdividing the latter by modality, and by the continuity or grouping of the message.

It is apparent from these charts that (a) there is a tendency for performance to deteriorate with age; (b) this trend is both more continuous and

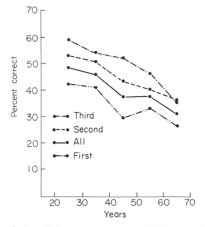

Fig. 4. Complete recall of nine digits, presented once (13), twice (9), or three times (3), and pooling all 25 trials; combining the four methods of presentation: means by five age groups.

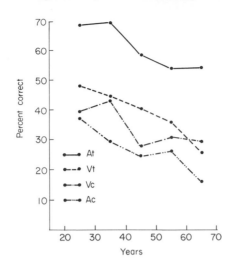

Fig. 5. Complete recall of nine-digit numbers according to method of presentation: auditory continuous (Ac), auditory triplets (At), visual continuous (Vc), and visual triplets (Vt); means by five age groups.

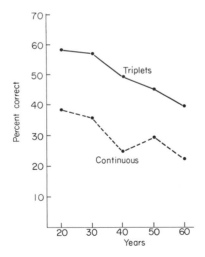

Fig. 6. Complete recall of nine-digit numbers presented without a break and presented in three triplets; means by five age groups.

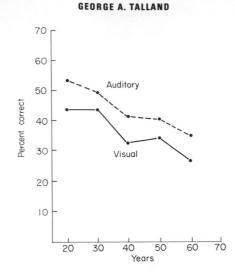

Fig. 7. Complete recall of nine-digit numbers presented aurally and visually; means by five age groups.

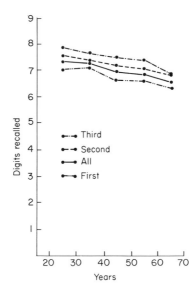

Fig. 8. Serial recall of items from nine-digit numbers presented once, twice, or three times, and pooling all 25 trials; percentage correct by five age groups.

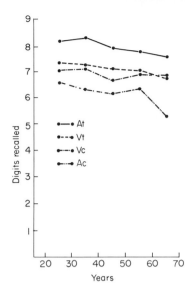

Fig. 9. Serial recall from nine-digit numbers according to method of presentation: auditory continuous (Ac), auditory triplets (At), visual continuous (Vc), visual triplets (Vt); percentage correct by five age groups.

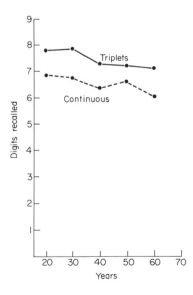

Fig. 10. Serial recall from nine-digit numbers according to continuous or grouped (triplets) presentation; percentage correct by five age groups.

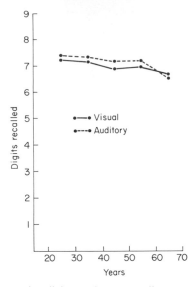

Fig. 11. Serial recall from nine-digit numbers according to sensory channel of input; percentage correct by five age groups.

slower when recall is evaluated by the number of digits recalled; and (c) that the trends indicated vary only slightly with method of presentation or with first or repeated exposure to the message. The effects of age and of its interaction with the several experimental variables on STR in this experiment were examined more exactly by analysis of variance. In these statistical tests the variances attributable to age were tested against the between-S variance, the variance attributable to the interaction of age with an experimental variable against the interaction of the same variable with differences among Ss.

Dividing the 80 subjects into five equal age groups according to decade, no significant effect attributable to age could be determined with either criterion of performance. The interaction between age and repetition was significant ($p < .01$) in regard to digits recalled but not to complete recall of messages. Further analysis disclosed that this interaction effect stemmed from the larger gain the three older decades derived from a first repetition, and the smaller additional gain they derived from a second repetition, of the message as compared with that of the two youngest decades. Moreover, the failure of the oldest decade to improve on its score after a first repetition, when the message occurred a third time, also contributed significantly to this source of variance. In other words, the interaction between age and repetition was significant if the sample of 80 subjects was divided into two groups, with either 40 or 60 years of age as the dividing line.

It is apparent from the graphs that the two youngest decades differed little in performance, and that men in their forties were as apt to fall behind those in their fifties as to exceed them. The Ss were therefore regrouped into three divisions, one comprising all the men under 40, another those between 40 and 59, and the third those over 60. With this threefold division, the variance contributed by age proved significant ($p < .05$), in complete recall, whereas none of the interactions with age, except continuity versus grouping into triplets, proved significant. The oldest decade derived less advantage from grouping the message into triplets than the men under 60. Judged by the number of digits recalled, there was no significant difference attributable to age or to interactions with age.

From these results it appears that there is indeed a progressive decrement in STR for messages of digits exceeding the span, and that over four decades it amounts to over 50%, if performance is evaluated by complete reproduction and the messages are presented vocally at a continuous rate of one item per second. With visual presentation, with messages broken into three groups of three digits, or judged by the number of digits recalled, the age-related decrement is considerably smaller. Even so, the loss in STR capacity over the adult years is larger with messages that exceed the immediate span of recall than with similar messages that do not exceed it.

The span itself, of course, is a statistical concept. We regard a string of nine digits as exceeding the span because none of the subjects of this or other experiments can reliably reproduce it under the conditions of presentation or testing. The remarkable fact is that, divided into three units and presented vocally, messages of nine digits were recalled without error in more than half the trials at all ages. Even under the least favorable conditions of presentation over one quarter of the trials was successful, although in the oldest age group the percentage was lower. Yet when STR was tested with lists of nine monosyllabic words, not one trial in 400 proved successful. Judged by the number of items correctly recalled, from lists with continuous auditory presentation, performance according to age groups in the present and preceding experiments is as shown in Table 1. Serial recall may not be more difficult, but it is no easier than free recall; the effect of a faster presentation rate is controversial, as Conrad and Hille (1958) found that it improved recall but Pollack, Johnson, and Knaff (1959), and Mackworth (1962) arrived at the opposite conclusion. It seems therefore that, Pollack's (1953) and Miller's (1956) arguments notwithstanding, the span of immediate recall is not independent of the vocabulary size or, in technical terms, of the information per message unit.

Comparing the age trends in the two experiments, it seems that the advantage of a smaller vocabulary drops off considerably above the age of 60 years. This conclusion would agree with other observations about age

TABLE I

MEAN NUMBER OF ITEMS CORRECTLY RECALLED PER TRIAL IN FREE RECALL
OF LISTS OF NINE WORDS AND NINE-DIGIT NUMBERS[a]

Type of item	Age group (years)				
	20–29	30–39	40–49	50–59	60–69
Words	5.2	5.4	5.2	5.3	5.0
Digits	6.6	6.3	6.2	6.4	5.3

[a]Details of experiments are presented in Section II, A and B.

changes in STR if the reconstruction of nine-digit numbers depended on filling in gaps by scanning the vocabulary for a missing item. The interaction between age and information per message unit, although supported by Heron and Craik (1964), still needs to be demonstrated.

The decline in STR for strings of digits in excess of the reproduction span is not a continuous function of age. There is a drop at about the age of 40 and another at about 60 years. That STR judged by the number of digits recalled shows no significant change with age confirms an observation, made in tests of reaction time (Talland, 1965c), that quite apart from a lowering of capacity, the effects of aging are manifested in a diminution of the probability that an S will perform at capacity level. If possible, he may compensate for this shortcoming by performing more consistently well just below that level than do younger people.

Regarding the principal experimental variables, there is little evidence that they interact with age in determining the span of STR. Whatever the mechanism by which repeated presentation of a nine-digit number raises the probability of its recall over that of its previous presentation, it is unimpaired by age. The gain from first repetition was confirmed by the experiment, and this gain increased with age over the five decades sampled. The additional advantage of a second repetition is also evident, and seems stable over the span embracing the first four decades of adulthood. It was not found in the performance of our men over 60 years of age, nor was it absent because of any increased susceptibility to proactive interference, the reason Heron and Craik (1964) advanced for the failure of their older Ss to show cumulative learning. The same slight trend of improved performance over the 25 consecutive trials was as evident in the performance of the oldest as in that of the younger groups.

The conventional method of presenting messages for immediate recall, i.e., auditory presentation at a constant rate, seems to be quite unfavorable, at any rate with lists exceeding the span. In order to take in messages of nine unrelated items, it helps considerably if they are broken down into smaller units. Other studies (Gill & Dallenbach, 1926; Fraisse, 1937) have demonstrated the advantage of grouping for STR, and the present experiment has shown that, contrary to the conclusion of Pollack, Johnson, and Knaff (1959), this advantage is quite effective with messages of known length, and is much more marked when the messages are presented vocally rather than in print. With visual presentation, it is not too difficult for the S to break up the message into segments of convenient size, and this is the most likely reason why performance was not so far apart under the two conditions of visual presentation. If this explanation is correct, it also follows that the efficiency with which messages are thus broken up does not diminish with advancing age.

McGhie, Chapman, and Lawson (1965) noted that the visual digit span deteriorates with age more than the auditory span, and attributed this difference to the processes by which visual input is transformed into acoustic messages for storage. In accordance with several other experimental findings, older people were found to be apt to lose more information in the course of such transformation than younger ones. Murdock (1966), moreover, has shown that the recency effect operates more strongly with auditory than with visual presentation in tests of STR; in other words, recall from auditory messages depends more on the terminal items. On this consideration also, as will be shown later, older people should derive a greater advantage from auditory presentation. In fact, however, they did not; it is also worth noting, though, that with auditory triplets performance was about the same in the three oldest decades.

III. Experiments with the Running Item Span

A.   Continuous Performance Tasks and the Running Digit Span

The experiment with nine-digit numbers has shown, as have other experiments, the advantage for STR of organization even as simple as the grouping of message units. The poorer the organization of the message, the less its availability. The lability of information in STR is especially marked in continuous monitoring tasks that keep on presenting the S with new signals while he is still processing or responding to earlier ones. Processing information from a continuous flow of input need not be a particularly difficult task as long as we may alternately take in suitable portions of the information and organize it or respond to it before more is added to it. The difficulty of this task increases at a steep rate, and rapidly becomes unmanageable if one has to pay attention to a series of unrelated consecutive items and always respond to that which arrived several steps back. Experiments demanding such delayed responses to signals that arrive in rapid succession have demonstrated how limited the human operator's capacity is in these circumstances (Mackworth & Mackworth, 1959; Mackworth, 1959) and that this capacity shrinks with age (Kay, 1953; Kirchner, 1958).

Tests of the running digit span, like certain tasks of continuous detection and inspection, demand a progressive shift in the focus of attention (that is, the discarding of some items while new ones are registered). Successful performance requires a continually changing separation of the message into noise and signal components. Items that constitute the signal rapidly lose that property, and information is easily lost in the course of this continual recoding of the input.

Unlike tests of the stable digit span, those of the running digit span call only for the reproduction of the terminal segment of the string. The extent of this segment, the reproduction range, can be limited to, e.g., the three, five, or seven last items, or it can be left open. Although Pollack, Johnson and Knaff (1959) studied the running digit span with messages of both known and unknown length, only the latter provides a proper test, for if the S knows in advance how many items there will be from beginning to end, he can ignore all that arrive before the final segment.

Whether the operations demanded by the running item span are also involved in the acquisition or retrieval of memories or not, empirically this test has been found to be sensitive to gross memory disorders, even where the standard digit span shows no deficit (Talland, 1965a; Talland, Mendelson, Koz, & Aaron, 1965). Patients with the Korsakoff syndrome or senile dementia performed very poorly on this task because they tended to reproduce the initial items of the list instead of the terminal ones. They seemed incapable of ridding themselves of the first part of the message, and whatever they retained of it occupied their slender storage capacity.

Since the loss of capacity observed in the normal course of aging, particularly the decline in memory function, has at times been viewed as an intermediate stage between intact and pathological function, for example, as in senile dementia (Inglis, 1965), it is of interest to examine the effect of age on the running memory span. The first question is whether the ability to discard the initial items diminishes with the advancing years. If it does, there could be still other reasons for declining proficiency in this type of performance, such as a differential utilization of the primacy and recency effects. Tests of the running item span, in addition to demanding considerable flexibility in information processing, also cut off an important source of the span of immediate recall by disallowing the initial segment of the list (Waugh, 1960).

Data collected in our laboratory from groups of 15–30 men and women representing each decade between the fourth and ninth, showed a gradual drop in the running item span in stages of 3.9, 3.7, 3.5, 3.4, 3.3, and 3.2 items. These means represent a decline no steeper than that observed with the standard digit span, and at no point reach the low levels characteristic of, e.g., amnesic patients. The procedure by which they were obtained consisted of four strings of digits and four strings of consonants 10, 18, 8, and 12 items long, with a reproduction range of five. Since the restriction to recall only the last five items may have differentially affected the different age groups, and because these were not matched on some possibly relevant attributes, a series of experiments was conducted expressly to test any effect that age may exert on the running item span.

Five experiments were conducted, each with different groups of men representing in equal numbers the five decades between 20 and 69 years. They were all employed or had all retired from clerical jobs and had no known record of chronic illness, especially of a psychiatric or neurological disorder. They were either made available for the study by their employer during working hours or were paid volunteers.

Every subject, except in Experiment II, was tested on the running item span under two different conditions, at the beginning and, the end of an experimental session that lasted about 2 hours and included other performance tests. Alternate representatives of an age group began with one or the other matched version.

A test consisted of a series of discrete trials. In all experiments but Ia sixteen strings of items were presented in an order randomized for length; three each were composed of 8, 9, 15, and 17; two of 14; and one each of 11 and 16 items. They were compiled either from the series of numbers between one and ten or from the consonants of the alphabet, excluding W. Presentation was auditory, by means of a recorded tape, and at a comfortable level of intelligibility. A soft buzzer marked the end of each string, and S was alerted to observe that signal. Items were presented uniformly at the rate of one per second; response was unpaced, its manner and terms were specified by the instruction given at the beginning of the test, and were demonstrated in two practice trials. For written response S received a scoring sheet with sixteen printed rows of twelve square boxes. The running item span was measured after each trial by the sun of items reported in the correct position—serial or absolute—from the end of the string back to a run of three errors or three blank spaces.

B. Experiment I: Spoken Letter Span with Limited Reproduction
    Range and Written Unlimited Digit Span

1. Method

Each of the five decades was represented by 40 Ss. Experiment Ia tested the running item span with strings of consonants constructed to avoid sequences resembling natural words. They ranged in length from 11 to 30 items, and were presented in a standard randomized order. The *S* was told that he would hear several lists consisting of meaningless sequences of letters, that they would vary in length and would be too long to be memorized in full. His task was to report the last seven letters from each list, or as many of these as he could remember, in the order in which he had heard them, and he was also warned that no credit would be given for letters other than the last seven.

Experiment Ib tested the running item span with thirty-two strings of digits, the first sixteen presented monaurally, the second sixteen binaurally. Monaural presentation meant that the messages were fed to one ear only, eight strings to the left and another eight to the right ear in an unbroken run. Binaural presentation was identical for the message, but each number was shadowed by the simultaneous presentation of a letter to the other ear. The instruction was to ignore the letters, and report the numbers only. Under both conditions the subject wrote down his answers, so that his record corresponded to the order of presentation, with the last number in the list on the extreme right but with no constraint to enter his responses in any particular order. Care was taken to explain this instruction and to test its observance by practice trials.

2. Results and Discussion

Figure 12 compares the mean letter spans of the five age groups with their digit span scored for order only, and with their reproduction of the last seven digits in the correct order. Figure 13 replicates the unlimited digit span for order, along with performance according to instruction, i.e., recording absolute positions, under both monaural and binaural presentation.

All estimates of the running item span show a downward trend with

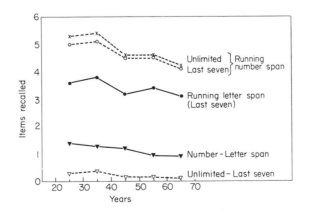

Fig. 12. Running item spans at five age levels for letters and digits (Experiments Ia and Ib).

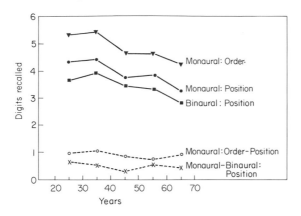

Fig. 13. Running digit spans, at five age levels, with monaural presentation of message and binaural input of noise with message (Experiment II).

increasing age, but that based on the letters was discontinuous, so that neither the linear trend nor the between-group difference proved to be significant when tested against within-group variability. The digit span declined progressively with age, whether scored for position of for order, whether it allowed for all correct responses or those limited to the last seven items. Forty and 60 years emerged as the critical ages for the running digit span. Mean scores of subjects above either of these age levels were significantly ($p < .01$) lower than of those representing the next youngest or two next youngest decades. The corresponding t ratios calculated on the running letter span were not statistically significant.

Product-moment correlation between digit and letter spans was .76 for the entire sample and between .57 and .81 within age groups. The mean difference between digit and letter spans dropped quite sharply about the age of 40 years, and more gradually beyond that stage. In this respect the two youngest age groups significantly differed from the three older ($t = 4.76$), but differences were not significant between adjacent decades above 40 years. Similarly, limiting the digit span to recall of the last seven items reduced the score of the men under 40 by a significantly wider margin ($t = 4.78$) than the score of those above that age. Differences between the three older age groups were not significant.

Scored for order, the digit span was of course larger than when based on correct absolute position, and the margin between the two scores remained fairly constant over the years. Noise arriving concurrently with the message reduced the digit span by a small margin, but significantly. This effect proved to be stable over the five decades; its drop in the forties does not represent a significant difference from either neighboring age group. Differences between the *S*s' digit span received through the more efficient

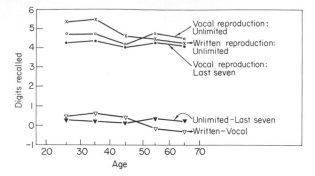

Fig. 14. Running digit spans at five age levels: vocal and written reproduction with limited and unlimited reproduction ranges (Experiments Ib and II).

and the less efficient ear also remained unchanged over the years, under both monaural and binaural presentation, as shown by Fig. 14.

Data on incorrect responses and indicating the effect of the distance of an item from the end of the string on its probability of recall will be given in the following subsection, under Experiment II.

Both the foregoing experiments show a contraction in the running item span with age, although not with the same degree of progressiveness or reliability. Either this capacity changes but little in the course of adulthood, and such decline as was observed must be attributed to some special condition of the testing procedure, or there is an age effect that was largely masked in the present test of the letter span. Performance proved remarkably poor with the letter span at all ages and, with so low a baseline, there would be less scope for a further drop with age. It is also possible that the adverse influence of age on the running digit span would not have been manifest but for the requirement to observe absolute as well as relative serial positions, and to write down rather than call out the responses. Of these two differences in instruction, observance of position could not account for the consistent superiority of the digit over the letter span; the manner of response, however, may have contributed to it.

Three more attributes distinguished the two experiments. The letter span demanded the reproduction of the last seven items, thus possibly setting a goal as well as a limit, and attempts to reach it may have interfered with the reproduction of those terminal letters that were still available for recall at the time of interrogation. Second, the letter span was tested with a larger number of strings that also varied within a wider range in length than those testing the digit span. In fact, this discrepancy in procedure does not explain the difference in results, since performance tended to improve with practice over repeated trials, and the letter span tended to increase with string length. Proactive interference was not a source of failure in recall.

Finally, the two experiments also differed in the class of message used. The vocabulary of consonants is larger than the vocabulary of digits and, as noted earlier as well as by the evidence of other experimenters (Brener, 1940; Crossman, 1960), this attribute of the message has been found to influence the span of STR. In our own pilot study 41 of the 75 Ss tested had a longer, and 23 a shorter, running digit span than letter span, and the difference was significant ($t = 2.89$).

The subsequent experiments were run to determine the contribution of each of these factors to the extent of the running item span and to its change with advancing age.

C. Experiment II: Spoken Unlimited Digit Span

1. Method

One hundred eighty men, 36 representing each decade between 20 and 69 years, served as Ss. Their one test of the running memory span employed the sixteen strings of digits presented monaurally in Experiment Ib, this time with the instruction to report vocally as many digits from the end of a series as the S could recall in the original order.

2. Results and Discussion

Figure 15 shows digit spans based on all responses and on those correspond-

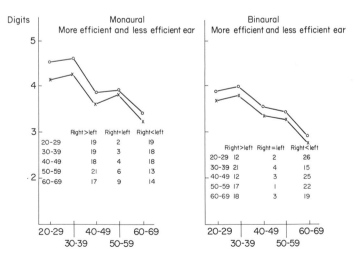

Fig. 15. The running digit span in five age groups, with the message presented to each S's more efficient and less efficient ear, and either no masking noise (monaural) or a simultaneous input of letters (binaural) to the other ear. The tabulation indicates the number of Ss in each group of 40 whose right or left ear proved more efficient.

TABLE II

PERCENTAGE OF RECALL OF DIGITS IN CORRECT ORDER ACCORDING TO
POSITION AT THE END OF A STRING[a]

Age (years)	N	$N-1$	$N-2$	$N-3$	$N-4$	$N-5$	$N-6$	$N-7$
			Experiment Ib					
20–29	96	89	84	78	67	52	35	16
30–39	97	91	88	78	65	51	34	22
40–49	96	87	80	71	52	36	22	9
50–59	96	84	82	74	53	34	18	10
60–69	94	85	81	68	46	25	9	4
			Experiment II					
20–29	90	79	82	64	55	39	28	18
30–39	95	86	80	63	56	41	25	18
40–49	94	86	78	60	39	28	15	10
50–59	92	84	83	63	50	41	26	18
60–69	92	81	76	57	51	33	21	15

[a]N = last digit.

ing to the seven terminal items, and reproduces comparable data from Experiment Ib. No significant differences were found between age groups. Limiting credit to the last seven items reduces the running memory span by a fairly stable margin at all ages. The digit span based on seven items was larger than the letter span in Experiment Ia at all ages. In contrast, the vocal running digit span was smaller than the comparable written span of the three younger age groups, but this relationship was reversed above the age of 50 years.

Correlations between length of string and running memory span were positive at all ages. Recall according to serial positions is shown in Table II with percentage correct in each position counted from the end of the string and scoring performance for order in Experiments Ib and II. The gain in written response accrued principally from the items four and five places from the end of the string. In position $N-3$ this gain was general, but in position $N-4$ it dropped off with advancing age.

Failure to respond correctly in Experiment Ib could be by wrong entry or by omission. The first type was predominant in the final four positions of the list but amounted to only a fraction of the omissions six places and more from the end. Age also influenced the ratio of the two types of failure: the proportion of incorrect responses dropped from 44% of the total in the two younger age groups to 32% in the forties and to 30% in the fifties and sixties. The ratio of incorrect to correct responses, however, barely changed with age in this or in the two experiments reported earlier. Over all trials and the entire sample of Ss this ratio was .36 in Experiment Ia, .33 in Experiment Ib (scored for order only), and .20 in Experiment II.

Since the additional requirement to observe the absolute position of digits could hardly improve their recall in sequence, the manner of reproduction seems the most likely source of the difference observed between the digit spans in Experiments Ib and II. Systematic bias in sampling might also account for it, but none could be discovered in comparing the groups of men who served as Ss in the two experiments. Writing down the answer evidently facilitated recall, but this gain dissipated as the Ss grew older.

Response interference by vocal report could possibly be reduced by writing the response (Mackworth, 1964); forgetting consequent upon delay, however, would increase. Probably any gain that appears in the written, as compared with the spoken, running item span derives from the S's freedom to report his responses in any order he pleases, as long as the original order appears on the record. This allows him to recover snatches of the message and to test and correct his responses before finally committing them to a record. Vocal reporting precludes these tactics or admits them only at the cost of considerably enhanced interference. At about the age of 50 these tactics cease to improve performance. Very likely, transposing auditory messages into written reports resulted in some forgetting at all ages, and with the advancing years this effect outweighed the advantage of a free order in reporting.

Analysis by serial position shows that writing increased the running memory span chiefly by extending it past the three terminal digits. It appears that these earlier items are remembered at the moment the buzzer sounds for vocal recall but the S may distrust his capacity to report them, and may play safe by getting the terminal items in first. This is sound strategy in free recall, for the late items are apt to be lost if not reported immediately (Waugh & Norman, 1965). Reciting the running memory span, however, is an example of serial recall; an item that has been by-passed may no longer be added to the record. With written reporting it may, and younger men benefit from this opportunity. Older men do not retrieve remote items with the same facility; indeed, they may have lost them before they jot down the first response. A strategy dictated by caution is characteristic of older people (Botwinick, 1966); it has been observed in several studies of age differences and has also been illustrated in the present experiment by an increased preference with age to avoid the response rather than risk an error.

While the proportion of errors by incorrect response varied with age, the ratio of these errors to correct responses was constant over the five decades in this as well as in the other two experiments. This measure may therefore be taken to indicate the strategies dictated by the experimental instructions. Report by writing, if it encourages the tactics just proposed, should increase the occasions for incorrect responses. So would also an instruction for a limited reproduction range if the limit set thereby were also viewed as a goal. Accordingly, the ratio of incorrect to correct responses was considerably lower in Experiment II than in either Experiment Ia or Ib. The larger vocabulary and higher probability of acoustic confusion of consonants than of digits may also have contributed to an increase in the proportion of false responses.

D.   Experiment III: Spoken and Written Digit Span with Limited and Open Reproduction Ranges

The effects of the mode of reporting on the running digit span and of a limit set on the number of items to be reported were tested by a further experiment.

1.   Method

Six men representing each decade between 20 and 69 years were tested on the running item span with sixteen strings of digits under two conditions. On one occasion the instruction was to reproduce the terminal items by reciting them in the original order; on the other it was to write them down so that the record correspond to the original order as it appears from left to right. The reproduction range was alternately open or limited to the last seven items. Both sets of experimental instructions were balanced in order across Ss in each age group.

2.   Results and Discussion

Mean digit spans as a function of age according to the four instructions are shown in Fig. 16. Analysis of variance, calculated with age, mode of reporting, and reproduction range as the three factors, indicated significant ($p < .01$) contributions from age, with 40 years as the dividing line but not with a fivefold division according to decades, and from the mode of reporting. The interactions of these two factors and of age with the reproduction range were also significant ($p < .01$). The age difference was not significant in regard to performance by vocal recall only.

The results confirmed the previous finding that writing the response offers the younger but not the older men an opportunity to increase their digit span over its vocal counterpart. So does an open reproduction range, even as compared with a limit as wide as seven terminal items that could hardly cut off information available at the time of interrogation. Faced with the challenge of reproducing seven items, many of the younger men may have reached back into a range of stored information where their grasp was

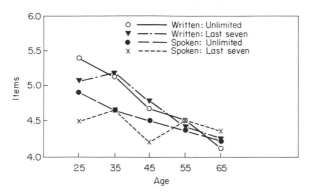

Fig. 16. Running digit spans at five age levels, with vocal and written reporting and with limited and open reproduction range (Experiment III).

uncertain, and in the process lost information that would have been accessible if recalled immediately. Older men were probably less tempted to aim past the limits of their STR capacity, and consequently performed neither better nor worse with an open than with a limited reproduction range.

E.   Experiment IV: Spoken Digit and Letter Span with Limited and Open Reproduction Ranges

Another test of the effect exerted by a limited reproduction range on the running item span was combined in this experiment with a direct test of the size of the vocabulary from which the message is derived.

1. Method

Six men representing each decade between the ages of 20 and 69 years were tested on the running item span with sixteen strings of consonants and sixteen strings of digits under two instructions: (1) to reproduce vocally as many items from the end of each string as they could recall in the original order, and (2) to reproduce vocally the last seven items in the original order. Messages by type of content and instruction were balanced in order.

2. Results and Discussion

Mean item spans are shown in Fig. 17; these performance scores were subjected to analysis of variance with age, type of message, and instruction for recall as the three factors. Age, with a twofold classification about either 40 or 50 years, but not according to decades, and type of content contributed significantly ($p < .01$) to the variance, but instruction, and first or second-order interactions did not. There were only three Ss whose letter span

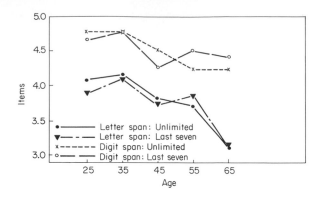

Fig. 17. Running item spans for letters and digits at five age levels, with limited and open reproduction ranges (Experiment IV).

exceeded the digit span, and two performed equally with the two types of message.

The experiment produced evidence once more that the running digit span is larger than the running letter span, and that this effect remains constant over the five decades sampled. Although the oldest group showed the widest discrepancy between the two types of message, it did not differ significantly in this respect from the group of Ss under 60 years. While the most immediate explanation of this consistent margin between the digit and letter span is the difference in information per message unit, acoustic confusion (Conrad, 1964) or other noninformational factors could also account for it. With telephone numbers, license plates, etc., to remember, most adults are practiced in recalling arbitrary sequences of digits, but only rarely do they have to reproduce consonants in randomly arrayed series.

In this experiment the effect of an open versus a limited reproduction range did not interact significantly with age, although once again the men over 40 performed about equally under the two instructions, while those below that age tended to do better when no limit was set to the items credited in recall.

F.   Experiment V: Digit Span Written in Order of Presentation

The purpose of this experiment was to test the hypothesis that younger Ss extend their running item span in written reports by starting their response with the terminal items and subsequently adding some of those further back in the list. The effect of observing the absolute as well as ordinal position of the items on the running digit span was also tested.

1.   Method

Six men representing each decade between 20 and 69 years were tested on sixteen strings of digits, instructed (1) to reproduce the final items in order, or (2) to enter them according to absolute position with blank places for digits they could not recall. Under both instructions the procedure differed from those in previous experiments by demanding that the response be actually written from left to right, i.e., in the same order as in vocal recall.

2.   Results and Discussion

Mean running digit spans for recall by order are shown in Fig. 18, along with corresponding curves based on Experiments Ib and II, i.e., written response without constraint on the order in which the rows of boxes were filled in, and spoken response. The requirement to write the digits in the order in which they had been presented shortened the span at all age levels. The younger Ss lost thereby the benefit they had derived from responding in writing without such a constraint and, moreover, lost additional information in the process of writing. The older Ss, who had gained nothing from writing their responses, were still further handicapped by the demands of the present instruction.

The difference between recall by relative and absolute positions was negligible and unrelated to age. When reporting digits in a forward order, the Ss only rarely left a gap in the rows of boxes. A comparison of recall by serial position from the end of the string with Experiment II shows that the slopes start at about the same level but drop more steeply in the

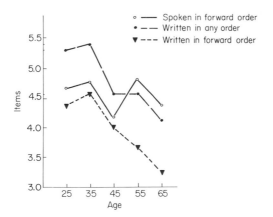

Fig. 18. Running digit spans by vocal report, written in forward order, and written without constraint of order, at five age levels (Experiments Ib, II, and V).

TABLE III

MEAN RUNNING LETTER AND DIGIT SPANS UNDER DIFFERENT
INSTRUCTIONS AND METHODS OF RECALL[a]

| | Unlimited order | | | | | | | Last 7 items | | | | | Unlimited position | |
| | Spoken | | | | Written | | | Spoken | | | | Written | Written | |
Age (years)	IID	IIID	IVD	IVL	ID	IIID	VD[b]	IIID	IVD	IL	IIID	IVL	ID	VD[b]
20–29	4.7	4.8	4.8	4.1	5.3	5.4	4.4	4.5	4.7	3.6	5.1	3.9	4.3	4.5
30–39	4.8	4.7	4.8	4.2	5.4	5.2	4.6	4.7	4.8	3.8	5.2	4.1	4.4	4.4
40–49	4.2	4.5	4.5	3.9	4.6	4.7	4.1	4.4	4.4	3.2	4.8	3.7	3.7	4.2
50–59	4.8	4.4	4.3	3.7	4.6	4.5	3.7	4.5	4.5	3.4	4.4	3.8	3.8	3.7
60–69	4.4	4.3	4.3	3.1	4.2	4.1	3.3	4.4	4.4	3.1	4.3	3.3	3.3	3.2

[a]Roman numerals in column heads refer to Experiments listed; D and L to type of message presented, i.e., digits or letters.

present instance. The widest differences between the two experiments were found in the records of the oldest age groups in positions $N - 2$ to $N - 5$.

Table III summarizes the mean running item spans obtained in the five experiments discussed in this section. It is evident that the running item span does tend to decline with advancing age and that, of all the experimental variables tested, writing the response is that which most accentuated this aging effect.

Transposing messages from an acoustic store into written records may indeed involve operations that deteriorate with age; it also takes longer than vocal recitation, and memory traces could fade progressively faster with the advancing years. The freedom to write down the items of the response in any order chosen can more than offset the disadvantages inherent in recall by writing, and does so for younger persons, who first set down the terminal items of the list and then fill in some of the positions to the left. Writing the number offered them no advantage when they were not allowed to proceed in this manner.

The older men did not gain from the opportunity to write down the terminal items first and then add on whatever items they recalled from further back. This could happen either because they had forgotten those earlier items by the time they reached the end of the list, or because they forgot them while they were writing down the terminal items. If, as Waugh and Norman (1965) propose, there is a separate "primary memory" store for the last items of a list and another "secondary memory" store for those all the way back, it is conceivable that the latter store shrinks in capacity with age while primary memory remains unchanged. Such a conclusion, however, should not be taken as evidence for a decline in storage capacity rather than for an increased susceptibility to response interference with age. The experiments with the word span presented in Section II, A, as well as studies with the dichotic digit span (Craik, 1965; Inglis & Ankus, 1965) and similar procedures (Broadbent & Gregory, 1965), and also Talland 's (1967) finding that the recall of infraspan messages after very brief delays and under conditions that prevent rehearsal is unrelated to age, all accord with the latter interpretation.

According to that interpretation, older *S*s are less efficient than the young in holding certain items of the message while delivering others, possibly because this can be done only by using the same limited-capacity system for both operations, and by alternating at a rapid rate between the two operations. It seems quite probable that the speed of alternation demanded by this task undergoes deleterious changes with age similar to those observed in other central processes of information processing and skilled performance (Welford, 1958).

In this sense the capacity to shift or divide attention would indeed appear to diminish with age. It is equally evident from these experiments with the running item span that no general statement is warranted about changes with age in the capacity to shift or divide attention. To distinguish between signals and noise arriving simultaneously, as in the bimodal version of Experiment Ib, also demands a division of attention, and that capacity remained unchanged with age within the limits tested. This finding also confirms Inglis's (1965) conclusion that the experiments with dichotic input of signals demonstrated a loss with age in STR, and more specifically in recall, rather than in perception.

The experiments reported here have also shown that merely to shift the focus of attention with the changing flow of message input, and to shed the redundant items while taking in the potentially relevant, are operations that hold up reasonably well with advancing age. In the normal course of aging the running span of STR is curtailed far less than it is in senility, and for reasons different from those that explain the impeded performance of senile or other amnesic patients. Whatever deficit in performance distinguishes older from young adults stems, not from a reduction of information intake, but primarily from an increased suscep-tibility to response interference.

IV. Conclusions

As tested by the span of immediate recall, human capacity to transmit information diminishes with advancing age between the ages of 20 and 70 years, more under some conditions than under others. This loss of capacity associated with age seems to occur at certain critical stages, particularly at about 40 and again at about 60 years, rather than to progress at a continuous rate. Under the conditions tested, the deficit shown at older ages was comparatively slight; it can, however, be increased considerably, e.g., by fast pacing (Canestrari, 1963; Arenberg, 1965; Eisdorfer, 1965 and Chapter 7, this volume), or by demanding operations of discrimination and choice (Rabbitt, 1965 and Chapter 2, this volume).

The span of immediate recall, as has been argued earlier here, represents a limiting case in the transmission of information, free from the complexities of most life situations. Its contraction with age under favorable conditions of operation, therefore, indicates that the capacity to transmit information is also apt to diminish, although that effect can often be offset by compensatory aptitudes. The span of STR is most likely to contract with age if the operations testing it create more than the usual interference with the retention of the message. Mere enumeration or selection, although undoubtedly sources of interference, do not change in their disruptive effect with age. Holding one part of the message while reporting another part, or reverting to an earlier section after reproducing a later section, are operations that increasingly impair STR with advancing age.

There is some evidence that messages exceeding the span are transmitted with relatively more loss of information by older persons than messages within the span. Whether the span itself narrows with age is a matter that depends on the criteria of its determination. The limits of the STR span change with age less than does the probability of performing at the limit of capacity. The advantage derived from splitting long messages into groups is unaffected by age, and so—by inference—is the ability to divide a continuous visual message into segments in the course of its registration. The observation that STR for visually presented messages declines with age more than STR for auditory messages has not been confirmed in this study. The incremental effect of a repeated presentation of the message does not diminish with age, but past 60 years no additional gain was found with a second repetition.

Recalling the terminal segment from a continuous stream of unrelated items is a task that can be performed quite efficiently at all ages tested in this study. Up to 70 years, at any rate, the ability to shift one's attention with the flow of information input is well preserved; the ability to shut out unwanted messages confined to a special channel of auditory input is also unimpaired.

The various experiments reviewed have shown that the span of STR declines with age when the conditions of recall allow for its extension by means of retrospective selection, ordering, matching, and gap filling. Learning at the level of cognitive assimilation, the registration of observations for future recall, always involves such operations by which the new information is organized and aligned within the available categories of reference. An incoming message must be held, transposed, checked, and recoded, while other parts of it are being embedded in the fitting matrix. With advancing age more of the information is liable to be lost in that process, lost immediately and irrevocably. To this extent the reduced span of STR is indeed crucial to the learning and memory deficit of old age. Similar operations are also necessary in the recall of information that has not been overlearned, and consequently older people could be further handicapped when trying to remember recent information.

REFERENCES

Anderson, N. S. Post-stimulus cuing in immediate memory. *J. exp. Psychol.*, 1960, **60**, 216–221.

Arenberg, D. Anticipation interval and age differences in verbal learning. *J. abnorm. soc. Psychol.*, 1965, **70**, 419–425.

Botwinick, J. Cautiousness in advanced age. *J. Geront.*, 1966, **21**, 347–353.

Botwinick, J., Brinley, J. F., & Robbin, S. S. Task alternation time in relation to problem difficulty and age. *J. Geront.*, 1958, **13**, 414–417

Brener, L. R. An experimental investigation of memory span. *J. exp. Psychol.*, 1960, **26**, 467–482.

Broadbent, D. E. *Perception and communication.* New York: Macmillan (Pergamon), 1958.

Broadbent, D. E., & Gregory, M. Some confirmatory results on age differences in memory for simultaneous stimulation. *Brit. J. Psychol.*, 1965, **56**, 77–80.

Broadbent, D. E., & Heron, A. Effects of a subsidiary task on performance involving immediate memory by younger and older men. *Brit. J. Psychol.*, 1962, **53**, 189–198.

Bromley,D. B. Some effects of age on short term learning and remembering. *J. Geront.*, 1958, **13**, 398–406.

Buschke, H. Retention in immediate memory estimated without retrieval. *Science*, 1963, **140**, 56–57.

Caird, W. K. Aging and short-term memory. *J. Geront.*, 1966, **21**, 295–299.

Canestrari, R. E., Jr. Paced and self-paced learning in young and elderly adults. *J. Geront.*, 1963, **18**, 165–168.

Conrad, R. Acoustic confusions in immediate memory. *Brit J. Psychol.*, 1964, **55**, 75–84.

Conrad, R., & Hille, B.4. The decay theory of immediate memory and paced recall. *Canad. J. Psychol.*, 1958, **12**, 1–6.

Craik, F. I. M. The nature of age decrement in performance on dichotic listening tasks. *Quart. J. exp. Psychol.*, 1965, **17**, 227–240.

Crossman, E. R. F. W. Information and serial order in human immediate memory. In C. Cherry (Ed.), *Information theory. London & Washington, D. C.: Butterworth, 1960.*

Crossman, E. R. F. W., & Szafran, J. Changes with age in the speed of information-intake and discrimination. *Experientia (Suppl.)*, 1956, **4**, 128–134.

Eisdorfer, C. Verbal learning and response time in the aged. *J. genet. Psychol.*, 1965, **107**, 15–22.

Fraisse. P. Etudes sur la mémoire immédiate: I. L'appréhension des sons. *Année psychol.*, 1937, **38**, 48–83.

Gilbert, J. G. Mental efficiency in senescence. *Arch. Psychol.*, 1935, **27** (No. 188).

Gilbert, J. G. Memory loss in senescence. *J. abnorm. soc. Psychol.*, 1941, **36**, 73–86.

Gill, N. F., & Dallenbach, K. M. A preliminary study of the range of attention. *Amer. J. Psychol.*, 1926, **37**, 247–256.

Gladis, M., & Braun, H. W. Age differences in transfer and retroaction as a function of intertask response similarity. *J. exp. Psychol.*, 1958, **55**, 25–30.

Hebb, D. O. *The organization of behavior.* New York: Wiley, 1949.

Hebb, D. O. Distinctive features of learning in the higher animal. In J. F. Delafresnaye (Ed.), *Brain mechanisms and learning.* Oxford: Blackwell, 1961.

Heron, A, & Craik, F. Age differences in cumulative learning of meaningful and meaningless material. *Scand J. Psychol.*, 1964, **5**, 209–217.

Hulicka, Irene M., & Grossman, J. L. Age-group comparisons for the use of mediators in paired-associate learning. *J. Geront.*, 1967, **22**, 46–51.

Hulicka, Ipene M., & Weiss, R. L. Age differences in retention as a function of learning. *J. consult. Psychol.*, 1965, **29**, 125–129.

Inglis, J. Immediate memory, age and brain function. In A. T. Welford & J. E. Birren (Eds.), *Behavior, aging and the nervous system.* Springfield, Ill.: Charles C. Thomas, 1965.

Inglis, J., & Ankus, M. N. Effects of age on short-term storage and serial rote learning. *Brit. J. Psychol.*, 1965, **56**, 183–195.

Kay, H. *Experimental studies of adult learning.* Unpublished doctoral thesis, Cambridge Univer., 1953.

Kay, H. Theories of learning and aging. In J. E. Birren (Ed.), *Handbook of aging and the individual*, Chicago, Ill.: Univer. of Chicago Press, 1959.

Kirchner, W. K. Age differences in short-term retention of rapidly changing information. *J. exp. Psychol.*, 1958, **55**, 352–358.

Klemmer, E. T. Communication and human performance. *Human Factors*, 1962, **4**, 75–79.

Korchin, S. H., & Basowitz, H. Age difference in verbal learning. *J. abnorm. soc. Psychol.*, 1957, **54**, 64–69.

Mackworth, J. F. Paced memorizing in a continuous task. *J. exp. Psychol.*, 1959, **58**, 206–211.

Mackworth, J. F. Presentation date and immediate memory. *Canad. J. Psychol.*, 1962, **16**, 42–47.

Mackworth, J. F. Auditory short-term memory. *Canad. J. Psychol.*, 1964, **18**, 292–303.

Mackworth, N. N. H., & Mackworth, J. F. Remembering advance cues during searching. *Brit. J. Psychol.*, 1959, **56**, 69–75.

McGhie, A., Chapman, J., & Lawson, J. S. Changes in immediate memory with age. *Brit. J. Psychol.*, 1965, **56**, 69–75.

Melton, A. W. Implications of short-term memory for a general theory of memory. *J. verb. Learn. verb. Behav.*, 1963, **2**, 1–21.

Miller, G. A. The magical number seven, plus or minus two: some limits of our capacity for processing information. *Psychol. Rev.*, 1956, **63**, 81–97.

Murdock, B. B. Visual and auditory stores in short-term memory. *Quart. J. exp. Psychol.*, 1966, **18**, 206–211.

Pollack, I. The assimilation of sequentially encoded information. *Amer. J. Psychol.*, 1953, **66**, 421–435.

Pollack, I., Johnson, L. B., & Knaff, P. R. Running memory span. *J. exp. Psychol.*, 1959, **57**, 137–146.

Posner, M. I. Immediate memory in sequential tasks. *Psychol. Bull.*, 1963, **60**, 333–349.

Postman, L. Short-term memory and incidental learning. In A. W. Melton (Ed.), *Categories of human learning.* New York: Academic Press, 1964.

Rabbitt, P. M. A. Age and discrimination between complex stimuli. In A. T. Welford and J. E. Birren (Eds.), *Behavior, aging and the nervous system*, Springfield, Ill.: Charles C. Thomas, 1965.

Ruch, F. L. The differentiative effects of age upon human learning. *J. gen. Psychol.*, 1934, **11**, 261–286.

Sperling, G. The information available in brief visual presentations. *Psychol. Monogr.*, 1960, **74** (No. 11).

Talland, G. A. Age and the effect of expectancy on the accuracy of perception. *J. Geront.*, 1959, **14**, 202–207.

Talland, G. A. The effect of age on speed of simple manual skill. *J. genet. Psychol.*, 1962, **100**, 69–76.

Talland, G. A. *Deranged memory: a psychonomic study of the amnesic syndrome.* New York: Academic Press, 1965. (a)

Talland, G. A. Three estimates of the word span and their stability over the adult years. *Quart. J. exp. Psychol.*, 1965, **17**, 301–307. (b)

Talland, G. A. Initiation of response and reaction time in aging, and with brain damage. In A. T. Welford and J. E. Birren (Eds.), *Behavior, aging and the nervous system.* Springfield, Ill.: Charles C. Thomas, 1965. (c)

Talland, G. A. Performance studies in human aging and their theoretical significance. *Psychiat. Digest*, 1966, **27**, 37–53.

Talland, G.A. Age and the immediate memory span. *The Gerontologist.* 1967, **7**, 4–9.

Talland, G. A., Mendelson, J. H., Koz, G., & Aaron, R. Experimental studies of the effects of tricyanoaminopropene on the memory and learning capacities of geriatric patients. *J. psychiat. Res.*, 1965, **3**, 171–179.

Taub, H. A., & Greiff, S. Effects of age on organization and recall of two sets of stimuli. *Psychonomic Sci.*, 1967, **7**, 53–54.

Waugh, N. C. Serial position and the memory span. *Amer. J. Psychol.*, 1960, **73**, 68–79.

Waugh, N. C., & Norman, D. A. Primary memory. *Psychol. Rev.*, 1965, **72**, 89–104.

Wechsler, D. A study of retention in Korsakoff psychosis *Psychiat. Bull. N. Y. State Hosp.* 1917, **2**, 403–451.

Wechsler, D. *Manual for the Wechsler Adult Intelligence Scale.* New York: The Psychol. Corp., 1955.

Welford, A. T. *Aging and human skill.* London & New York: Oxford Univer. Press, 1958.

Welford, A. T. Changes in the speed of performance with age and their industrial significance. *Ergonomics*, 1962, **5**, 139–145.

Wimer, R. E. Age differences in incidental and intentional learning. *J. Geront.*, 1960, **15**, 79–82.

Yntema, D. B., & Trask, F. P. Recall as a search process. *J. verb. Learn. verb. Behav.*, 1963, **2**, 65–74.

Zangwill, O. L. Clinical tests of memory impairment. *Proc. roy. Soc. Med.*, 1943, **36**, 571–576.

Short-Term Memory and the Aging Process

F. I. M. CRAIK

Birkbeck College,
University of London,
London, England

I. Background and Literature Review

A.   Age Differences in Learning Ability

It has long been believed that learning ability declines from youth to old age and this popular belief concerning old dogs and new tricks was generally upheld by the results of a series of early descriptive studies reviewed by Ruch (1933). In a more recent review, Birren (1964) came to the more optimistic conclusion that age changes in the primary capacity to learn were small under most circumstances and that the results of global descriptive studies that apparently showed age decrements in learning might rather have been due to age deficits in perception, set, or attention.

In general, more recent studies have attempted to specify the conditions under which age-related decrements in learning appear. Ruch (1934) for example, hypothesized that as learning must involve changes in neural organization and as senescence probably causes lowered plasticity of tissue, then learning that involves reorganization of existing habits should be performed less well by old subjects (Ss). He thus predicted that the rote learning of associations that run contrary to past experience, such as false equations (e.g., $6 \times 3 = 5$), should be differentially harder for older Ss than the learning of nonsense equations (e.g., $F \times P = V$) and much harder than the learning of meaningful word pairs (e.g., WALK − CAR). His results apparently supported his point of view, but Welford (1958) pointed out that while learning of the meaningful associations showed the smallest age decrement, there was little difference in percentage declines with age between the nonsense equations and false equations. Also, Korchin and Basowitz (1957) repeated Ruch's experiment and were unable to demonstrate a relative age difference in the learning of nonsense and false equations. They did find that the older Ss were at less of a disadvantage with meaningful associates, but also pointed out that since the learning task was paced (4 sec for reading the stimulus, selecting and reporting a response), it was possible that old Ss required more time for the integration of a response. It is also possible that this effect was more severe for the nonsense and false equations.

Gilbert (1941) examined age differences in memory for several types of material. She found very slight age differences in auditory and visual digit span but significant age deficits in several other tests, including paired associates and items from a Turkish-English dictionary. Gilbert interpreted these results as showing substantial age losses in retention, but Jerome (1959) pointed out that acquisition and retention were inextricably associated in Gilbert's experiment. Evidence that the age differences were due, partly at least, to acquisition deficits comes from a study by Gladis and Braun (1958). They used the retroactive inhibition paradigm and found that although uncorrected scores showed a greater liability to interpolated interference on the part of old Ss, when scores were corrected for differences in original learning, there were no age differences in retroactive interference.

The differential age decrements with various types of material found by Gilbert—that is, the least familiar and meaningful materials showing the greatest age decrements—could be interpreted as showing greater interference from past learning in the older Ss. The results of Gladis and Braun and of Korchin and Basowitz make it appear more likely, however, that novel material is more difficult for the older person to acquire and that the manner and speed of presentation of the material may further handicap older Ss.

B. Short-Term Memory and Learning Decrements

In an attempt to analyze the process of learning in greater detail, Welford (1958) distinguished seven essential stages: (1) perception and comprehension of the material; (2) short-term memory; (3) establishment of a durable trace; (4) endurance of this trace; (5) recognition of a further situation demanding the reuse of the material; (6) recovery of the material from memory; and (7) production of a response. Welford further suggested that the key to understanding age deficits in learning and performance might lie at stage 2. An age decrement in short-term memory (STM) would account for the observed decline in overall learning ability and would locate the difficulty in the acquisition stages, a conclusion in line with the results discussed in Section A. A breakdown with age in STM could also explain age deficits in problem solving and in skilled performance. Finally, Welford suggested that there was some physiological basis for his argument: the smaller number of brain cells in the aged brain, lowered general activity, and disorganization of the electroencephalogram (EEG) all pointed to the probability that STM traces would be shorter lasting and more liable to disruption by other brain activity.

Once attention is focused on STM, there is no lack of experimental evidence to show that this function does in fact become less efficient with increasing age. Aspects of the results of experiments by Kirchner (1958), Bromley (1958), Talland (1961), and Griew and Davies (1962) were attributed to this cause. However, there are also situations where no decline in short-term retention is apparent. Several workers, including Gilbert (1941) and Bromley (1958), have reported little or no age decrement in digit span, whether auditory or visual. As digit span seems to be a reasonably pure measure of STM, this poses a problem, but Welford (1958) suggested that it was in situations that demanded an alternation between taking in information for retention and making responses that age deficits were observed. That is, in the digit-span situation all information is received before any response is required, whereas this was not true of other experimental situations.

Studies by Kay (cited by Welford, 1958) and by Kirchner (1958), for example, revealed large age decrements in STM. *S*s faced a row of twelve lights with a telegraph key below each light. In the simplest form of the task the lights came on in random order, one light at a time at 1.5-sec intervals. *S*'s task was simply to press the key underneath the light that was on. In the "one-back" condition *S* pressed the key under the light that had just gone out, and this task was extended to "two-back" and "three-back." Kirchner compared the performance of young (18–25) and old (64–78) *S*s and found that although old *S*s performed virtually as well as the young group at the no-back task, their performance had fallen to 38% of the young group's level on the two-back task. Kirchner attributed this deficit to the slowing down of the ability to organize the continuous interchange of incoming and outgoing information. It seems that in the case where *S*s are merely required to store information "passively" and then recall it (as in the digit-span procedure), there is little age decrement. Where the task demands that

Ss manipulate or reorganize the material, on the other hand, old Ss are at a disadvantage. This way of looking at Kirchner's results is supported by the finding (Gilbert, 1941; Bromley, 1958) that while digit span forward is little affected by aging, reversed digit span is significantly impaired. It is also supported by an experiment carried out by Talland (1965). He gave Ss lists of words in which all words occurred twice except one. A significant age decrement was found in the condition where Ss recalled all words but left until last the one unrepeated word. There was no decrement under free-recall conditions or in the condition where Ss had to recall only the un-repeated word.

On the basis of Kay's and Kirchner's results, Welford (1958) suggested that STM is increasingly liable to interference by other activity as age advances. This interference could take several forms, and Welford cited an experiment by Speakman (Welford, 1958) to show that not all potentially interfering material was more disrupting for old Ss. Speakman's Ss were asked to turn over numbered cards one by one until a specified card was reached, and to count the number of cards turned. In one form of the experiment, Ss were read a four-figure number. They repeated the number and then proceeded to turn and count the cards. Ss of all ages from 11 to 63 were able to count the cards and correctly recall the four-figure number after the specified card had been found. Thus apparently if the material to be remembered is short and is adequately registered in STM, interpolated activity has no greater interfering effect with age.

In a second form of his experiment, Speakman presented the four-figure number without warning to Ss performing the card-counting task. In this case, although Ss of all ages performed the counting task correctly, the older Ss were less able to correctly recall or recognize the four-figure number. When Speakman repeated this form of the experiment, old Ss remembered the number but did poorly on the card-counting task. Welford concluded from these results that it was the interfering effect of *simultaneous* activity that was especially disrupting and became more so with advancing age. It also seems clear from this experiment that older Ss were less able to divide their attention between perception and retention, and this conclusion is confirmed by the results of Broadbent and Heron (1962).

Other forms of interference that might give rise to greater retention losses with age are proactive inhibition, intralist interference, and response interference. There is little evidence relating to age differences in the first two categories, although some evidence will be presented in Section II that experimentally induced proactive inhibition is no stronger in old Ss. Welford (1958) stated: "It would seem that some process involved in responding exerts a serious interfering effect upon the information stored in short-term memory" (p. 251). Inglis (1965) and Taub (1966) have also suggested that response interference may be greater in the elderly. In the light of Speakman's results and those of Gladis and Braun (1958), however, it would seem that any greater interfering effect of response activity with age is limited to the period before the retained material has been adequately registered in STM. Welford (1958) predicted that for material exceeding the span, retention would be poorer for older people, since the responses made in rehearsing or recalling some of the material would interfere with the storage of the rest; evidence on this point is also cited in Section II.

This section has dealt largely with Welford's (1958, 1962, 1964a) point of view. He has suggested that age deficits in learning and problem-solving, as well as on intelligence tests and perceptual motor tasks, are due basically to a decline with age in the efficiency of STM. He has further suggested that this decline is not due to a decrease in the capacity of the short-term store, but to increased liability to interference caused by shifts of attention between perceptual and memory functions. This view is plausible and is in accordance with the experimental evidence, but we should like to know something more about the precise mechanisms and stages involved. There is mounting evidence (Broadbent & Heron, 1962; Murdock, 1965) that perception and STM are mediated at least in part by the same mechanism, so the performance of older Ss suggests either that their total "capacity" to be divided between STM and perception is reduced or that their ability to rapidly switch attention between the two functions has declined.

Two possible defects in the "attention–STM complex" that would account for the experimental results may be distinguished. The first is that if the STM trace decays unless attention is turned to storage rather than perception or response, then distracting factors, an additional task, or the making of responses would reduce the attention paid to storage and accelerate decay. It is likely that this decay is fastest before the trace is adequately registered in STM, so the diversion-of-attention factor would be most potent at the moment of reception of the material to be stored. It is also plausible that this initial rapid decay of the STM trace is faster in older Ss. The second possible defect is that in older people there is a narrowing of attention. This would mean that less incoming information could be processed in a given time, and if the input exceeded the limits, some material would necessarily be excluded and would not be registered in STM. Under conditions of slow or moderate input rates this defect would not affect older Ss; it would only become crucial when the amount of information per unit time was increased (as when a second task was added or responding became necessary) or when the rate of arrival of items was stepped up. It is well known that older Ss are at a disadvantage on paced tasks where items must be dealt with in rapid succession (Welford, 1958), so again this possibility would fit the facts.

At any rate, the importance of an age deficit in STM has been established.

The following subsections examine experiments that have attempted to specify more clearly the nature of this deficit.

C. Dichotic Listening Experiments

Broadbent (1958) developed a model of STM partly on the basis of dichotic listening studies. In these experiments, two short series of digits were presented simultaneously, one series to each ear. Ss typically recalled all digits from one series before recalling those from the other and the first series recalled was usually more accurate. Broadbent postulated that the first series recalled went straight into a perceptual system, whereas the second was held briefly in a preperceptual short-term store until the perceptual system was free.

Broadbent's model provided the basis for a series of studies carried out by Inglis and his associates (Inglis & Caird, 1963; Mackay & Inglis, 1963; Inglis, 1965; Inglis & Ankus, 1965). Inglis argued that if STM was in fact the locus of age-related learning deficits, then in the dichotic digit situation old Ss should show no decrement in the first series reproduced, as this would not involve the short-term store, but there should be a marked age decrement on the second series, which had been held briefly in STM. The results obtained by Inglis and Caird (1963) strikingly confirmed these predictions. Using "half-spans" of one to six digits presented to each ear, they found no evidence for an age decline in the first half-set recalled, but found consistently significant age decrements in recall of the second half-set. This result was confirmed with different Ss by Mackay and Inglis (1963).

These results appeared to rule out the possibility raised by Jerome (1959) that age deficits in learning and retention were due to lack of motivation; it is difficult to see why a motivation deficit would affect one half-set but not the other. Further studies (Inglis & Ankus, 1965) in which the series to be recalled first was not specified until after presentation appeared to rule out the further possibility that the original result was due to age losses in attention or perception. Craik (1965) also concluded that age decrements in the dichotic listening situation were due to memory rather than attentional factors. His results showed age declines in both half-sets, however, and he interpreted them as showing that all digits were held in memory "tagged" for ear of presentation and position in series. The digits were retrieved at recall after a search process (Yntema & Trask, 1963) and errors could occur through fading of the tags. Finally, Broadbent and Gregory (1965), using the eye and ear as the two channels, also obtained significant age differences in simultaneous stimulation.

D. Age Differences in Registration and Retrieval

Results from the dichotic listening experiments just reviewed suggest that the locus of STM deficit in older Ss is storage. That is, the material to be remembered is initially as firmly registered in STM for old and young Ss, but performance at recall is poorer for the elderly because of faster decay or greater liability to interference. However, other studies suggest that there may also be age decrements in the initial registration of the material and in the efficiency of the retrieval process.

Wimer and Wigdor (1958) found that when young and old Ss learned a paired-associate list to the same criterion and then engaged in some comparatively noninterfering activity, there was no age difference in retention over a 15-min period. This result agrees with the findings of Gladis and Braun (1958) and suggests that once the material has been adequately registered there are slight age losses in memory. Work discussed by Canestrari (1966; chapter in this volume) also supports the notion of an age decrement in registration.

Against the point of view that registration is the locus of age deficits in STM are the results of the dichotic listening experiments carried out by Inglis and his colleagues. Their studies have repeatedly shown an age decrement in the second half-set recalled but none in the first, while an age deficit in registration should presumably be evident in the first half-set also. The results reported by Craik (1965) did show an age decrement in both half-sets, however. There are obviously some points in this area that await clarification from further experimental work.

It is also plausible that retrieval processes are less efficient in the elderly, but this notion is not yet well supported by experimental data. Hurwitz and Allison (1965) made the clinical observation that old people suffering from diffuse cortical atrophy can recall the names of things they see, hear, or touch but have the greatest difficulty in recalling them without such stimuli. Thus apparently the names are still stored in memory but retrieval has failed. Schonfield (1965) has reported a study in which Ss learned lists of words and subsequently recalled them or recognized them from within a small group of irrelevant words. He found significant age deficits in recall but none on the recognition task, so again concluded that retrieval was at fault. Finally, from an analysis of errors on the dichotic listening task, Craik (1965) concluded that errors due to faulty retrieval increased with age.

E. Further Relevant Factors

Although Wimer and Wigdor (1958) found no age differences in retention of a paired-associate list over a 15-min period, a subsequent study by Wimer (1960) did find an age decrement in the same type of task when retention was studied over 24 hours. He suggested that if consolidation takes up to 1 hour, then an age decrement in this process might not become evident until retention intervals of an hour or more were studied.

Caird (1964, 1966) has examined the ability of aged *S*s to establish long-term memory (LTM) using a cumulative learning technique developed by Hebb (1961). Caird (1964) found the cumulative learning effect to be absent in elderly memory-disordered psychiatric patients but present in elderly patients free from memory disorder. Caird speculatively explained his result in terms of lowered cerebral reverberatory activity in the memory-disordered group and anticipated (Caird, 1966) that the cumulative learning effect would be greater in young *S*s than in old *S*s. His results failed to confirm this expectation, however. Heron and Craik (1964) also found that both young and old *S*s could show cumulative learning under certain conditions.

Several studies have shown that visual STM is more impaired by aging than auditory STM (Bromley, 1958; McGhie, Chapman, & Lawson, 1965). This could be due either to a less stable short-term visual trace or to less efficient recoding of verbal material into an auditory store.

In conclusion, attention is drawn to several points that await experimental clarification. The general loss in speed with age (Welford & Birren, 1965) may mean slower responses and thus longer time in store for the material to be remembered. It would be useful to have more response time data from STM experiments. Second, the larger age differences found when material to be remembered is presented simultaneously with other material requiring attention or response may be due to switching of attention between STM and perception (Welford, 1964a) or to a reduced "input capacity" leading to less efficient registration. Finally, it is possible that all three processes of registration, storage, and retrieval become less efficient as aging progresses. There appears to be no compelling evidence to show that storage is poorer in the elderly once the material has been unequivocally registered, but proof of this registration demands a response, and it may be in the period before the first response that STM is particularly vulnerable.

II. Experimental Studies

A. Age Differences in Word Span for
Meaningful and Meaningless Material

The series of experiments to be reported here had its starting point in an observation from a previous study (Heron & Craik, 1964) that examined age differences in cumulative learning of meaningful and meaningless material. The meaningless material used in part of the study was a recording of the digits 1 to 9 spoken in Finnish, while the equivalent digits in English

TABLE I

MEAN DIGIT SPANS FOR ENGLISH Ss IN FINNISH AND ENGLISH AND
SCORES ON MILL HILL VOCABULARY TEST (MHV)

Group	Finnish	English	MHV
Young	3.6	8.3	35.5
Old	3.6	6.8	35.8

formed the material for the meaningful lists. After a familiarization session in which Ss heard and repeated the sound of the Finnish digits several times, they were given a standard digit-span forward test with auditory presentation and immediate verbal recall. Two lists of each length from 3 upward were presented at 1 digit per second and the span was taken as the highest level at which at least one list was correctly recalled, taking order into account. This procedure was later repeated with English digits; the results are shown in Table I. Two groups of Ss were used: a young group (age range 23–35; mean age 29.9) and an old group (age range 60–72; mean age 65.9). The groups were matched on verbal intelligence on the basis of their scores from the Mill Hill Vocabulary (MHV) test. The mean MHV scores shown in Table I represent the 85th percentile approximately.

Table I shows that although the Finnish digit spans were identical for both groups, young Ss had somewhat higher scores than the old group on English digit span. When the difference between English and Finnish spans was taken as a score for each S, a highly significant age difference ($t = 4.14$, $p < .001$) was found to exist between the two sets of scores.

Thus it appears that when Ss are matched in the way described earlier, old Ss are no worse at immediate recall of meaningless sounds but are at a disadvantage, relative to younger Ss, when the material to be remembered is meaningful. This result could be explained in terms of a reduced efficiency with age of some recoding or chunking process. That is, immediate recall of Finnish digits may reflect a fairly pure retention mechanism, whereas English digits are considered to be more amenable to chunking and will thus be registered in STM in a more efficient fashion.

This tentative conclusion would support the notion referred to in Section I, D that at least some of the age deficit in STM is due to less effective registration of the memory trace. The conclusion is opposed, however, by the results of previous workers who have manipulated the familiarity or meaningfulness of material to be learned or remembered. It has been widely reported (Ruch, 1934; Gilbert, 1941; Korchin & Basowitz, 1957; Kay, 1959) that old Ss are at a *disadvantage* with unfamiliar, meaningless material, as in this case they can derive little benefit from their past experience.

There may be some difference between the immediate recall and longer-term learning situations that is differentially affected by the nature of the material, but this seems unlikely. Two short experiments in which the "chunkability" of the material was varied were thus designed to explore further this difference in conclusions.

B. Experiment I: Memory Span for Three Types of Verbal Material*

1. Introduction

The memory span for three types of verbal material was obtained for Ss ranging in age from 20 to 79. The first type of material, English text sentences, was considered to be highly familiar, meaningful, and amenable to recoding procedures. The second type of material, color names, was not so amenable to chunking. For the third type of material, common proverbs with their word order scrambled were used; this was considered to be an example of material that would be disruptive to normal coding procedures. On the basis of the foregoing discussion, it was predicted that an age decrement would be found on the first and third types of material but not on the second. That is, old Ss would be at a disadvantage when the material was amenable to coding (text) and when inappropriate recoding was possible (scrambled proverbs), but no age difference would be found with material that merely had to be stored and recalled in relatively uncoded form (color names).

2. Procedure

S was told to repeat back verbally each list of words exactly as he heard them. E read each list (the text sentences at a slow conversational speed and the other lists at 1 word per second); S then recalled each list immediately after presentation. Digit-span technique was used, the number of words in successive lists being increased each time until S failed to recall the list correctly. Two lists were given at each length and the score was taken to be the longest string length at which at least one list was correctly recalled, taking items and correct order into account. The lists were presented in the same order to each S: text, color names, and finally, scrambled proverbs.

3. Subjects

Five men and five women represented each decade age group from the twenties to the seventies. Each group was matched on vocabulary level, as this is a measure known to decline little with age. The mean score on Mill Hill Vocabulary Set B Synonyms (Raven, 1958) was 36.0 for all groups.

*Experiments I and II were carried out in collaboration with Mr. P. A. Masani.

MEMORY SPAN FOR THREE TYPES OF VERBAL MATERIAL
OBTAINED FROM Ss AGED 20–79

Material	Age groups					
	20–29	30–39	40–49	50–59	60–69	70–79
Text sentences	20.5	19.8	20.8	20.0	18.5	17.2
Color names	6.2	6.1	6.6	6.2	6.0	5.9
Scrambled proverbs	7.0	7.0	6.9	6.4	6.4	6.3

4. Results

The mean number of words correctly recalled is shown for each type of list and each age group in Table II. Trend analyses of variance were carried out to assess age differences in the length of list recalled. An age decrement was found in ability to recall text ($F = 8.26$, $p < .01$) and scrambled proverbs ($F = 8.08$, $p < .01$), but was not found in ability to recall color names ($F = .50$; not significant).

5. Discussion

These results are in accordance with the predictions made in the Introduction (subsection B, 1) and support the hypothesis that older Ss exhibit a deficit in coding and registration. That is, where the possibility of transforming or chunking verbal material is at a minimum (color names), old Ss can remember as many items as younger Ss; when this possibility is present (text lists), however, young Ss can make more use of it. Thus while Ss of all ages can remember longer lists of text than of color names, the older Ss are less able to make use of the structure and redundancy in meaningful verbal material. The age decrement in retention of scrambled proverbs might be interpreted as showing the use of inappropriate coding procedures by the older Ss: they still group words in their most likely order. Alternatively this decrement might be looked on as demonstrating the greater interfering effect on the older Ss of intrusion of the correct order of the proverbs.

C. Experiment II: Approximations to English

1. Introduction

A second exploratory experiment on age differences in the retention of verbal material was carried out on the same Ss. In this case codability was manipulated by varying the degree of contextual constraint between words.

The word lists of different orders of statistical approximation to English generated by Miller and Selfridge (1950) were used as material. The lists chosen were those of 10 and 30 words at zero, first, third, and fifth orders of approximation to English, as well as lists of standard text. The predictability of words in these lists, due to increasing semantic and syntactic constraint, increases as the lists go from zero order to text.

The author's prediction, from the argument that coding efficiency decreases with age and that this deficit is most obvious with highly codable material, was that age differences should be least with the zero-order lists (randomly chosen words with very low transitional probabilities) and greatest with the text lists. On the other hand, if it is true that old Ss are least handicapped when they can make most use of their past experience and deeply ingrained habits, presumably the old group should show most deficit with the lists of unrelated words and least deficit with the lists of text.

2.   Procedure

The 10-word and 30-word lists generated by Miller and Selfridge (1950) were recorded on tape at 1 word per second. In each case the five lists were recorded in the same order (0, 1, 3, 5, and text). Ss, who were tested individually, were instructed to listen to each list as it was played back and then to write down as many of the words as they could, in any order. All Ss were given the lists in the same order (10-word lists, zero order to text; then 30-word lists, zero order to text) and the score calculated was the number of words correctly recalled regardless of order.

3.   Subjects

Ss were the same as those in Experiment I. Thus the ages 20–79 were represented and age groups were matched on vocabulary level.

4.   Results

For ease of presentation the results were grouped into three large age groups, each of twenty Ss: Young (twenties and thirties); Middle (forties and fifties), and Old (sixties and seventies). The mean numbers of words recalled for each age group and experimental condition are shown in Table III. This table shows that a ceiling effect was in operation for the 10-word lists in that virtually all Ss correctly recalled the fifth-order and text lists. The 10-word lists were therefore not included in further analyses except in one particular, mentioned later. Trend analyses of variance were carried out on the 30-word-list data and the significance of the slopes (zero order to text) is given in Table IV. Table III also shows that the Young group's recall scores on the 30-word lists increased markedly between zero order and text,

TABLE III

MEAN NUMBER OF WORDS RECALLED BY Ss OF THREE AGE GROUPS FROM
WORD LISTS OF DIFFERENT STATISTICAL APPROXIMATION TO ENGLISH

	Order of approximation to English				
Age group	0	1	3	5	Text
		10-word lists			
Young	4.6	5.6	8.3	9.8	9.9
Middle	4.0	5.2	8.3	9.8	9.8
Old	3.6	3.9	6.4	9.5	9.7
		30-word lists			
Young	5.8	8.9	13.5	15.5	20.1
Middle	5.1	8.1	11.5	13.3	18.5
Old	3.1	5.9	9.0	10.4	13.9

while the Middle and Old groups' scores increased to a lesser extent. The significance of differences between these rates of improvement was also assessed by the trend analyses.

Table IV shows that all three age groups improved their recall scores very significantly from zero order to text. The difference in slopes between the Young and Middle groups is not significant, the Middle–Old difference approaches significance, and the Young–Old difference is significant beyond $p = .05$. Thus it can be concluded that while all Ss recalled more words as the approximation to English increased, the younger Ss were able

TABLE IV

SIGNIFICANCE OF SLOPES FROM TREND ANALYSES OF VARIANCE[a]

	F	p
	Difference of slope from zero	
Young	148.1	$< .001$
Middle	184.8	$< .001$
Old	121.9	$< .001$
	Difference between slopes	
Young–Middle	0.78	NS[b]
Middle–Old	3.02	NS
Young–Old	5.92	$< .05$

[a]Data from Table III.

[b]NS = not significant.

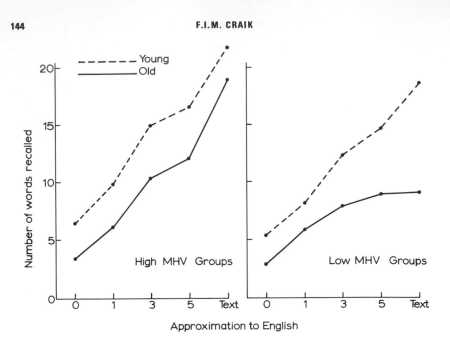

Fig. 1. Mean recall scores from 30-word lists of approximations to English.

to make more use of the contextual constraints inherent in the higher-order approximations. Older Ss are thus at a relative disadvantage when dealing with highly structured meaningful material, a conclusion that is in accordance with the present author's hypothesis.

Although the difference in slopes between the Young and Old groups shown in Table IV reaches significance, the differences between the means given in Table III are not very great. It seemed possible that the absence of marked differences was due to the tested Ss being of extremely high verbal intelligence. Accordingly, the Young and Old groups were split into two subgroups, each of ten Ss: those of very high verbal intelligence (mean MHV = 38.5; groups referred to as Young-high and Old-high) and those of moderately high verbal intelligence (mean MHV = 33.6; groups referred to as Young-low and Old-low). It should be pointed out that the low groups are so only relatively; they still represent the 75th percentile of MHV scores, whereas the high groups represent the 95th percentile. The mean recall scores of these subgroups (from the 30-word lists) are shown in Fig 1, which reveals that the Young-low group's scores are at a slightly lower level than those of the Young-high group, but there is no difference in their rates of improvement as text is approached. This rate of improvement is at least maintained by the Old-high group, although again their scores are at a lower absolute level. Ss in the Old-low group, however, are much less able to make use of the increasing contextual constraints in the higher-order lists. Thus there is no age difference in ability to make use of contextual constraint in Ss of very high verbal intelligence (Young–Old difference between slopes, $F = .03$; not significant), whereas there is a marked age difference in this ability in Ss of moderately high verbal intelligence (Young–Old difference between slopes, $F = 14.6$, $p < .01$. This analysis shows that when a more typical group is considered, older Ss are at more of a relative disadvantage when dealing with higher-order lists than the results shown in Tables III and IV indicate. On the other hand, this relative disadvantage is not shown by Ss of very high verbal intelligence.

5.   Discussion

Before going on to discuss the interim conclusions from Experiments I and II, an attempt will be made to deal with some possible alternative interpretations. It might be objected that since old Ss are known to write significantly more slowly than young Ss (Birren and Botwinick, 1951), the results on the Miller and Selfridge word lists are due to this factor. That is, old Ss take longer to write the first few words and this additional delay gives more time for decay of further material. In addition, this effect would be intensified as text was approached, since a greater amount of material is written during recall of the higher-order lists. This factor may well be operating, but that it is not the sole cause of the observed result is shown by the fact that the same result was obtained from the verbal recall of text and color names in Experiment I. In that experiment a significant age decrement was observed with text lists but none with lists of color names.

A second objection might be that since all Ss were given the Miller and Selfridge lists in the same order, the observed effect might be the result of the more potent effects of proactive interference in old Ss. Proactive interference presumably increases with greater similarity between items in successive lists. If a proactive effect was operating in this situation, it would therefore show itself in recall of color names. As no age decrement was found for that material, it is concluded that an age difference in proactive interference was not a relevant factor in these experiments.

A third objection to the present writer's interpretation is that if ratios, rather than arithmetic differences, between young and old Ss' scores are taken, the age differences on the Miller and Selfridge lists look somewhat different. When the Old group's score is expressed as a percentage of the Young group's score, the results are:

list:	0	1	3	5	text
$\frac{O}{Y}(\%)$:	53	67	67	67	69

Thus, looked at in this way, old Ss appear to be at the greatest disadvantage when dealing with the unrelated word lists. This conclusion is strengthened by the fact that there is a fairly large age difference with the zero-order lists, while the author's point of view should predict little or none.

The explanation suggested to account for this feature of the results is that, basically, old Ss *can* remember as many unrelated words as young Ss (as shown by their retention of color names in Experiment I), but that their score was depressed by their greater liability to interference when the word span is exceeded. The possibility that old Ss are more prone to supraspan interference has previously been suggested by Welford (1958) and Kay (1959). If this factor was indeed operating in the present situation, it follows that there should be much less of an age difference in recall of unrelated words from the 10-word lists, since in this case there is less supraspan material. Table III shows that this is so; age differences are smaller on the zero-order 10-word list than on the equivalent 30-word list, as are the corresponding t ratios calculated on differences between old and young (2.84 for the 10-word list, 6.14 for the 30-word list).

Table V also shows that young Ss recalled more words from the 30-word list than from the 10-word list. It seems, therefore, that another factor working in the opposite direction to supraspan interference must be postulated. This is probably the factor described by Murdock (1960), who found that, from a list of unrelated words, his student Ss recalled a constant number of words plus a percentage of the total, regardless of the length of the list. On the basis of these present results it appears that although young Ss can recall more unrelated words as the list length increases, for old Ss this factor is outweighed by the negative effects of greater amounts of supraspan interference.

It is therefore concluded that for lists of unrelated words, the age difference is caused (or at least greatly amplified) by supraspan interference. This interference becomes smaller in amount as the Miller and Selfridge lists approach text; therefore the age difference with lists of text must be attributable to another factor, judged here to be the older Ss' inability to make as full use of the structure and redundancy inherent in spoken English.

TABLE V

MEAN NUMBER OF UNRELATED WORDS RECALLED BY YOUNG AND OLD Ss

Group	10-word lists	30-word lists
Young	4.65	5.85
Old	3.60	3.10
	$t = 2.84$	$t = 6.14$

6. Conclusions from Experiments I and II

The two main conclusions that are drawn from Experiments I and II are, first, that old Ss are at a greater disadvantage when dealing with material that is highly amenable to chunking, and second, that they are more vulnerable to the effects of supraspan interference.

The hypothesized difficulty that older Ss have in chunking and thus in efficient registration of verbal material might be regarded as a deficit in temporal integration. That is, words in spoken or written discourse are held and integrated over time in the S's attention or perceptual system and are then transferred to memory in suitably encoded chunks. Thus the input systems must simultaneously perceive, hold, integrate, and store the verbal material. In the case of unrelated words, digit sequences, or color names, there is little opportunity for integrating and recoding the material into a more economical form and in these instances there is relatively little age decrement. When the sequential dependency between words is high, however, as in written or spoken English, there is much more opportunity for integration and recoding; it appears to be with this part of the process that old Ss have difficulty.

This interpretation is in general agreement with the results of Wallace (1956). She found that when parts of visual displays were shown serially, so that Ss had to integrate the material in order to identify the total display, older Ss were nearly as good as a young group at identifying simple displays, but there was a progressive age decrement as the material became more complex. The greater difficulty that older Ss experienced with the complex material was attributed largely to the greater amount of temporal integration required with such material. It is suggested that there is a close parallel between increasing complexity of display in Wallace's experiments and increasing contextual constraint in the present experiments.

Some recent experiments by Lachman and Tuttle (1965) are also relevant here. They concluded that the superiority of free recall with high orders of approximation to English was not due to facilitation at perception or at retrieval, but that the human storage system is biased for material with high contextual constraints. This conclusion could be modified to state that such material was more efficiently registered in storage.

The deficit shown by older Ss in recoding and integration could be attributed to one of two factors: either old Ss have forgotten to some extent the structure of language, and so verbal material carries less redundancy for them, or the difficulty might be due basically to the necessary switching of attention between the operations of perception and integration. Both factors are possible sources of the age decrement, although the second explanation is more in line with conclusions from previous studies described in Section 1, B. An age decrement in the ability to switch attention between aspects of perception and storage would also account for the second finding of the present experiments, that older Ss are more vulnerable to the effects of supraspan interference.

The generally accepted point of view that older Ss show least decrement when they are dealing with familiar meaningful material seems at first to conflict with the conclusions presented here. There may not be an opposition of views, however, since all the material used in the present experiments was equally familiar but varied in its amenability to chunking. On the other hand, Welford's (1962) proposal that old Ss have an improved coding ability is certainly not in accordance with the present writer's conclusions. Welford's view is a plausible one but there is no compelling experimental evidence to support it. It seems certain that coding and chunking ability improves from childhood to maturity but it does not necessarily follow that this ability continues to improve from maturity to old age.

Two brief exploratory experiments, carried out to examine the proposals discussed in the foregoing, are now reported. The first examined possible age differences in the redundancy inherent in a short English sentence and the second experiment was carried out to test the hypothesis that old Ss are more vulnerable to the effects of supraspan interference.

D.   Experiment III: Age Differences in Redundancy

1.   Introduction

Written or spoken English is highly redundant in the information theory sense, and this feature makes the material relatively easy to code into memory. One possibility discussed in the previous section was that older Ss find English less redundant, as they have forgotten to some extent digram and word probabilities and other structural rules of the language.

Attneave (1959) described a letter-guessing technique for estimating the redundancy in a short sequence of words. The technique, originated by Shannon, requires Ss to guess the successive letters of a simple sentence or phrase. Thus on each trial S guesses a letter or says "space" if he thinks that a word has ended. E informs him if he is right or wrong and S proceeds to the next letter or guesses again. S attempts to guess the whole sentence in as few trials as possible and the average number of guesses per letter is related inversely to the redundancy carried by the sentence. If English involves as much redundancy for old Ss as for young, then presumably they should guess the sentence in as few trials. If, on the other hand, older Ss have forgotten the probability structure of the language to some extent, they will require more guesses per letter. The following short experiment tested the hypothesis that English was less redundant for older Ss and that they would require more guesses in the letter-generation situation.

2. Procedure

Ss were tested individually and were told that E had in mind a short simple English sentence. They were required to guess the sentence letter by letter and would be informed after each guess whether it was right or wrong. Ss were instructed to guess the sentence in as few trials and in as short a time as possible—the number of guesses and the time taken were equally important. They were asked to write down each correct letter and were also provided with sheets with the alphabet plus "space" printed on them several times. Thus Ss could check their wrong attempts to guess any letter and no memory was involved for correct or faulty guesses. When S fully understood the task he started to guess the letters; E corrected any failure to comply with instructions and measured the time to completion of the task by stopwatch. The sentence used was: "There is a big house on top of the hill."

3. Subjects

Two groups of twenty Ss performed the experiment: a young group (age range 18–30; mean age 22.3) and an old group (age range 60–69; mean age 65.2). They were matched on vocabulary level, with mean MHV scores of 33.4 and 33.5. The young Ss were mostly students, while the old Ss were people who had volunteered to participate in experiments on aging. There were ten men and ten women in each group.

4. Results and Discussion

As the distributions of time and trials per letter were heavily skewed, medians were taken to express the group results. These medians and the significance of the age differences assessed by the Mann-Whitney U test are shown in Table VI. This table shows that old Ss took significantly longer to guess the letters and required significantly more trials.

TABLE VI

MEDIAN TIME AND TRIALS PER LETTER FOR A LETTER-GUESSING TASK

	Time per letter (sec)	Trials per letter
Young	4.92	1.71
Old	12.82	2.33
Mann-Whitney U (Y–O)	16^a	83.5^a

[a] $p < .01$.

This result suggests that older *S*s have in fact forgotten the probability structure of English to some extent and that this may be a factor in their hypothesized difficulty with coding and registration. An alternative interpretation is that the result shows a *retrieval* deficit with age. That is, older *S*s retain such language habits as probability structures, but in this somewhat artificial situation they have more difficulty in retrieving the most probable letter or the most probable word. The results of the next experiment to be reported also suggested a retrieval deficit in the elderly.

E.   Experiment IV: Supraspan Interference with Digit Lists
1.   Introduction

This study was not run as a separate experiment but is an abstraction of data from a large-scale investigation reported by Heron and Chown (1967). This investigation involved the collection of data from a large number of volunteers on a selection of psychological and physiological tests. One such test was the immediate recall of digit lists varying in length from 4 to 9 digits and presented both auditorily and visually. The results of a group of young and old male *S*s matched on digit span forward were therefore selected from the total available. It was predicted that if supraspan material was more interfering for the elderly, then the recall scores of both age groups would be identical up to the span, but that after this point the performance of the young group would be superior. That is, an interaction between age and list length was predicted.

2.   Procedure

*S*s were tested individually and were told that they would be presented with a series of digit lists ranging from 4 to 9 digits in length. They were to listen to, or watch, each list as it was presented and then attempt to recall as many digits as they could, in the correct order. In the auditory series, a warning signal sounded and was followed by the digits presented at 75 digits per minute over a loudspeaker. The end of each list was also marked by a tone and after this second signal, *S*s recalled the digits verbally and at their own speed. *S*s' responses were recorded by *E* and checked against the correct list. The digit lists had been prerecorded on tape, two practice lists followed by thirty test lists, five lists at each length. The lists were arranged randomly so that *S* did not know how long each list was going to be until it was presented.

The visual series consisted of the same lists but in a different random order. Lists were again preceded and terminated by a warning signal (in this case a red light), the presentation rate was 75 digits per minute and *S*s responded verbally after each list had been presented. The digits appeared serially on a small screen about 3–4 feet from *S*.

The score considered here is the number of digits correct in their correct position in the list. Only the last four lists at any list length were scored.

3. Subjects

The results of 50 male Ss in their twenties and 50 male Ss in their seventies were available. These groups were representative of the local population on such factors as social class and occupational class. 'Subgroups were selected from the total groups, so that the final Ss considered were matched for digit span forward. This measure was also obtained from the data and taken to be the longest list length on which S correctly recalled at least two of the four lists. Ss with digit spans of 4, 5, and 6 were selected since this gave some scope for supraspan interference to operate. This procedure yielded two groups, each of 23 Ss, for the auditory presentation (mean age for young Ss, 24.1; for old Ss, 73.5) and two groups of 20 Ss for the visual presentation (mean ages, 24.4 and 73.4, respectively).

4. Results and Discussion

Figure 2 shows the mean recall scores for the two modes of presentation. The age differences are obviously slight and this was confirmed by statistical analysis. The results of analyses of variance on the auditory and visual data are given in Table VII. This table shows that list length was a significant

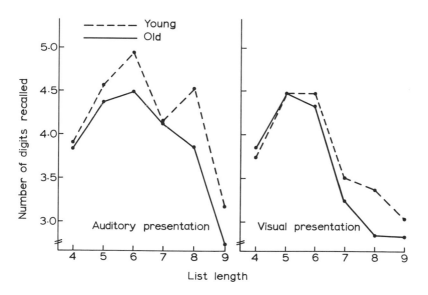

Fig. 2. Mean recall scores for two age groups from digit lists.

TABLE VII

ANALYSES OF VARIANCE[a]

Variable	Auditory		Visual	
	F	p	F	p
Age	8.01	< .01	1.59	NS[b]
List length	20.14	< .001	16.76	< .001
Age × list length	0.91	NS	0.53	NS

[a]Data from Fig. 2.

[b]NS = not significant.

factor in both cases, age had a significant effect only with the auditory presentation, and the interaction between age and list length was not significant in either case.

The failure of the interaction to approach significance shows that with these groups, supraspan interference was as potent for the young as for the old Ss. This result goes against the present writer's prediction and the hypothesis of Welford (1958) and Kay (1959) that supraspan interference is more disruptive for the elderly.

It is difficult to reconcile the absence of an age difference in supraspan interference in these data with the apparent presence of the effect in the recall of unrelated words reported in Section II, C, 5. One difference between the two experiments was that the unrelated words were recalled and scored without regard to order, whereas order was important in the digit study. When the digit data were reworked, scoring items correct regardless of order, the same result of no interaction between age and list length was obtained, however.

A second suggestion is that the apparent difference in results between the two experiments was caused by the different material used. If retrieval from memory becomes less efficient with age, it is plausible to suggest that this effect is more marked with lists of unrelated words, where the cues for retrieval are not so effective. That is, if Ss must perform a search through memory to retrieve the words in the list, this search process will obviously be facilitated where the possible vocabulary is very small (as with digits 0–9) and be at its least efficient when the possible vocabulary is large (as with unrelated words). The age difference reported with unrelated words might have been due to an age-related retrieval deficit rather than to supraspan interference. It is suggested that this deficit becomes more obvious as the cues for retrieval become less effective—in this case as the vocabulary from which stimulus words are drawn becomes larger.

Murdock (1960) found that Ss recalled a constant number of words plus a percentage of the total number in the list. This suggests that a plausible model for immediate recall would be a primary store that holds a constant number of words and a secondary longer-term store with a much larger capacity. Recall from the primary store would be augmented by a search process through the secondary store. If it is postulated that the primary store is not much affected by aging but that the search process is, this would explain the finding (from Experiment II) that there was a greater age difference with lists of 30 words than with 10-word lists. In the case of the longer lists, the search process would play a bigger part and young Ss would thus be at a greater advantage.

An experiment was therefore designed to test the notion that the interaction between age and list length increases as the vocabulary from which words are drawn increases in size. The ideas of a primary and secondary store would also be further explored.

F. Experiment V: Age Differences in the Recall of Word Lists

1. Introduction

This experiment was designed to test the hypothesis, just discussed, that older Ss have a less efficient memory retrieval system. It was postulated that this deficit would be most apparent when cues for retrieval were poor, as when the total possible vocabulary was large and the search process was necessarily extensive. It was also postulated that for any type of material, age differences in recall would be greatest when there was greatest reliance on the search process, that is, when the lists were long. An interaction between age and list length was therefore predicted and the further prediction was made that this interaction would increase with vocabulary size, that is, that the three-factor interaction between age, list length, and vocabulary size would be significant.

Four different types of common verbal material were used. In order of increasing vocabulary size these were: digits 0—9; English county names; animal names; unrelated words. For the last type of material only AA words from the Thorndike-Lorge word count were used; thus all words used in the experiment were well known to all Ss. Lists of words from one or another of these vocabularies were presented to S for immediate free recall in the manner described below.

The experiment was designed in such a way that other hypotheses could some results of their experiments to greater proactive interference with age; data from the present experiment were examined for supporting evidence. Also, in view of the recent application of signal detection theory to studies of memory (Norman, 1966) and the fact that the present writer has reported a significantly more cautious decision criterion in signal detection for an old group (Craik, 1966), it seemed possible that some at least of the age differences in memory were the result of more cautious decision criteria in the elderly. Accordingly, responses from the word-list experiment were examined for age differences in intrusive errors (false positives) as well as for accuracy in recall.

2. Procedure

Lists of words representing the various types of material were constructed as follows. The digit lists ranged in length from 5 to 10 digits; two lists were presented at each length. No digit appeared more than twice per list and easy runs were avoided. With these constraints, lists were constructed from random number tables. The other lists ranged from 5 to 20 words in lengths of 5, 6, 7, 8, 9, 10, 15, and 20. One list was presented at each length, but two complete sets were constructed for the county, animal, and unrelated word lists. Half the Ss in each age group were given set A and half set B; the point of this was to minimize effects due to the particular words chosen. In the county lists no county was repeated within a list but counties were necessarily repeated between lists, since the total number of English counties is 39. In the animal and unrelated word lists no word was repeated throughout the lists. The animal lists included names of birds, fish, and insects. Ss were informed beforehand of the principles of list construction.

Ss worked through all the lists of one type of material in a block, and within each age group Ss were given the different types of material in a counterbalanced order—that is, each block was equally often first, second, third, or fourth. Within each block of lists the order of list length was also counterbalanced, so that over a group of Ss the long and short lists were equally often first, second, third, and so on. S was informed before each block what kind of words would be in the lists and he was told the length of list before each presentation. Because of the complex design, lists were not prerecorded but were read by E at a rate of 48 words per minute. Ss recalled the words verbally, in any order and without time limit. E checked S's responses on typed copies of the lists and noted any intrusive errors. The score taken was simply the number of words correctly recalled.

Ss were tested individually and were told that E would read lists of words that they were required to recall immediately after presentation, in any order. The types of material to be used and the construction of the lists were described and all reasonable questions relating to the task were answered.

3.   Subjects

*S*s were the same as those used in Experiment III and described in Section II, D, 3. That is, two groups of *S*s matched on vocabulary level performed the task, a young group (mean age 22.3) and an old group (mean age 65.2).

4.   Results

The effect of proactive interference was assessed by transforming each *S*'s recall score on each list to a percentage of the total list. This was necessary as all list lengths were represented at each order of presentation position (first, second, third, etc.). The mean percentage correct at each position was then calculated for the two groups and the results are shown graphically in Fig. 3. There were twelve positions of presentation for the digit lists, as each of the lengths 5 through 10 was presented twice to each *S*; there were eight positions for the other lists.

Figure 3 shows that the young group performed better throughout but that there was little effect of order of presentation and little sign of an interaction between age and order of presentation. Analyses of variance were carried out for each type of material and the results may be summarized as follows. Age was a significant factor in all four types of list; order of presentation was significant only in the case of county names ($p < .01$), and Duncan's Multiple Range Test revealed that this significant effect was

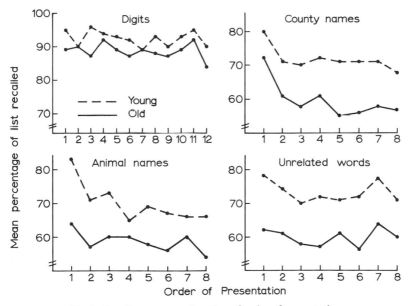

Fig. 3. Recall scores as a function of order of presentation.

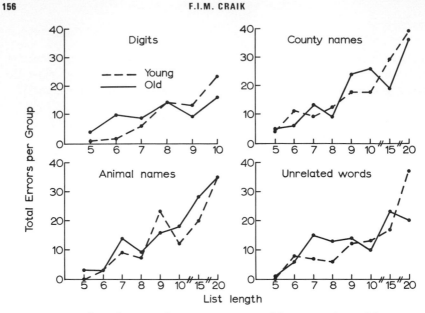

Fig. 4. Intrusion errors for two age groups and four types of material.

due entirely to the difference between the first lists and subsequent lists; the age × order of presentation interaction was not significant for any type of material. This last result means that there were no age differences in proactive interference in the present experiment. The finding gives no support to the notion that the effects of intraexperimental proactive interference increase with age, although it is possible that an age difference would become apparent in a situation where proactive interference exerted a more powerful effect.

Intrusion errors for both age groups and each length of list are shown in Fig. 4. Analyses of variance were carried out for each type of material and the results may be summarized as follows: age was not a significant factor in any case; list length had a highly significant effect ($p < .001$) for all types of material; the age × list length interaction was significant ($p < .01$) only in the case of the digit lists. It thus seems that there were no age differences in willingness to guess or make false positive errors except on the digit lists where, as Fig. 4 shows, young Ss were somewhat less prone to this type of error with the shorter lists but more prone with the longer lists. The hypothesis that older Ss are at a disadvantage in recall situations because of a more cautious decision criterion and a greater reluctance to guess is thus not confirmed by these results.

When the experiment was designed it was felt that, for free recall, lists of 10 digits would be long enough to show the predicted effects and that longer lists of digits would be treated rather differently by Ss. For the word material, however, lists of up to 20 words were presented. This feature of the design implied some problems for analysis, so several analyses were carried out and are described here. The first was a series of two-variable analyses of variance within each type of material on list lengths 5–10; the second was a further series of two-variable analyses of variance on lists 5–20 for the county names, animal names, and unrelated words; the third analysis was a three-variable analysis of variance on lists 5–20. The three variables were thus list length (5–20), type of material (county names, animal names, unrelated words), and age (young and old). As there was a tendency for the variance of recall scores to increase with list length, transformed data were used for the analyses just described. The original data were transformed according to the formula $X' = (X + \frac{1}{2})^{\frac{1}{2}}$ (Winer, 1962). The results of the analyses of variance are given in Tables VIII and IX and the mean recall scores are shown graphically in Fig. 5.

Figure 5 shows that the performance of the young group was superior throughout and that the age discrepancy became greater as vocabulary size increased. Tables VIII and IX confirm that age had a significant effect but, whereas Table VIII shows that the significance of the age effect increased from digits to unrelated words, the three-factor analysis summarized in Table IX did not yield a significant age × type of material interaction. Similarly, while Table VIII shows that the significance of the age × list length interaction increased from county names to unrelated words,

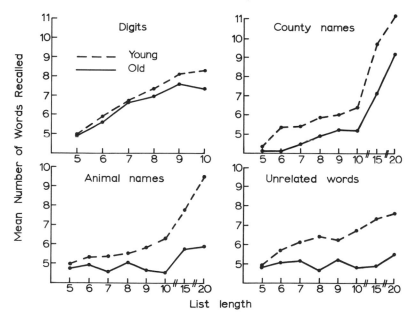

Fig. 5. Mean recall scores for two age groups and four types of material.

TABLE VIII

RESULTS OF TWO-VARIABLE ANALYSES OF VARIANCE (F VALUES) ON
DATA FROM EXPERIMENT V

Material	List lengths 5–10			List lengths 5–20		
	Age	Lists	Age × Lists	Age	Lists	Age × Lists
Digits	6.71^a	174.46^b	2.65^a	—	—	—
County names	13.68^b	12.55^b	1.29	14.95^b	85.04^b	2.22^a
Animal names	15.80^b	0.88	2.33^a	27.48^b	17.15^b	4.26^c
Unrelated words	33.72^b	3.87	4.80^b	33.52^b	6.13^b	4.61^b

$^a p < .05.$
$^b p < .001.$
$^c p < .01.$

TABLE IX

RESULTS OF THREE VARIABLE ANALYSIS OF VARIANCE (F VALUES)
ON DATA FROM EXPERIMENT V

Main effects		Interactions	
Age	$F = 33.82^a$	Age × Lists	$F = 7.83^a$
List length	$F = 75.16^a$	Age × Material	$F = 0.28$
Type of material	$F = 5.62^b$	Lists × Material	$F = 15.53^a$
		Age × Lists × Material	$F = 1.19$

$^a p < .001.$
$^b p < .01.$

Table IX shows that, contrary to prediction, the age × list length × type of material interaction did not reach significance.

The age × list length interaction for digits shown in Table VIII is larger than expected, but this may be a function of the significant age × list length interaction for intrusive errors described earlier. That is, young Ss probably increased their recall scores on the longer lists of digits by guessing, and thereby increased the size of the age × list length interaction for recall scores on this type of material.

Other features of the results may be mentioned briefly. Recall scores generally increased with increasing list length and decreased with increasing vocabulary size; the effect of list length in adding to the number of words recalled became significantly less powerful as vocabulary size increased, however (as shown by the list length × type of material interaction, Table IX). Finally, the significant age × list length interaction shown in Table IX signifies that, over all types of material, young Ss improved their recall scores relative to the old group as list length increased.

One further measure taken from the data was the word span for each S. This was defined as the longest list from which S recalled all the items, regardless of order, so the measure was slightly different from the standard digit span. The results for the two age groups and different types of material are shown in Table XI. The significance of age differences was tested by t test and these results are also shown. Table XI shows that there was no significant age decrement in digit span but that the age difference increases, more or less, with vocabulary size until the spans for unrelated words show a highly significant decrement with age.

How do all these results fit the picture of a deficit in the retrieval process with age? A model for STM was briefly described in the discussion of Experiment IV (Section II, E, 4). This speculative model will be discussed in greater detail in the following section, but the basic concept is that immediate recall involves two storage systems: a limited-capacity primary memory store whose traces decay rapidly and are coded in terms of acoustic qualities; and a secondary larger longer-term store where traces are coded in a much more complex fashion. This coding in the secondary store almost certainly involves acoustic and semantic attributes and it is in this store that organization of the material, recoding, or chunking are important factors. Retrieval from the primary store would be a direct readout of the traces that are still viable, whereas retrieval from the secondary store involves a search process. It is further postulated that age differences are slight in the primary memory system, but that in the secondary system there are large age deficits in both registration and retrieval.

This speculative model predicts that for short lists, slight age decrements should be observed since the material will be retrieved largely from the primary store. As list length increases, however, there is greater reliance on the search process to augment the primary memory component, and therefore there should be greater age deficits. The search process will be facilitated when the vocabulary from which words are drawn is small, and in this case older Ss are at little disadvantage. It is postulated that as vocabulary size increases, the extent of the search process is increased and older Ss show progressively greater decrements in recall.

The results of the present experiment give partial support to this model. The age decrement increases as list length increases (shown by Fig. 5 and confirmed by the significant age × list length interaction, Table IX). Recall is more difficult as vocabulary size increases (shown by the significant main effect of type of material, Table IX) and the effect of increased list length leading to higher recall scores is reduced with the larger vocabularies (shown by the significant list length × type of material interaction, Table IX). The model predicts larger age decrements as vocabulary size increases and this is borne out by Fig. 5 and by the two-variable analyses of variance in Table VIII, but it is not supported by the nonsignificant age × type of material interaction from the three-variable analysis (Table IX). Similarly, the age × list length interaction should increase with vocabulary size, and this is generally supported by the results shown in Table VIII, but the age × list length × type of material interaction (Table IX) does not reach significance. Thus the results of the experiment are in the predicted direction, although not all are statistically significant.

The results of the word span measurement (Table XI) do support the model quite well. The age decrement increases more or less with vocabulary size, that is, with less guidance for the search process. Thus old Ss are less able to augment their primary store component with words retrieved from the secondary store. The finding of a highly significant age difference in free recall of unrelated words conflicts with the results of Talland (1965). He found no such age decrement in free recall; at present, no explanation is offered to account for this discrepancy.

5. *Primary and Secondary Components in Immediate Recall*

The model of STM proposed in the foregoing has much in common with the model suggested by Waugh and Norman (1965). Some speculative additions or changes have been made to their model, however. It is proposed that the capacity of the primary memory (PM) is governed by the acoustic content of the material to be remembered (e.g., number of syllables) but is otherwise independent of the nature of the material (e.g., vocabulary size or information content). To borrow a term from Waugh and Norman, the primary store behaves as an "echo box"—although the term is used here to describe the whole store rather than cells within the store. Registration into secondary memory (SM) would depend on the amenability of the material to coding or chunking. Retrieval is seen as consisting of a direct readout of the material in PM plus a search process through SM. The efficiency of the search process will depend upon such factors as the effectiveness of the original registration and the presence of such cues for retrieval as knowledge of the vocabulary or ensemble from which stimuli were drawn: the smaller the vocabulary, the less extensive and more efficient the search process. Finally, it is postulated that aging primarily affects registration into and retrieval from SM.

It follows from the foregoing propositions that if recall scores from the present experiment could be broken down into PM and SM components, several predictions could be made relating these components to changes with age and vocabulary size. First, the PM component should remain approximately the same for both age groups and for all types of material. Second, the SM component for any one list length should be larger for the smaller vocabularies, and for any given condition the SM component should be smaller for the old group.

The result of Murdock's (1960) experiment seemed to provide a possible method for isolating the PM and SM components. Murdock presented word lists of various lengths for immediate recall and he found that for lists of 5–400 words, recall scores were well fitted by the linear equation

$$R = m + kt$$

where R = recall score, t = total presentation time (thus a function of list length), and m and k are constants. Murdock suggested that the intercept constant m was the memory span and thus, for any length of list, S recalled the number of words in his span plus a small percentage of the total list.

It is proposed here that m may be the PM component while k may be a function of search process efficiency in SM. In view of the predictions made earlier, it follows that m should remain approximately constant for all types of material and both age groups, whereas k should decrease with increasing vocabulary size and from young to old. Best-fit linear equations were therefore calculated (by the least squares method) from the group means for each list length and type of material. The equations are given in Table X in the form $y = m + kx$ where y = number of words recalled and x = length of list. This does not conflict with Murdock's formulation, since presentation speed was constant and may be taken as 1.

Table X shows that the data confirm three of the predictions but that one prediction is not supported. That is, the slope constant k decreases regularly from digits to unrelated words for both groups; it is also smaller for the old group at each vocabulary size—both of which findings accord with prediction. The constant m shows no systematic age differences, as in two cases it is larger for the young group and in two

TABLE X

BEST-FIT LINEAR EQUATIONS FOR FOUR TYPES OF WORD LIST
MATERIAL AND TWO AGE GROUPS[a]

Material	Young	Old
Digits	$y = 1.70 + 0.69x$	$y = 2.50 + 0.54x$
County names	$y = 2.11 + 0.47x$	$y = 2.09 + 0.34x$
Animal names	$y = 3.31 + 0.30x$	$y = 4.12 + 0.09x$
Unrelated words	$y = 4.86 + 0.15x$	$y = 4.74 + 0.03x$

[a]Where y = number of words recalled, x = list length.

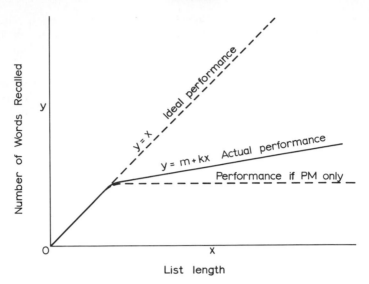

Fig. 6. Three theoretical recall functions.

cases smaller, again in accordance with prediction. However, Table X shows that for both age groups, m increases fairly regularly with vocabulary size and this finding goes against prediction.

Another formulation was therefore proposed (this suggestion was first made by Dr. David Legge) and is illustrated in Fig. 6. This figure shows the theoretical graph of words recalled in an immediate free-recall situation as list length increases. Several possible functions relating number of words recalled to length of list are illustrated: the first is the ideal slope—that is, all words are recalled; the second function is the number of words recalled in practice: if the list is very short, S recalls all words, but for lists longer than a critical length he performs less than perfectly and from this point his recall score increases linearly (Murdock, 1960); the third function is the one that would hold if recall were totally dependent on a primary store of limited capacity: recall would increase up to the capacity but would thereafter remain at that level despite increases in list length.

If the assumption is made that all three functions diverge from a common point, the y value of this point (which will be the capacity of the primary store) may be found, as it is also the intersection of the ideal and actual recall functions. The equation of the ideal slope is $y = x$ and the equation of the actual slope after it departs from the ideal slope is $y = m + kx$. If these equations are simultaneously solved for y, this gives a value of y that is an estimate of the capacity of PM. Accordingly, best-fit linear equations were calculated for each S's recall scores on each type of material and mean values of the intersection points are shown in Table XI.

The first column of Table XI shows the values of y calculated as described in the preceding paragraph; this gives an estimate of PM capacity in units of words. The values are fairly similar except for county names, where the values are somewhat lower. If the capacity of PM is governed by acoustic content, as suggested earlier, it is more logical to measure y in syllable units. The mean numbers of syllables per word for the lists of digits, county names, animal names, and unrelated words were 1.09, 2.65, 1.74, and 1.61, respectively. When the mean number of words was multiplied by the relevant number of syllables, an estimate of PM capacity in syllables was obtained and is shown in the second column. The indices of search efficiency (k) are virtually identical to the values given in Table X; the slight discrepancies are the result of having used individual data rather than group means for the calculation. Last, word span values are shown.

The age differences for each measure were assessed by t tests, the results of which are also shown in Table XI. The age differences in PM capacity are all nonsignificant, as predicted, except in the case of unrelated words. The index of search efficiency (k) shows a significant drop with age for each type of material, again according to prediction. The word-span results have been discussed earlier.

TABLE XI

MEAN VALUES OF PRIMARY MEMORY CAPACITY (y), SEARCH EFFICIENCY (k), AND
WORD SPAN FOR TWO AGE GROUPS AND FOUR TYPES OF MATERIAL[a]

	Primary memory capacity (y)						
	Words	Syllables	t	Search (k)	t	Span	t
Digits							
Young	4.96	5.41	0.99	0.69	2.38[b]	8.30	1.86
Old	5.33	5.81		0.54		7.60	
County names							
Young	3.52	9.33	0.97	0.46	2.11[b]	5.65	2.67[b]
Old	2.92	7.74		0.34		4.50	
Animal names							
Young	4.48	7.80	0.00	0.28	3.96[c]	6.10	2.13[b]
Old	4.48	7.80		0.09		5.25	
Unrelated Words							
Young	5.73	9.23	4.77[c]	0.15	3.20[c]	6.70	4.35[c]
Old	4.87	7.84		0.03		5.35	

[a]Values of t given are for the age difference in each case.
[b]$p < .05$.
[c]$p < .01$.

The differences between types of material generally support the predictions. The PM capacity in syllables is remarkably constant for the last three types of material: estimates range only from 7.7 to 9.3 syllables. The values from the digit lists are somewhat lower, however. The obtained values of k decrease regularly from digits to unrelated words for both age groups as predicted.

These results give good support to the proposed model of STM. Two features of the data require explanation, however: the much lower estimates of PM capacity from the digit lists and the highly significant age difference in PM capacity for unrelated words. There are arguable reasons for the first discrepancy: digits are somewhat different from the other verbal material and may have been treated differently by Ss. For example, some Ss reported checking mentally which of the digits 0–9 had been presented once or twice in a list; this procedure implies a greater reliance on recoded memory traces and less on a "passive" echo box. More simply, the fact that digit lists extended only to 10 in length means that the shorter lists had a greater weighting effect on the best-fit linear equation than was the case for the other types of material. Thus the digit slopes may have been relatively steeper and the obtained values of y consequently lower. The finding of a significant age difference in PM capacity for unrelated words is more difficult to account for and no explanation is offered for this discrepancy at present.

In summary, a model of STM that postulates the involvement of two stores, a limited-capacity primary memory (echo box) and a longer-term memory, was supported fairly well by the results of the present experiment. With regard to aging, it was predicted that age has little effect on the amount of material recalled from the primary store, but that recall from the secondary store is detrimentally affected by age due to poorer registration and less efficient retrieval. These predictions were also borne out, in general, by the results.

G.   Conclusions

The experimental findings may be briefly summarized at this point. The original observation was that old Ss were no worse than a young group in their ability to recall novel meaningless material (Finnish digits), but there was an age decrement when English digits were used. It was suggested that this result might reflect a coding or chunking deficit with age—old Ss might be no worse at tasks demanding passive retention, but might be increasingly at a disadvantage as the material became more amenable to chunking procedures. This suggestion was supported by the results of Experiments I and II and the conclusion was drawn that the age deficit in coding led to poorer registration in the elderly. Experiment III showed that old *S*s required more time and more trials to guess the letters of a short sentence; this finding was taken to mean either that there is some forgetting of the statistical structure of language with age or that the structure is remembered but retrieval from memory is less efficient in the elderly. The results from Experiment II suggested that older *S*s are more vulnerable to the effects of supraspan interference, but in a direct test (Experiment IV), this hypothesis was not confirmed. It was then proposed that there is an age-related deficit in the retrieval process and that this deficit would be most apparent in the recall of lengthy word lists whose items were drawn from a large vocabulary. These predictions were borne out by the results of Experiment V.

In the light of these findings and of the results of such other workers as Murdock (1960) and Waugh and Norman (1965), a speculative model of STM was proposed. In essence it was postulated that immediate recall involves two storage systems: primary memory, which has a limited capacity for acoustically coded traces, and secondary memory, which is very much larger and whose traces are coded or chunked in a complex manner. Retrieval from PM is by direct readout of the remaining traces, whereas retrieval from SM involves a search process that would be guided by such heuristics as knowledge of the general sound or meaning of the word and by knowledge of the vocabulary from which the word was drawn. With regard to aging, it was postulated that PM is little affected by the advancing years but that there are age-related deficits both in registration into and retrieval from SM.

These postulates were reasonably well supported when estimates of PM capacity and search efficiency were obtained from the word list data (Experiment V). For the *S*s used in that experiment, PM capacity was 8–9 syllables and was reasonably independent of age and of material used. The efficiency of the search process, on the other hand, declined with age and with increased vocabulary size.

Other findings from these present experiments fit the model reasonably well. The immediate recall of Finnish digits presumably reflects fairly purely the capacity of PM: the mean span for both young and old groups was 8.3 syllables, which is in good agreement with the estimate given earlier. The finding of no age decrement in word span for color names (Experiment I) could be interpreted as showing no registration advantage to the young group (as the material cannot easily be recoded into chunks) and no retrieval disadvantage to the old group, as the words came from a limited vocabulary. With increasing order of approximation to English, presumably there is greater facilitation of retrieval, but the relative gains made by older *S*s in this respect may be outweighed by the greater recoding advantages for younger *S*s in the higher-order approximations. These factors may explain the relatively greater age decrement found on the higher-order lists in Experiment II. It was shown in Experiment III that old Ss required significantly more trials to guess letters in a sentence and this result was interpreted as showing either the forgetting of the statistical structure of language with age or as another manifestation of retrieval loss. It might be possible to distinguish between these interpretations by means of a recognition test for letter or word sequences, e.g., by presenting alternatives for the next letter in sequence. Presumably older Ss would show less decrement on this task if Experiment III shows a retrieval failure.

It is not proposed to discuss the literature reviewed in Section I in the light of the author's proposals, but there appear to be no serious conflicts with the present point of view. The suggested model of STM is presented in rather general terms, so it is not surprising that most of the existing evidence on age differences in STM may be fitted into the framework it provides. Obviously the model requires many refinements and additions; nothing has been said of the decay or interference characteristics of material held in PM and SM, or of the place of an attention mechanism. There are many other questions to answer: What about visual input, for example? Are visual stimuli recoded into the same primary store? Do stimuli enter PM and SM simultaneously or are they transferred from PM to SM? Do all stimuli enter SM or only some (Treisman, 1964)? What part, if any, does PM play in temporal integration and coding? What are the problems of ordered as opposed to free recall? Answers to these and many other questions will be found as research techniques become more sophisticated.

Finally, it is stressed that although the point of view advocated here may turn out to be wrong in many respects, it is felt that such analytic models can serve a useful function in stimulating relevant questions for experimental research on aging.

ACKNOWLEDGMENTS

The experiments reported here were carried out at the Medical Research Council Unit for Research on Occupational Aspects of Ageing, University of Liverpool. The author gratefully acknowledges the usefulness of many discussions that have taken place in Liverpool and at Birkbeck College.

REFERENCES

Attneave, F. *Applications of information theory to psychology.* New York: Holt, Rinehart, & Winston, 1959.
Birren, J. E. *The psychology of aging.* Englewood Cliffs, N.J.: Prentice-Hall, 1964.
Birren, J. E., & Botwinick, J. The relation of writing speed to age and to the senile psychoses. *J. consult. Psychol.,* 1951, **15,** 243–249.
Broadbent, D. E. *Perception and communication.* New York: Macmillan (Pergamon), 1958.
Broadbent, D. E., & Gregory, M. Some confirmatory results on age differences in memory for simultaneous stimulation. *Brit. J. Psychol.,* 1965, **56,** 77–80.

Broadbent, D. E., & Heron, A. Effects of a subsidiary task on performance involving immediate memory by younger and older men. *Brit. J. Psychol.*, 1962, **53**, 189–198.

Bromley, D. B. Some effects of age on short term learning and remembering. *J. Geront.*, 1958, **13**, 398–406.

Caird, W. K. Reverberatory activity and memory disorder. *Nature*, 1964, **201**, 1150.

Caird, W. K. Aging and short-term memory. *J. Geront.*, 1966, **21**, 295–299.

Canestrari, R. E. Age differences in verbal learning and verbal behavior. Paper presented at Colloq. Psychol. Functioning in Normal Aging and Senile Aged, Semmering, Austria, June, 1966.

Craik, F. I. M. The nature of the age decrement in performance on dichotic listening tasks *Quart. J. Exp. Psychol.*, 1965, **17**, 227–240.

Craik, F. I. M. The effects of ageing on the detection of faint auditory signals. *Proc. 7th int. Congr. Geront., Vienna*, 1966, pp. 145–147.

Gilbert, J. G. Memory loss in senescence. *J. abnorm. soc. Psychol.*, 1941, **36**, 73–86.

Gladis, M., & Braun, H. W. Age differences in transfer and retroaction as a function of intertask response similarity. *J. exp. Psychol.*, 1958, **55**, 25–30.

Griew, S., & Davies, D. R. The effect of aging on auditory vigilance performance. *J. Geront.*, 1962, **17**, 88–90.

Hebb, D. O. Distinctive features of learning in the higher animal. In J. F. Delafresnaye (Ed.), *Brain mechanisms and learning.* Oxford: Blackwell, 1961. Pp. 37–51.

Heron, A., & Chown, S. M. *Age and function.* London: Churchill, 1967.

Heron, A., & Craik, F. Age differences in cumulative learning of meaningful and meaningless material. *Scand. J. Psychol.*, 1964, **5**, 209–217.

Hurwitz, L. J., & Allison, R. S. Factors influencing performance in psychological testing of the aged. In A. T. Welford and J. E. Birren (Eds.), *Behavior, aging and the nervous system.* Springfield, Ill.: Charles C Thomas, 1965. Pp. 461–475.

Inglis, J. Immediate memory, age and brain function. In A. T. Welford and J. E. Birren (Eds.), *Behavior, aging and the nervous system.* Springfield, Ill.: Charles C Thomas, 1965. Pp. 88–113.

Inglis, J., & Ankus, M. N. Effects of age on short-term storage and serial rote learning. *Brit. J. Psychol.*, 1965, **56**, 183–195.

Inglis, J., & Caird, W. K. Age differences in successive responses to simultaneous stimulation. *Canad. J. Psychol.*, 1963, **17**, 98–105.

Jerome, E. A. Age and learning—experimental studies. In J. E. Birren (Ed.), *Handbook of aging and the individual.* Chicago, Ill.: Univer. of Chicago Press, 1959.

Kay, H. Theories of learning and aging. In J. E. Birren (Ed.), *Handbook of aging and the individual.* Chicago, Ill.: Univer. of Chicago Press, 1959. Pp. 614–654.

Kirchner, W. K. Age differences in short-term retention of rapidly changing information *J. exp. Psychol.*, 1958, **55**, 352–358.

Korchin, S. H., & Basowitz, H. Age differences in verbal learning. *J. abnorm. soc. Psychol.*, 1957, **54**, 64–69.

Lachman, R., & Tuttle, A. V. Approximations to English and short-term memory: construction or storage? *J. exp. Psychol.*, 1965, **70**, 386–393.

Maccoby, E. E., Jones, T. M., & Konrad, K. W. Selective listening in later life. Paper presented at Colloq. Psychol. Functioning in Normal Aging and Senile Aged, Semmering, Austria, June, 1966.

McGhie, A., Chapman, J., & Lawson, J. S. Changes in immediate memory with age. *Brit. J. Psychol.*, 1965, **56**, 69–75.

Mackay, H. A., & Inglis, J. The effect of age on a short-term auditory storage process. *Gerontologia*, 1963, **8**, 193–200.

Miller, G. A., & Selfridge, J. A. Verbal context and the recall of meaningful material. *Amer. J. Psychol.*, 1950, **63**, 176–185.

Murdock, B. B. The immediate retention of unrelated words. *J. exp. Psychol.*, 1960, **60**, 222–234.

Murdock, B. B. Effects of a subsidiary task on short-term memory. *Brit. J. Psychol.*, 1965, **56**, 413–419.

Norman, D. A. Acquisition and retention in short-term memory. *J. exp. Psychol.*, 1966, **72**, 369–381.

Raven, J. C. *Guide to using the Mill Hill Vocabulary Scale.* London: H. K. Lewis, 1958.

Ruch, F. L. Adult learning. *Psychol. Bull.*, 1933, **30**, 387–414.

Ruch, F. L. The differentiative effects of age upon human learning. *J. gen. Psychol.*, 1934, **11**, 261–286.

Schonfield, D. Memory changes with age. *Nature*, 1965, **208**, 918.

Talland, G. A. Effects of aging on the formation of sequential and spatial concepts. *Percept. mot. Skills*, 1961, **13**, 210.

Talland, G. A. Three estimates of the word span and their stability over the adult years. *Quart. J. exp. Psychol.*, 1965, **17**, 301–307.

Taub, H. A. Visual short-term memory as a function of age, rate of presentation, and schedule of presentation. *J. Geront.*, 1966, **21**, 388–394.

Treisman, A. M. Selective attention in man. *Brit. med. Bull.*, 1964, **20**, 12–16.

Wallace, J. G. Some studies of perception in relation to age. *Brit. J. Psychol* , 1956, **47**, 283–297.

Waugh, N. C., & Norman, D. A. Primary memory. *Psychol. Rev.*, 1965, **72**, 89–104.

Welford, A. T. *Ageing and human skill.* London & New York: Oxford Univer. Press, 1958.

Welford, A. T. On changes of performance with age. *Lancet*, 1962, **1**, 335–339.

Welford, A. T. Experimental psychology in the study of ageing. *Brit. med. Bull.*, 1964 **20**, 65–69. (a)

Welford, A. T. Ageing and personality: age changes in basic psychological capacities. In P. From Hansen (Ed.), *Age with a future.* Copenhagen: Munksgaard, 1964. (b) Pp. 60–66.

Welford, A. T., & Birren, J. E. (Eds.) *Behavior, aging and the nervous system.* Springfield, Ill.: Charles C Thomas, 1965.

Wimer, R. E. A supplementary report on age differences in retention over a twenty-four hour period. *J. Geront.*, 1960, **15**, 417–418.

Wimer, R. E., & Wigdor, B. T. Age differences in retention of learning. *J. Geront.*, 1958, **13**, 291–295.

Winer, B. J. *Statistical principles in experimental design.* New York: McGraw-Hill, 1962.

Yntema, D. B., & Trask, F. P. Recall as a search process. *J. verb. Learn. verb. Behav.*, 1963, **2**, 65–74.

Age Changes in Acquisition

ROBERT E. CANESTRARI, Jr.

Research Unit on Aging,

Veterans Administration Center,

Hampton, Virginia

I. Introduction

For some time we have been investigating a number of variables that may be involved in the often noted deficit behavior of elderly adults engaged in learning tasks. This report is based on some of our previously reported work in this area, as well as on two additional studies that attempt to isolate variables involved in this deficit behavior.

Much of our previous work has been concerned with the effect of pacing schedules on the ability of elderly persons to learn verbal material. In order to provide sufficient background it is necessary to briefly describe previously reported material. In an early study (Canestrari, 1963) a comparison of the performance of young and elderly Ss under paced and self-paced conditions revealed that the performance of the elderly S was greatly improved under the self-paced condition. Further, there was a marked decrease in omission errors (nonresponses) and very little change in errors of commission (overt errors). Similar results were obtained in a serial learning study by Eisdorfer, Axelrod, and Wilkie (1963). It was also observed that although Ss in our study had complete control over stimulus material under the self-paced schedule, the older Ss used the extra time available under the self-paced condition to gain additional response time rather than to study the pairs. It was concluded that the enhancing effect of the self-paced schedule was due to the increased availability of response time, which allowed the older S to make those correct responses that were in his repertoire. The assumption was that the older S had learned the material under the fast-paced condition, but did not have time to respond.

It should be noted, however, that self-pacing has the additional effect of increasing the interval between stimuli. Consequently, Welford's (1959) conception of the learning process suggests an alternative explanation of the data. He postulates a number of stages that are essential to the learning process. First, the material has to be perceived and comprehended. Having perceived the stimuli, the material must be held by some short-term storage mechanism that can store rapidly but impermanently. This storage is broken down by neuronal activity resulting from fresh stimulus input. Welford suggests that the short-term storage mechanism of the older person is less able to maintain an ongoing pattern in the face of fresh stimulus input. Stimulus events may be erased by incoming stimuli before adequate comprehension occurs, and consequently never reach a more permanent memory system. The improvement shown by the elderly under self-paced schedules may therefore have been a function of the increased interval between stimulus events. This hypothesis is supported by a study by Arenberg (1965) that addresses itself to this problem. Before concluding that older persons learn at a fast pace, but do not have enough time to respond, it is necessary to examine the effect of the interval between items and to measure how much is learned after each trial, without imposing time limits on responses. In Arenberg's study, young and elderly Ss learned paired-associate lists under two conditions. Groups learned lists under either a short or long anticipation interval. Interspersed through the acquisition process were self-paced trials in which only the stimulus word was shown and Ss had unlimited time to respond. If time to respond is crucial, then varying the anticipation interval should not have any effect on the error scores during the self-paced trials. Ss run under the longer anticipation interval had fewer errors than Ss run under the shorter anticipation interval, irrespective of whether they had to respond under paced or self-paced conditions. This suggests that the decrease in error scores under self-paced conditions is not due entirely to the additional time available to make a correct response, but rather to some increased susceptibility with age to the sort of erasure phenomenon suggested by Welford. The erasure hypothesis is further supported by a study, unrelated to aging (Averbach & Coriell, 1961), that demonstrated that ability to recall a visual signal varies as a function of the interval between an original stimulus and a signal that follows it.

A.   Experiment I: Age-Related Changes as a Function of Stimulus Intervals

For these reasons it was decided to design a paired-associate study in which the interval between pairs was systematically varied.

1.   Apparatus

In order to adequately control for interitem intervals, paired-associate material was presented by means of a motion picture projector. By counting frames, it was possible to precisely control both the duration of stimulus material and the interval between successive presentations of stimulus material. In this experiment three different blank intervals (0.0 sec, 0.5 sec, and 5.0 sec) between stimulus pairs were utilized. The pairs themselves were presented for 1 sec in all cases.

The paired-associate lists consisted of 10 one-syllable stimulus words obtained from the Kent-Rosanoff list and 10 response words, obtained from the Russell and Jenkins (1954) norms, that occurred only once in one thousand presentations. The list was presented to each *S* in five varying orders, and at the end of a run *S*s were presented with each stimulus word and asked to give the appropriate response. Response time in this situation was unlimited.

2. Subjects

Data were gathered on 152 *S*s ranging in age from 30 to 69. *S*s were divided into four age decades (thirties, forties, fifties, and sixties) and were randomly assigned to one of the three interval conditions within each age decade. *S*s were obtained from various clerical and housekeeping personnel on our station and from veterans receiving outpatient medical services. The groups were of similar socioeconomic and educational backgrounds. *S*s were told that they were taking part in a memory experiment and were given the usual instructions for a paired-associate task. The pertinent identifying data and performance scores are presented in Table I.

3. Results

The number of correct responses was utilized as an index of learning and was analyzed by means of a 3 × 4 analysis of variance (Winer, 1962), which is presented in Table II. The analysis indicates that there are significant age and interval differences as well as a significant age by interval interaction. Since the age by interval interaction was significant, simple analyses of variance were obtained for each age decade to determine the contribution each of the age groups was making to the overall interaction. These analyses indicated that the intervals had no significant effect in the 30-year-old and 50-year-old groups, whereas the effect of the interval was significant for both the 40- and 60-year-old groups.

4. Discussion

Certain aspects of the data analysis are not surprising. The age differences in learning and the effect of the intervals on performance were to be expected. However, the important aspect of the findings is related to the significant age by interval interaction. This interaction indicates that the elderly adult exhibits a differentially greater deficit than the young adult when the in-

TABLE I

MEAN AGE, EDUCATION, AND PERFORMANCE SCORES FOR ALL *S*s IN EXPERIMENT I[a]

	30–39				40–49			
	Age	Educ.	Score	*N*	Age	Educ.	Score	*N*
5 sec M	33.44	11.56	7.22	9	44.79	8.86	7.07	14
SD	3.13	1.26	2.09		1.86	3.92	2.19	
0.5 sec M	34.14	12.25	5.21	14	43.27	10.45	6.64	14
SD	2.85	1.76	2.68		2.26	3.17	2.01	
0 sec M	33.11	12.94	6.56	9	44.57	9.79	3.86	14
SD	2.56	1.67	2.22		2.95	3.80	3.44	
	50–59				60–69			
5 sec M	55.17	11.17	5.33	12	66.40	11.67	5.33	15
SD	2.88	2.44	1.69		2.70	4.60	2.98	
0.5 sec M	54.69	11.23	3.77	14	65.60	10.60	1.33	15
SD	2.64	2.19	2.45		2.82	3.81	1.62	
0 sec M	53.44	11.11	4.00	9	63.87	10.60	1.73	15
SD	2.67	1.29	2.58		2.73	2.58	1.77	

[a]Scores reflect number of correct responses. Education is given in years.

terval between pairs is short, even in a situation where response time is unlimited. Further, the data suggest that the deleterious effect of the short interval may make its presence felt in middle life, since the simple analyses of variance indicated that the short intervals were resulting in significantly inferior performance in the 40-year-old group as well as in the 60-year-old group. However, the nonsignificant *F* ratio obtained in the 50-year-old group dictates a degree of cautiousness regarding the latter hypothesis.

The disruptive effects of the shorter interval on the performance of the

TABLE II

ANALYSIS OF SCORES AS A FUNCTION OF AGE AND INTERVALS

Source	*df*	MS	*F*
A (interval)	2	91.9234	13.89[a]
B (age)	3	74.8707	11.31[a]
AB	6	14.6524	2.21[b]
Within cell	140	6.6187	

[a]$p < .01$.
[b]$p < .05$.

elderly S suggest that he is more susceptible to an erasure phenomenon. It is possible, however, that the poorer performance of the elderly Ss was associated with increased susceptibility to interitem interference. An analysis of the type of errors made under the differing intervals was therefore undertaken for the 60-year-old Ss. It seemed reasonable to assume that if poorer performance were associated with increased interitem interference at the shorter intervals, this should be reflected by an increase in "intrusion errors." Intrusion errors are defined as any overt reponses that involve the incorrect placement of any stimulus or response member of the list. The analysis of variance presented in Table III indicates that there was no significant difference in intrusion errors as a function of the intervals. The

TABLE III

ANALYSIS OF VARIANCE FOR INTRUSION ERRORS IN 60-YEAR-OLD GROUP

Source	df	MS	F
Between groups	2	2.2220	1.48
Within groups	42	1.50477	

poorer performance was primarily the result of an increase in omission errors and, to a smaller extent to overt errors, which consisted of the popular or stereotyped response to a given stimulus word. Although this analysis is not a definitive test of an erasure hypothesis, it is certainly not contradictory and does not support an interference hypothesis.

B. Experiment II: The Effects of Mediators on Acquisition in Two Age Groups

There is an additional aspect of increased intervals between stimuli that warrants consideration. Riegel (1965), in his studies on speed of verbal performance, has demonstrated that association time is greater for the elderly as compared with young adults. Further, his data indicate that older Ss are more handicapped when they have to make associations when redundancy between test and response words is small. This is exactly the situation that is obtained in paired-associate learning when the linkage between stimulus and response words is made deliberately obscure. Increasing the interval between stimulus events in a paired-associate task may also enhance performance because it allows the older S sufficient time for the development of mediators. For this reason we have begun to investigate the use of mnemonic devices by young and elderly adults in paired-associate learning. (This research was undertaken by Mr. Franklin Knill as part of the requirements for the degree of Master of Arts at the University of Richmond and was directed by the author. Mr. Knill has graciously consented to its inclusion in this paper.)

These devices appear to be employed extensively in this type of learning. Woodworth and Schlosberg (1954) refer to these tactics, but treat it as a contaminating variable. However, Miller, Galanter, and Pribram (1960) view the process as important in its own right. Underwood and Schulz (1960) also discuss the process and report a study with young adults that attests to its pervasiveness in a paired-associate task. For example, in this study there were 280 possible pairs of words, and Ss reported that they utilized no mediators in only 27% of the pairs.

There are several studies with young Ss that demonstrate the effectiveness of the use of such tactics in a paired-associate task. Wallace, Turner, and Perkins (1957) instructed Ss to "form a mental picture" connecting each pair of words to be learned. They found that Ss were able to remember 99% of the word pairs presented with lists up to 500 items and 95% of a 700-pair list, although each pair was presented only once. Other studies (Gruber, Kulkin, & Schwartz, 1965; Paivio, 1965a; Runquist & Farley, 1964) have also demonstrated that mnemonic devices have a facilitating effect in paired-associate learning tasks.

However, the use of mnemonic devices by aged Ss has not received a great deal of attention until recently. There is some indirect evidence that older Ss might encounter some difficulty in forming mental pictures or connections. This evidence comes from studies of memory and creativity in aging. Jones (1959) comments that there is a reduction in the ability of older Ss to form and integrate new connections. Several studies, using a variety of approaches (Bromley, 1956; Prados & Fried, 1947; Chesrow, Wosika, & Reivitz, 1949), report an "associative impoverishment" among older persons.

In a more direct investigation, Hulicka (1965) found that elderly Ss reported using mediators less often than young Ss in a paired-associate task. In a subsequent study (1966a) she found that older Ss reported 20% of the pairs were too odd to form a connection whereas the young Ss rarely complained of this difficulty.

Although old Ss have difficulty in developing mediators, Hulicka (1965) found that instructing them to do so resulted in improved performance. A pilot study run in our laboratory indicated that aged Ss could develop connections to some degree when instructed and that this ability was positively related to paired-associate performance.

Returning to Welford's stages of learning, it is quite possible that in the initial stage of learning Ss are organizing the material and attempting to develop mediators. Since the previously cited evidence suggests that older

Ss have difficulty and require more time in developing such mediators, the lengthened time interval may possibly enhance their performance by allowing them more time to develop these mediators before fresh stimuli disrupt the process.

Before going further it is necessary to point out that there is a distinction to be made between verbal mediators and visual mediators. The majority of studies where such a dichotomy has been assumed do not report the criterion used to make the distinction. For the most part the instructions to form a mental picture have sufficed for an operational definition. Indeed, Jenkins (1961) poses the question whether all such mediators are not verbal. At this point it would appear that we will have to rely on a commonsense approach for distinguishing between the two. For the purpose of this study verbal mediators will be defined as linkages based on the formal syntactical characteristics of the words (such as grammatical linkage and connecting phrases), and visual imagery as those linkages that appear to be descriptive of some picture or image. This, unfortunately, introduces an element of arbitrariness into the matter that must be kept in mind when considering the ensuing discussion.

In a study with young adults, Paivio (1965b) found that the reaction time of verbal mediators increased with an increase in the associative variety of the words. This is important since Hulicka (1965) found that aged Ss report using more verbal mediators than visual ones. These data, when coupled with the general assumption that the verbal repertoire of an individual increases with age, suggest that the older adult needs more time to develop mediators.

In Hulicka's mediation study a deficit between the two age groups was still observed. One explanation for this deficit lies in the fact that older Ss, even after being instructed to use mediators, could not develop as many as did the young Ss. However, an additional factor may also have been contributing to this deficit. Paivio, Yuille, and Smythe (1965) found, in a study using young Ss, that visual mediators are more effective than verbal ones. It has previously been noted that elderly Ss tend to use verbal mediators when instructed to develop mediators. It is conceivable, therefore, that these verbal mediators are not as effective as the visual ones being utilized by the young Ss.

The implications of the foregoing discussion are as follows: young Ss report using mediators more extensively than do older Ss. The literature indicates that elderly Ss appear to have difficulty in developing mediators and that they also require more time to develop mediators. Also, additional time may be needed by elderly Ss because of their tendency to use verbal mediators that require more time to develop as a result of their larger verbal repertoire.

These factors may partially account for the improved scores of elderly

Ss on self-paced schedules, since there is more time to form mediators during the short-term storage before the disrupting effects of new stimulus input.

When instructed to use mediators, evidence indicates that the elderly S's performance shows relatively more improvement than that of the young S. However, there is still a deficit. Two concurrent factors may be responsible for this deficit. Elderly Ss still do not report the use of as many mediators as do young Ss, and the ones they do use are most often the presumably less effective verbal ones. It follows, then, that the deficit could be further reduced if the elderly Ss were aided in developing the more effective visual mediators. The most efficient way to do this would be to present them with an image along with the word pair to be learned.

The purpose of the present study was to observe the effects of just such a procedure. Ss were presented pairs of words accompanied by a black and white sketch that illustrated both words. In a further attempt to more directly study the effects of visual and verbal mediators, a second condition was included where Ss were presented pairs of words accompanied by a phrase that contained both of the words.

It was predicted that the performance of young Ss would be superior to the performance of elderly Ss over all conditions. Further, the use of mediators would lead to superior performance when contrasted with the standard procedures for paired-associate learning in both age groups. It was also hypothesized that the visual mediators would lead to superior performance when contrasted with the verbal mediators in both age groups. Finally, it was predicted that the mediators would lead to a relatively greater improvement in the elderly adults as compared with the young adults.

1.   Subjects

Thirty elderly Ss were drawn from the domiciliary population of the Hampton Veterans Administration Center. Their ages ranged from 50 to 73 (mean age 62.44). Thirty young Ss were drawn from the population of the State Prison Farm, Southampton, Virginia. This institution is for young men who have been convicted of their first offense as adults. The age range of this group was from 16 to 27 (mean age 20.19). The use of young Ss from such a population made it possible to obtain two groups of roughly comparable socioeconomic background and educational level. In order to test the intellectual level of the two groups, both were given the Wechsler Adult Intelligence Scale (WAIS) vocabulary subtest.

2.   Apparatus

The pairs were printed in large print on 3 × 5-inch cards. A modified Wisconsin General Test Apparatus was used. This consists of a piece of plywood separating the examiner from the *S* with a small opening at the bottom through which a tray containing the stimulus cards and the sketches can be pushed.

3. List

Following Canestrari's (1963) procedure, 30 one-syllable stimulus words were chosen from the Russell and Jenkins (1954) norms and were paired with a response word that occurs only once in one thousand presentations of the stimulus word. These 30 pairs were randomly divided into three lists.

4. Sketches

Simple sketches were made that illustrated both words of the pair. All except two were black and white; the exceptions were those accompanying the pairs "loud–tie" and "red–heart." The sketch for the former was done in color to depict a loud tie and that for the latter was also done in color to depict a red heart.

5. Verbal mediators

A phrase was made up that contained both of the words. These phrases were very short, sometimes formed by merely adding the indefinite article to a pair, as, "a short box." Some phrases were in the form of equations: "Needle + nurse = hypo." In all cases except one the words were kept in the same stimulus-response order. The exception was with the pair "bed–twin," which was reversed to read "twin bed."

6. Procedure

a. Condition I. Each *S* was instructed that he would be shown a pair of words and that on subsequent trials he would be shown only the first word of the pair and would be asked to provide the second. He was also informed that previous studies had indicated that if a person sees a picture that contains the words it makes remembering easier. He was then instructed that such a sketch would accompany each pair and that he was to look at the pair and the picture.
b. Condition II. S was instructed concerning the presentation of pairs of words and was given instructions similar to those in Condition I, with the word "phrase" being substituted for "picture."
c. Condition III. S was instructed only as to the procedure of presentation of the pairs and to the recalling of the response words. No instructions were given to induce any kind of strategy.

Throughout all conditions, on each trial subsequent to the first presentation, each response word was shown again with the stimulus word, regardless of the appropriateness of the S's response. In Conditions I and II the mediator was also shown each time with the stimulus and response words.

Trials for all Ss were presented under a self-paced conditions. Ss were instructed that they could take as much time as they liked to look at the pair and to respond to the stimulus word. The time between the withdrawal of a pair together and the presentation of the next stimulus word was approximately 5–10 sec.

The dependent measure was the number of errors committed in reaching a criterion of one perfect recitation of a list. These errors were further broken down into errors of omission (no response) and commission (overt incorrect response).

d. Design. A Latin square design was used, whereby each of the two main groups were subdivided into three groups. Each of these subgroups was exposed to each of the three lists and each of the three conditions. The order of presentation of the conditions was counterbalanced with the order of lists being disregarded.

7. Results

Initially 30 Ss from each age group were to be used. In the latter stages of the study, however, one of the young Ss was transferred to a different location, thereby necessitating the random dropping of 5 more Ss. The results, then, are based on 27 Ss in each age group.

As was stated earlier, an attempt was made to match both experimental groups on the basis of socioeconomic background and intellectual ability. The elderly group scored significantly higher ($t = 4.35$, $p \leq .01$) than the younger group on the WAIS vocabulary subtest. Since this had the effect of working against our hypothesis, no further attempt was made to match the groups on the basis of the vocabulary scores.

a. Total Errors. The critical measure of learning was the number of errors committed in attaining one perfect recitation. The data were analyzed by $3 \times 3 \times a$ Latin square analysis of variance with repeated measures (Winer, 1962).

Figure 1 graphically represents the difference between the two groups in regard to total errors committed. Table IV indicates that the young Ss committed significantly fewer errors than did the elderly ones. The data analysis further indicates a significant age by treatment interaction. This interaction is represented graphically in Fig. 2. A test for simple effects of the treatment factor with the old group and the young group is summarized in Table V. From this table and Fig. 2 it is evident that the two mediators had a greater effect in reducing errors in the old group that in the young group. A further F test ($F = .16$) indicated that the difference

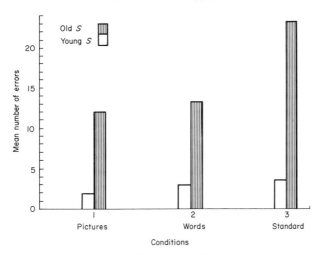

Fig. 1. Comparison of young and elderly Ss on total errors.

in error scores between treatments 1 and 2 in the old group was not significant.

b. Errors of Commission. Total errors were further broken down into errors of commission and errors of omission. Errors of commission were those overt responses that were incorrect. The difference between age groups

TABLE IV

ANALYSIS OF TOTAL ERRORS

Source	df	MS	F
Between Ss	53		
C (Age)	1	6548.76	23.66[a]
AB (between)	2	699.43	
ABC (between)	2	640.03	
Ss within groups	48	276.83	
Within Ss	108		
A (List)	2	96.40	1.37
B (Condition)	2	702.01	9.95[a]
AC	2	216.99	3.08
BC	2	382.23	5.42[a]
AB'	2	74.71	
ABC'	2	137.70	
Error	96	70.52	

[a] $p < .01$.

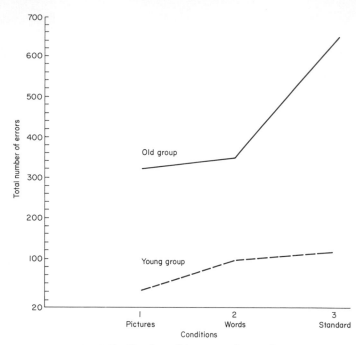

Fig. 2. Profile of condition × age interaction.

for these errors is represented in Fig. 3. An analysis of variance indicated that the young adults made significantly fewer errors ($F = 18.90, p < .01$) of this type than did the elderly adults. There were no significant treatment effects.

c. Errors of Omission. Errors of omission were those errors where no responses were given. The differences between groups on this measure are graphically represented in Fig. 4. An analysis of variance indicated that

TABLE V

SIMPLE EFFECTS FOR INTERACTION BETWEEN CONDITIONS AND AGE

Source	df	MS	F
Conditions at level c_1 (old Ss)	2	1047.64	14.86[a]
Conditions at level c_2 (young Ss)	2	36.60	0.52
Error (within)	96	70.52	

[a] $p < .01$.

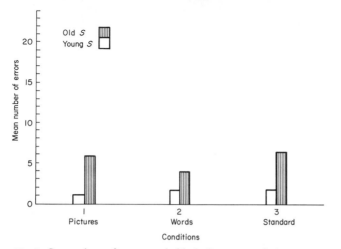

Fig. 3. Comparison of young and elderly *S*s on commission errors.

the young adults made significantly fewer errors ($F = 17.44, p < .01$) than did the older adults.

In addition, the age by treatment interaction was significant. This interaction represented graphically in Fig. 5. suggests that the two types of mediators had a greater effect in reducing errors of omission in the older group than in the young group. A further analysis of variance indicated that the two types of mediators were equally effective in reducing the errors of omission of the older *S*s.

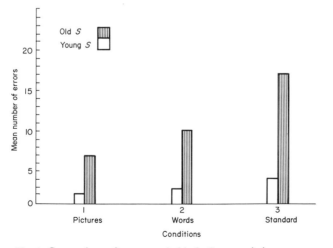

Fig. 4. Comparison of young and elderly *S*s on omission errors.

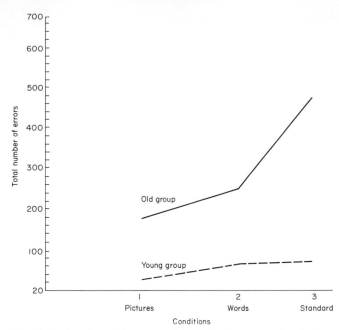

Fig. 5. Profile of condition × age interaction for errors of omission.

8. Discussion

The results of this study indicate an age-related difference in performance. The young Ss' performance on the task was superior to that of the elderly ones, regardless of the condition. This finding is in agreement with previous studies.

The data further indicate that providing Ss with mediators resulted in a differentially greater improvement of performance by the elderly Ss. This finding supports one of the hypotheses of the study. The results obtained did not confirm the prediction that visual mediators would improve the performance of all Ss more than verbal mediators. This prediction was based on Paivio's study (Paivio *et al.*, 1965) with young Ss in which visual mediators were found to be more effective than verbal ones. A closer look at the procedure used by Paivio and his colleagues provides a possible explanation for the disparity between the present results and those of the Paivio study. In the latter, each word of the pairs was rated before the experiment on the basis of ease of eliciting imagery. The words were paired to obtain combinations of high and low ratings. After the task, Ss were given a questionnaire with the pairs listed and asked to mark whether they used visual, verbal, or no mediators. It is obvious, as Paivio himself points out, that the Ss might not have been reporting what actually happened during acquisition. Instead, they might have been responding to the high imagery of the words listed on the check list.

The design of the present study partially eliminated this source of contamination by providing the Ss with ready-made mediators. Another explanation of the noted discrepancy in results is suggested by an examination of the performance of the young Ss in the present study. The data indicate that neither of the mediating conditions resulted in a significant improvement in the performance of the young Ss. This is not in keeping with previously cited evidence. It is possible that the lists in the present study were not difficult enough, resulting in a ceiling effect with the young group. If the lists had been more difficult, the results might have more closely paralleled those of Paivio *et al.* in regard to the effectiveness of the two types of mediators. Indeed, it is possible that the age by treatment interaction obtained would have been reduced. While the possibility of such a ceiling effect makes it difficult to evaluate the relative effectiveness of both types of mediators in the younger Ss, no such ceiling effect was observed with the older group.

As was mentioned earlier, elderly Ss verbalize a preference for verbal mediators (Hulicka, 1965) and they respond more with regard to grammatical form in word-association tasks (Riegel, 1965). The preference may be based on the fact that they have become accustomed to responding to various situations with stereotyped verbal responses and transfer this tendency to the paired-associate task. Nevertheless, the results of this study indicate that when the mediators are provided, they are able to use visual and verbal mediators equally well.

The analysis of the breakdown of total errors committed into those of commission and omission indicate that the elderly Ss committed more errors of commission, but the mediators had no effect on this type of error. In contrast, the elderly Ss also committed more errors of omission than the young Ss and the mediator conditions sharply reduced the number of this type error for the elderly.

There are two interpretations of the latter results. First, providing mediators helps the older Ss to develop the association necessary for storing the pair in a manner that makes it more available for recall. The second interpretation is based on Korchin and Basowitz's (1957) hypothesis that elderly Ss are more cautious and will not make a response unless they are confident of its correctness. Providing elderly Ss with the mediators could have resulted in raising their confidence. Either or both of these explanations could account for the reduction in omission errors.

The results of this study combined with other evidence cited tend to support the basic argument developed in the Introduction (Section I), namely, that the observed performance deficit of aged Ss is reduced when the interval between presentations of stimuli is lengthened. It has been suggested that the short-term storage mechanism of the elderly S needs more time to transfer material to be learned before the disrupting effects of fresh incoming stimuli. One activity that may take place in this short-term storage is the development of mediators between items in a pair. The evidence on hand indicates that elderly Ss have more difficulty and need more time in developing these mediators. Therefore they require extra time at this stage of acquisition.

Other evidence suggests that even though they are allowed more time to develop mediators, the elderly Ss still do not develop as many as the young Ss. This suggestion is based on the fact that further reduction in the deficit is observed when elderly Ss are instructed to develop mediators under self-paced conditions. Even under these conditions, however, they still report having more difficulty in forming connections and still develop fewer than do young Ss.

Based on the evidence cited earlier, it was suggested that directly aiding elderly Ss to develop mediators would reduce the deficit even further. The results of the present study support the validity of this suggestion.

An important question that remains unanswered is why the elderly Ss' ability to develop mediators is lost or impaired in the first place. There are two possible explanations for this impairment.

First, it might be due to experiential factors. The technique of developing mediators is most likely to reach its peak of efficiency during those years when an individual is engaged in formal education. Consequently, the older Ss' inability to develop such mediators might be the result of disuse or less frequent practice. This is opposed to the situation of younger Ss, who generally tend to be either actively engaged in, or at least chronologically closer to, academic exercises. A study by Sorenson (1930) provides some indirect support for this notion. In this study he correlated the achievement scores of a class of adults in an education course with the length of time that they had been out of school. The only reliable negative correlations he obtained were those with the group whose members had been out of school longer.

The second explanation is that the elderly Ss lose this ability through physiological changes in the central nervous system. Several studies (Andrews, 1956; Kety, 1956; Sokoloff, 1959) indicate a general decline in cerebral blood flow, oxygen consumption, and cell loss and deterioration. Studies with the electroencephalogram (EEG) (Obrist, 1954; Silverman, Busse, & Barnes, 1955) reveal a decreasing number of normal EEGs with increasing age, including a lowering of alpha rhythm and increasing temporal lobe abnormality. With regard to one of these findings, Hulicka (1966a) points out that one effect of oxygen deprivation on young Ss is a reduced ability to remember and perform other cognitive tasks. Indeed, the work of McFarland (1963) indicates that there are striking similarities between the behavior deficit seen in high-altitude situations and the behavioral deficit often observed in the aged. The elderly person's cognitive functioning (which is inextricably related to his ability to abstract and develop mediators) may be impaired by physiological change.

At present it is impossible to determine the relative contribution of these hypotheses. However, we do have some preliminary data that are relevant to the latter hypothesis. We have obtained rheoencephalographic records on a number of elderly males and have correlated various indices obtained from these records with behavioral data obtained from a paired-associate task and a number of psychomotor measures. Rheoencephalography is an impedance plethysmographic technique that involves the study of changes in impedance of the head to the passage of an electric current. The electrical impedance varies with relative changes in blood volume and the resulting wave form can be recorded.

There is some evidence (Jenker, 1962; Lifshitz, 1963; McHenry, 1965) that the technique may be used to obtain an index of diffuse cerebral vascular disease. We have quantified some features of the wave form and correlated them with the previously mentioned behavioral measures. Interestingly enough, paired-associate learning has correlated with an index obtained from the left side of the brain, while the psychomotor tasks (reaction time and tapping speed) have correlated with an index obtained from the right hemisphere. Although these results must be evaluated with caution until further intensive work is complete, they do add further support to the hypothesis that cerebral ischemia is a factor in performance changes associated with senescence.

II. Summary

The data gathered to date indicate that variables affecting the registration process need to be investigated more thoroughly. The hypothesis that the elderly S is more susceptible to an erasure phenomenon seems tenable in view of the evidence at hand. The fast pace schedule of presentation seems to be debilitating, even under those conditions where response time is unlimited. It is therefore assumed that a part of the deficit of the elderly may be related to an inability to maintain an ongoing neuronal pattern in the face of fresh stimulus input. Stimulus events may be erased before adequate comprehension occurs and consequently may never reach a more permanent memory system.

Age differences in the ability to develop and utilize mediators may also play a part in the performance deficit exhibited by the aged adult. Evidence has been presented indicating that the elderly person develops fewer mediators than the young and needs longer to develop these mediators. The evidence also indicates that the elderly S can utilize mediators when they are provided. Further, it is evident that the utilization of provided mediators sharply reduced the number of omission errors given by the elderly *S*. It is possible that the mediators help the older person to develop the association necessary for storing the pair in a manner that makes it more available for recall. A second possibility is related to the hypothesis that the elderly are more cautious and will not provide a response unless they are confident of its correctness. Providing mediators could result in increased confidence.

An important question that remains unanswered is related to the elderly person's inability to develop mediators. This loss may be related to a lack of practice in the utilization of this strategy or to a loss of abstractive ability resulting from central nervous system changes that occur with age.

ACKNOWLEDGMENTS

The work of Mr. Larry C. Gaskins, chief of medical illustration at the Veterans Administration Center, Hampton, Virginia, in preparing photographic materials used in Experiment I is gratefully acknowledged.

REFERENCES

Andrews, W. Structural alteration with aging in the nervous system. *J. chronic Dis.*, 1956, **3**, 575–596.

Arenberg, D. Anticipation interval and age differences in verbal learning. *J. abnorm. Psychol.*, 1965, **70**, 419–425.

Averbach, E., & Coriell, A. S. Short term memory in vision. *Bell System Tech. J.*, 1961, **40**, 309–328.

Bromley, D. B. Some experimental tests of the effect of age on creative intellectual output. *J. Geront.*, 1956, **11**, 74–78.

Canestrari, R. E. Paced and self-paced learning in young and elderly adults. *J. Geront.*, 1963, **18**, 165–168.

Chesrow, E. J., Wosika, P. H., & Reivitz, H. H. A psychometric evaluation of aged white males. *Geriatrics*, 1949, **4**, 169–177.

Eisdorfer, C., Axelrod, S., & Wilkie, F. L. Stimulus exposure time as a factor in serial learning in an aged sample. *J. abnorm. soc. Psychol.*, 1963, **67**, 594–600.

Gruber, H. E., Kulkin, A., & Schwartz, P. The effect of exposure time on mnemonic processing in paired associate learning. Paper presented to Eastern Psychol. Assoc. meeting, Atlantic City, New Jersey, April, 1965.

Hulicka, Irene M. Age group comparisons for the use of mediators. Paper presented at Southwestern Psychol. Assoc. meetings, Oklahoma City, Oklahoma, April, 1965.

Hulicka, Irene M. Age changes and age differences in memory functioning. Unpublished manuscript, D'Youville College, Buffalo, New York, 1966.

Hulicka, Irene M., Sterns, H., & Grossman, J. Age group comparisons of paired associate learning as a function of paced and self-paced association and response times. Unpublished manuscript, D'Youville College and The State University of New York at Buffalo, 1966.

Jenker, Fritz L. *Rheoencephalography.* Springfield, Ill.: Charles C Thomas, 1962.

Jenkins, J. J. Comments on Professor Goss' paper. In C. N. Cofer (Ed.), *Verbal learning and verbal behavior.* New York: McGraw-Hill, 1961. Pp. 69–74.

Jones, H. E. Intelligence and problem solving. In J. E. Birren (Ed.), *Handbook on aging and the individual.* Chicago, Ill.: Univer. of Chicago Press, 1959.

Kety, S. S. Human cerebral blood flow and oxygen consumption as related to aging. *J. chronic Dis.*, 1956, **3**, 478–486.

Knill, F. P. The effect of visual and verbal mnemonic devices on the paired associate learning of an aged population. Unpublished master's thesis, Univer. of Richmond, 1966.

Korchin, S. H., & Basowitz, H. Age differences in verbal learning *J. abnorm. soc. Psychol.*, 1957, **54**, 64–69.

Lifshitz, K. Rheoencephalography: I. Review of the technique. *J. nerv. ment. Dis.*, 1963, **135**, 388–398.

McFarland, R. A. Experimental evidence of the relationship between ageing and oxygen want: in search of a theory of aging. *Ergonomics*, 1963, **6**, 339–366.

McHenry, L. C. Rheoencephalography: a clinical appraisal. *Neurology*, 1965, **15**, 507–517.

Miller, G. A., Galanter, E., & Pribram, K. H. *Plans and the structure of behavior.* New York: Holt, Rinehart, & Winston, 1960.

Obrist, W. D. The electroencephalogram of normal aged adults. *EEG clin. Neurophysiol.*, 1954, **6**, 235–244.

Paivio, A. Abstractness, imagery, and meaningfulness in paired associate learning. *J. verb. Learn. verb. Behav.*, 1965, **4**, 32–38. (a)

Paivio, A. Latency of verbal associations and imagery to noun stimuli as a function of abstractness and generality. Res. Bull. No. 3, Dept. of Psychol., Univer. of Western Ontario, 1965. (b)

Paivio, A., & Oliver, Margaret. Denotive generality, imagery, and meaningfulness in PA learning of nouns. *Psychonomic Sci.*, 1964, **7**, 183–184.

Paivio, A., Yuille, J. C., & Smythe, P. C. Stimulus and response abstractness, imagery and meaningfulness, and reported mediators in paired associate learning. Res. Bull. No. 2, Dept. of Psychol., Univer. of Western Ontario, 1965.

Prados, M., & Fried, E. G. Personality structure of the older age groups. *J. clin. Psychol.*, 1947, **35**, 411–422.

Riegel, K. F. Speed of verbal performance as a function of age and set: A review of issues and data. In M. A. Welford & J. E. Birren (Eds.), *Behavior, aging and the nervous system.* Springfield, Ill.: Charles C Thomas, 1965. Pp. 150–190.

Runquist, W. N., & Farley, F. H. The use of mediators in the learning of verbal paired associates. *J. verb. Learn verb. Behav.*, 1964, **3**, 280–285.

Russell, W. A., & Jenkins, J. J. The complete Minnesota norms for responses to 100 words from the Kent-Rosanoff Word Association Test. *Studies on the role of language in behavior.* Tech. Rept. No. 11, 1954.

Silverman, A. J., Busse, E. W., & Barnes, A. H. Studies in the processes of aging. Electroencephalograhic findings in 400 elderly subjects. *EEG clin. Neurophysiol.*, 1955, **7**, 67–74.

Sokoloff, L. Circulation and metabolism of brain in relation to the process of aging. In J. E. Birren. H. A. Imus. & N. F. Windle (Eds.). *The process of aging in the nervous system.* Springfield, Ill.: Charles C Thomas, 1959.

Sorenson, H. Adult ages as a factor in learning. *J. educ. Psychol.*, 1930, **21**, 451–459.

Underwood, B. J., & Schulz, R. W. *Meaningfulness and verbal learning.* New York: Lippincott, 1960.

Wallace, W. H., Turner, S. H., & Perkins, C. C. Preliminary studies of human information storage. Signal Corps Project 1320, Inst. for Cooperative Res., Univer. of Pennsylvania, 1957.

Wechsler, D. *Wechsler Adult Intelligence Scale.* New York: Psychol. Corp., 1955.

Welford, A. T. Psychomotor performance. In J. E. Birren (Ed.), *Handbook of aging and the individual.* Chicago, Ill.: Univer. of Chicago Press, 1959. Pp. 562–613.

Winer, B. J. *Statistical principles in experimental design.* New York: McGraw-Hill, 1962.

Woodworth, R. S., & Schlosberg, H. *Experimental psychology,* New York: Holt, Rinehart & Winston., 1954.

Arousal and Performance: Experiments in Verbal Learning and a Tentative Theory

CARL EISDORFER

Duke University
Durham, North Carolina

I. Introduction

Aged persons do not learn as well as do the young. This deficit in aging adults has been commonly accepted as a correlate of the generalized decline hypothetically seen in man's postmaturity. While the aged are generally credited with wisdom, and some investigators, notably Sorenson (1930), have stated that "up to the age of 50 there is no decline in learning ability with age for those who are actively engaged in study" (p. 459), even the earliest reviews of the experimental literature (Ruch, 1933) support the thesis that aging is accompanied by a decline in verbal learning behavior. A variety of theoretical approaches may be taken in attempting to understand this phenomenon. Shock (1962) has suggested that cell dropout may be implicated in the aging process and that a loss in the population of functional neurons may be the basis for diminished central nervous system functioning. Cumming and Henry (1961) offer the hypothesis that a disengagement process is associated with advancing age and that the older person has gradually withdrawn from the environment and is not sufficiently motivated to participate in many situations, thus causing an apparent decline in functioning. Thorndike (Thorndike, Bregman, Tilton, & Woodward, 1928) suggested that there must be a decline in motivation since older individuals feel that they have learned all they need to learn. Hulicka and Rust (1964) observed that the old are resentful and lacking in interest, therefore less inclined to make use of their cognitive skills in a learning task. A number of recent studies have questioned whether impairment of learning with advancing age after maturity is not in fact the result of a decline in the efficiency of registration of new information and the short-term storage processes (Inglis, 1964; Inglis & Ankus, 1965; Caird, 1965). Inglis and Ankus (1965) do report, however, that there was still an effect of age on rote learning after the influences of short-term storage had been parcelled out. According to others (Ruch, 1934), interfering associations may be intimately involved with the recall deficit in aged persons. Since the aged have far more associations than the young, inhibition in the form of interference from old associations might be expected to produce greater difficulties in recall in the aged.

Welford (1958) cited earlier work that he felt included systematic biases in design that acted to impair the performance of aged Ss compared with younger controls. He contended that experiments that required Ss to perceive, learn, and respond under relatively rapid pacing might be expected to selectively impair the performance of the aged. In his own work, Welford demonstrated that older men could function considerably more effectively at untimed unpaced jobs than under time pressure (Welford, 1951). In a study of paired-associate learning in the aged, Korchin and Basowitz (1957) proposed that older persons might benefit from more time to learn than would young persons. They suggested three postulates upon which they based their prediction: (1) that older Ss were more cautious and thus inhibited correct responses; (2) that the aged require more time for the integration of a response; and (3) that older individuals presumably learn principally by forming discrete stimulus-response (S-R) combinations rather than through the conceptualization that response items belong "somewhere in the series" of stimuli. It was the contention of Korchin and Basowitz that a slower pace might lead to improved learning in the aged S by permitting him more time to respond and, consequently, more opportunity to learn through the testing of an increased number of correct (as well as incorrect) S-R hypotheses.

A. Experiment I: Effect of Stimulus Exposure Time on Verbal Rote Learning by the Aged

Eisdorfer, Axelrod, and Wilkie (1963) undertook a study of verbal rote learning in the aged. They proposed that an increase in the exposure time of stimuli would facilitate learning for the aged to a greater extent than for the young. Their study was conducted with two groups of men divided on the basis of age. The Ss in group Y (young) were selected from among recuperating nonpsychiatric patients of the Durham Veterans Administration Hospital. All were cleared medically (as free of any serious physical disorder) and contacted individually in order to request their participation. Virtually all the patients so contacted agreed to participate. Group Y was composed of 28 men aged 28 – 49 (mean 37.3) years. The 33 men in group O (old), aged 60 – 80 (mean 66.5) years, were recruited through the Durham office of the North Carolina Employment Security Commission and were paid for their services.

The vocabulary subtest score of the Wechsler Adult Intelligence Scale (Wechsler, 1955), which does not decline appreciably with age and correlates highly with full-scale IQ scores (Doppelt & Wallace, 1955; Eisdorfer & Cohen, 1961) was used as a measure of intelligence. Only those Ss obtaining scaled scores in the range 7–12 were included in this experiment.

Eight lists were composed from the following eight five-letter disyllabic words: pupil, river, today, jewel, metal, honey, woman, and dozen. These words are highly familiar, occurring at least 41 times in a million as rated by Thorndike and Lorge (1944) in their word count and highly meaningful as defined by Taylor's (1959) study, in which all words were associated to within 2.5 sec by at least 80% of Taylor's Ss (college students). The lists were constructed so that a given word appeared in a different position in each list; all lists were begun with an asterisk. The lists were assigned to Ss in each group in random sequence and presented individually by means of a slide projector with timing controlled electronically. The letters measured 2.2 inches in height at 6 feet from the seated S and were easily read by all Ss.

The Ss were shown the words one at a time in the usual serial rote learning paradigm and encouraged to respond (guessing if necessary) by giving the next word to appear. A 2×3 factorial design was used involving two age levels (Y and O) and three stimulus exposure intervals, 4, 6, or 8 sec per word. A 1-sec interword interval and a 40-sec intertrial interval were maintained for all conditions. The Ss learned to a criterion of two consecutive errorless trials or until 15 trials were run.

The results of this first study are shown in Fig. 1. Within the time dimensions used, the aged seemed to profit more from increasing exposure time than did the young. This observation is supported by statistical analysis. The mean effect of age is significant ($F = 63.79$, $df = 1/75$, $p < .01$), as is the interaction ($F = 5.03$, $df = 2/75$). The mean number of errors made by the old Ss decreased monotonically from the 4-sec to the 8-sec condition ($t = 2.43$, $p < .05$). The errors were further analyzed and subdivided according to whether they were errors of omission or commission. While the number of errors of each type was virtually the same for the younger Ss, this was

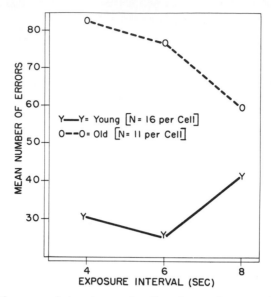

Fig. 1. Mean errors in learning as a function of age and exposure interval.

not the case for the aged. The omission errors of old Ss decreased monotonically as exposure time increased from 4 to 8 sec. This decrease was significant ($t = 2.21$, $p < .05$) and entirely paralleled the decline in total errors found in the older Ss from 4 to 8 sec.

The results were interpreted to indicate that the improvement found with increasing interval was related more to increased responsivity, a performance variable involving time to respond rather than time needed to form new associations. This hypothesis was put forward in view of the different rates of decline of the two types of error. It was assumed that if the effects of the increasing exposure time were primarily on the formation of new associations, then both errors of omission and commission should decline at the same relative rate. As is seen in Fig. 2, this is not the case. Commission errors in the aged did not change with stimulus interval. It was also found that at every exposure interval older Ss gave a higher ratio of omission to total errors than did younger Ss ($F = 10.0$, $df = 1/75$, p < .01). In addition, if the increased exposure time served primarily as an opportunity for Ss to rehearse the stimulus words, it might be expected, that the learning curve of the 8-sec group would be more rapidly decelerating at the outset than that for the 4-sec group (since each trial of the former would be equivalent in opportunity for practice to two trials of the latter). The error curves plotted per trial for the three older groups (4, 6, and 8 sec; Fig. 3) are parallel and statistical analysis shows no significant difference between their shapes (Lindquist, 1953, type 3 design). It is interesting to note in this regard that no difference in shape was found among the three curves for the younger Ss.

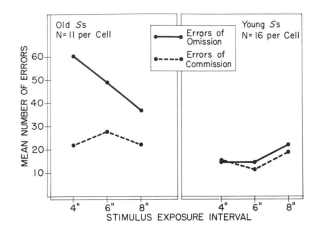

Fig. 2. Errors of omission and commission in relation to age and exposure interval.

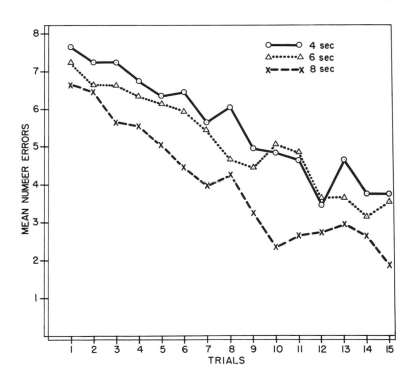

Fig. 3. Mean number of errors for the old group as a function of exposure interval and trial.

B. Experiment II: Relation of Varied Stimulus Exposure Time to Verbal Rote Learning by the Aged

As a further examination of the hypothesis that the improvement of older Ss (with increasing exposure interval) was related more to performance than to learning, it remained to be demonstrated that the superiority of the 8-sec condition over the 4-sec condition was not due merely to total time spent viewing the stimulus. The study that was performed next was virtually identical in method with that just described. In this case, Ss were 48 aged men recruited from the Durham Veterans Administration Hospital. Though stimuli, mode, and method of presentation were the same, the pattern of presentation of the word lists was changed. Ss were randomly assigned to two groups ($N = 24$ for each group) and learned under 4-8-4 or 8-4-8 conditions. Those learning under the 4-8-4 condition received the first seven trials with the stimulus words presented at 4-sec of exposure as described. At trials 8 and 9, the words were exposed for 8 sec, then the 4-sec exposure interval was resumed for the remaining trials (10 through 15). The 8-4-8 group received 8-sec exposures of the stimuli for trials 1 through 7

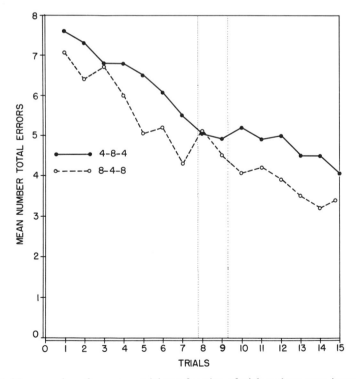

Fig. 4. Mean number of errors per trial as a function of trials and exposure intervals.

and 10 through 15, and 4-sec exposure of the stimuli at trials 8 and 9. The criteria for S selection were the same as those described earlier. The mean age of the 4-8-4 group was 68.5 and their vocabulary scaled score was 9.12; the mean age of the 8-4-8 group was 66.9 and mean vocabulary scaled score 8.29; these differences were not significant.

In this instance the initial instructions to Ss included the warning that the exposure time would be changed at some time during the study. Following the completion of the seventh trial Ss were informed that exposure time was to be changed at that point; after the ninth trial they were told that the original schedule was to be resumed. Figure 4 shows the mean number of total errors per trial for each of the two groups. As expected, analysis of the overall performance of the two groups (with trials 8 and 9 omitted from each S's error score) demonstrated that the 4-8-4 group made significantly more errors than the 8-4-8 group ($t = 2.14$, $df = 46$, $p < .05$). Analysis of the performance between the two conditions at the critical trials and their adjacent trials shows that although the 8-4-8 group shows fewer errors than the 4-8-4 group at trials 7 and 10 (trial 7: $t = 2.04$, $df = 46$, $p < .05$; trial 10: $t = 2.08$, $df = 46$, $p < .05$), there was no appreciable difference between the two conditions for trials 8 and 9. The patterns of omission and commission errors for the study are shown in Figs. 5 and 6. A decrease in omission errors for trials 8 and 9 of the 4-8-4 group and the reverse pattern for the 8-4-8 group is apparent. At the same time, there is an abrupt rise in commission errors with the (abrupt) increase in stimulus exposure time. It may be seen that, for the 8-4-8 group, the increase in omission errors is largely responsible for the poor performance in the critical trials. An increase in commission errors in trials 8 and 9 for the 4-8-4 condition is also notable. The results clearly support the hypothesis that all subjects perform better under an 8-sec trial than under the 4-sec condition even when the 4-sec condition follows exposure to the 8-sec experience. As anticipated, when the critical trials in this study were eliminated, the group that had the predominantly 4-sec exposure interval made significantly more errors than the 8-4-8 group.

This superiority of the 8-sec over the 4-sec exposure seems to relate to two possible factors: (1) the duration of the stimulus to which Ss were exposed, and (2) the increased opportunity for Ss to respond during a longer interval. The results, however, suggest that the improvement at the 8-sec period cannot be attributed solely to the increased duration of exposure of the stimulus. The increase in errors on the critical (4-sec) trials of the 8-4-8 group demonstrates that, although the cumulative exposure and its attendant opportunity to view and rehearse was greater on trials 8 and 9 than on trial 7, Ss made more errors at these 4-sec trials, even though they were well forewarned of the oncoming change. Analysis of the pattern of errors reveals that the principal component of the increase in mistakes was an

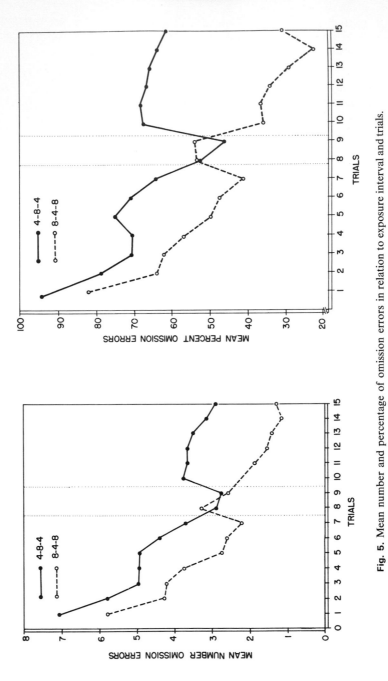

Fig. 5. Mean number and percentage of omission errors in relation to exposure interval and trials.

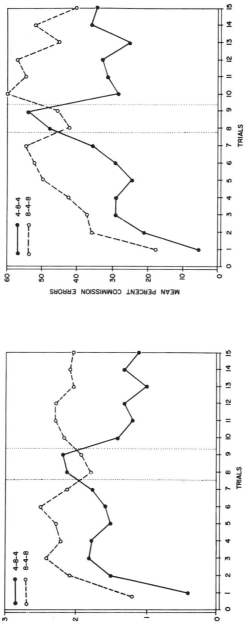

Fig. 6. Mean number and percentage of commission errors in relation to exposure interval and trials.

increase in omission errors on the critical trials. These data led to the conjecture that, under the 8-sec condition, Ss used the additional time to respond and that the change from an 8-sec to a 4-sec exposure blocked the opportunity to make such responses. It was demonstrated that the first and second postulates of Korchin and Basowitz (1957) may be correct in that the aged Ss in both studies did give a higher ratio of omission to total errors than did younger Ss and did seem to profit from increased time to organize their responses.

Upon further analysis, however, the results show a different finding than what would have been predicted from Korchin and Basowitz's third postulate. In Experiment II, there was an increase in commission with a decrease in omission errors at the critical trials of the 4-8-4 group. The increased exposure time, 8 sec, presented after the 4-sec trials, yielded a general increase in responses and offered a greater opportunity to learn from one's mistakes. This was not seen, however, in the 8-sec trials of the 8-4-8 group. For the moment, then, it would appear that the Ss having seven trials at 4 sec took the opportunity of an 8-sec exposure interval to produce and test more S-R hypotheses, whereas the group having most of its trials at 8 sec tended to inhibit all responses when shifted to a 4-sec rate. These results led to the general assumption that the improvement in the learning of old Ss with longer exposure intervals could be accounted for on the basis of an increase in opportunity to respond, and therefore the performance component of the learning deficit in the aged was implicated.

Since the improvement from 4 to 8 sec was monotonic, it remained a question of empirical verification to determine the asymptote of improvement. In a further study extending the exposure of the stimulus words to 10, 12, and 14 sec, a comparison of old and young Ss showed that the aged subjects improved monotonically as exposure duration increased from 4 to 10 sec but not beyond (Eisdorfer, 1963). This improvement in learning with lenghtened exposure is associated with an increase in the absolute number of responses (reduction in errors of omission) on the part of the aged subjects.

C.   Experiment III: Time Used for
     Verbal Learning Performance by the Aged

Although it has been suggested that the improvement of older Ss under longer exposure conditions could be accounted for "on the basis of an increase in opportunity to respond" and that old Ss "did not have sufficient time to produce their responses" (Eisdorfer et al., 1963 p. 140), the length of time that was used by aged Ss in order to produce a response during the learning situation remained to be determined. We also felt that it would be appropriate to further examine the proposition that the opportunty to view the stimulus was not a critical factor in the improved learning of the aged with increasing stimulus duration.

For this study, the method adopted was essentially the same as that of Experiment I. In this instance, however, the stimulus words were exposed for 4 sec with a 7-sec interstimulus interval; thus there was a total of 11 sec from the onset of a given stimulus to the onset of the succeeding one. This time sequence was chosen because the exposure time was identical with the 4-sec condition of the earlier experiments, but the total time from the onset of one stimulus to the succeeding one was identical to the previously used 10-sec exposure condition, which had a 1-sec interstimulus interval, making a total of 11 sec. As in the previous studies, a 40-sec interlist time was used and Ss learned to a criterion of two consecutive errorless trials or a maximum of 15 trials.

The apparatus was modified to include a voice key that activated a recorder. A small (1 cm $\times$ 3 cm) photosensitive cell placed in one corner of the projection screen was used to record the exposure time of each stimulus word on the same writeout; consequently, it was possible to determine how soon after the stimulus exposure the S made his response. A technician monitoring the projection equipment and recording S's responses was also able to keep track of noise artifacts in the experimental situation.

The Ss in this case were 15 men drawn from the North Carolina Employment Security Commissin in Durham. All were over 60 years of age (mean 71.6) and were screened on the vocabulary subtest of the Wechsler Adult Intelligence Scale. They represented essentially the same pool of Ss as that recruited for the earlier experiments.

The results were compared with those obtained previously from 66 Ss under conditions of 4, 6, 8, 10, 12, and 14 sec of exposure (with 1-sec interstimulus intervals, as discussed earlier). In Table I age and vocabulary scores of Ss from this study are compared with those of the aged Ss in all of the conditions just described. It should be noted that vocabulary scores are not different between groups of Ss under any of the conditions, as examined by a simple randomized analysis of variance design. Figure 7 illustrates the mean total number of errors made under the 4-sec-on and 7-sec-off (4_7) exposure condition. Performance under this condition appears to be at the same level of learning as with the 8-sec-on and 1-sec-off and the 10-sec-on

TABLE I

MEAN AGES AND MEAN VOCABULARY SCORES

Mean	Exposure time (sec)						
	4	6	8	10	12	14	4_7
Age	67.4	66.3	65.9	66.3	67.5	70.4	71.6
Vocabulary	7.9	8.2	8.9	8.3	8.3	8.8	8.7

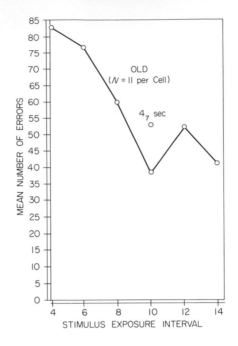

Fig. 7. The mean errors in learning as a function of exposure condition and interstimulus interval.

and 1-sec-off exposure. This is true for total omission and commission errors. In contrast, an analysis of variance and subsequent t tests (using $msw = 74$ as the df) demonstrated significant differences in total performance between the 4_7-sec condition and both the 4-sec and 6-sec exposure conditions ($t = 3.17$, $p < .01$ and $t = 2.40$, $p < .05$). Omission errors follow the same pattern of difference as do total errors but commission errors are not different (Fig. 8). It would thus appear that the old Ss profited more from the total time available than from the exposure time given the individual stimulus words.

Table II shows the time at which the subjects responded. The correct placement of a word three times in succession or twice in succession (if this involved the last two trials) was considered to indicate learning of the word. Those words beginning with the correct series were tabulated as postlearning; those responses made prior to the correct series were considered prelearning. The mean response time for the prelearning conditions was 5.01 sec, for postlearning responses, 3.39 sec. The results were further studied by responses was 5.21 sec; for correct responses it was 3.73 sec. Interestingly, analyzing all correct responses and all incorrect responses without regard to their having been learned. The mean response time for all incorrect the differences between prelearning and postlearning and between incorrect and correct responses are significant ($p < .01$) by t test analysis.

Our earlier studies had led to the hypothesis that time to respond was a significant factor in the learning deficit of aged persons and that increasing exposure of stimuli served primarily to allow the older person additional time to make his response. This study undertook a more definitive examination of the question by measuring the time that was used by the aged person to respond. It should be noted then that mean response times of aged Ss fell within the time intervals available under the more rapidly paced conditions. Thus a prelearning mean response time of 5.01 sec is within the limits of the 6-sec-on and 1-sec-off condition and almost approximates the 4-sec-on, 1-sec-off situation. It is also important to note that the mean postlearning response time (i.e., 3.39 sec) is well within the limits set by both of these exposure conditions. At this point, it should be reemphasized that there were significantly more responses and fewer errors made in the 4_7 condition than in either the 4-sec exposure or 6-sec exposure condition.

The results of this study support the thesis that rapid stimulus pacing and decreasing responsivity contribute to a deficit in verbal learning in the aged, but this is not a simple function of the inability of older persons to respond during the available time. Quite the contrary, it would appear that the aged person can formulate and produce the required response relatively rapidly. It is also clear that under moderately rapid pacing the older person is less likely to respond at all.

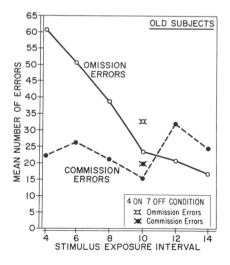

Fig. 8. Errors of omission and commission as a function of exposure condition and interstimulus interval.

TABLE II

RESPONSE TIME FOR CORRECT AND INCORRECT RESPONSES

	Response time (sec)			
Parameter	Correct	Incorrect	Difference	t
Mean	3.73	5.21	1.48	4.12^a
SD	1.38	1.70		

$^a df = 14, p < .01.$

D. Experiment IV: Effects of Learning on the Process of Lipid Mobilization in Man

In order to discuss the implications of these data, some relevant material derived from a somewhat different source is now described. In a study of physiological response patterns observed in a learning task, Powell, Eisdorfer, and Bogdonoff (1964) assayed the effects of learning in old and young Ss upon the process of lipid mobilization in man. It had been demonstrated that the level of free fatty acid (FFA) in the plasma component of blood was intimately related to the level of autonomic nervous system arousal (Bodgonoff, Weissler, & Merritt, 1960; Bogdonoff, Estes, Friedberg, & Klein, 1961; Bogdonoff, Estes, Harlan, Trout, & Kirschner, 1960). With an indwelling needle placed in the S's forearm, it is possible to collect sequential samples of blood during the course of a learning situation without causing pain or undue discomfort to the S. The following procedure was used.

The Ss were 48 male patients hospitalized on the medical and surgical services of the Duke University Medical Center. There were two groups, divided by age: young, between 20 and 48 years (mean 38.1), and old, over the age of 60 (mean 71.4). Patients with illnesses known to either alter fat metabolism or impair central nervous system functioning and those who presented psychiatric disorders, or were manifestly obese were also excluded. Ss were given the vocabulary subtest of the Wechsler Adult Intelligence Scale (WAIS) and only individuals scoring in the range of 7–12 were used.

The stimulus material and learning paradigm were identical to those used in Experiment I. For this study the young and old groups were further subdivided into three subgroups: one subgroup received the words projected for 4 sec, another group for 7 sec, and the third group for 10 sec. A 1-sec interword interval and a 40-sec interlist interval were maintained for all conditions. The word lists were presented for a total of fifteen trials. In this study, the sequence was interrupted at the end of the fifth, tenth, and fifteenth trials for the purpose of collecting blood samples. All Ss were fasted after the evening meal on the preceding day. They were permitted water ad lib but were instructed not to smoke or exercise the morning of the testing. *S*s were brought to the laboratory and seated comfortably in a wheelchair before the screen. All conversations were reduced to a minimum: A # 18 Cournand needle was placed, under local (procaine) anesthesia, in a forearm vein to facilitate sequential sampling of venous blood. A total of nine samples were collected at 30, 15, and 0 min prior to the learning task, at the end of the fifth, tenth, and fifteenth learning trials, and then every 15 min for the ensuing postlearning hour. All samples were collected and analyzed for plasma FFA content after the method of Dole as modified by Trout, Estes, and Friedberg (1960).

Older *S*s did less well in learning the lists than the young *S*s (t = 3.09, p < .01), scoring a mean of 70.1 errors (SD = 29.7) as against 44.3 (SD = 28.6). Figure 9 illustrates the mean plasma FFA values for the old and young *S*s during the study. It should be noted that (a) the plasma FFA level is higher (p < .01) for the older *S*s than for the younger at all points in the study, and (b) both groups demonstrate a decrease in plasma FFA level during initial resting phase of the study (samples 1–3); the rate of FFA decline for both groups is not different. A third finding is that both groups manifest a considerable rise in FFA following the initiation of the learning task (there were no exceptions in either group). The peak mean level for

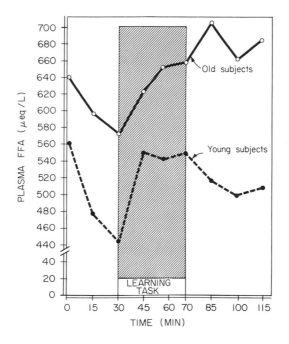

Fig. 9. Plasma FFA levels before, during, and after a learning task.

the older Ss was 732 μeq/liter; in the young Ss, it was 616 μeq/liter. In each group the peak significantly rose over the last (third) resting sample ($p < .01$). Our fourth finding is that the pattern of FFA release across time is different for the two age groups. As did the young, older Ss showed a rise in plasma levels of FFA in response to the onset of learning. For the young Ss, however, the peak elevation of plasma FFA was at the first sample drawn after the onset of learning. The elevation was sustained during the learning task and then proceeded to drop during the postlearning rest period. The peak FFA response for older individuals was observed in the sample drawn 15 min after completion of the learning, and the plasma FFA level remained elevated throughout the rest period. At the outset, the levels of plasma FFA were significantly higher in the older age group. Using the same type of interpretation of plasma FFA levels employed previously (namely, that in the nonexercising, nonobese, fasted individual, the higher the concentration of plasma FFA, the greater the degree of autonomic activation), these higher levels in the aged group may indicate that its members enter into the experimental situation at a significantly greater degree of autonomic arousal. Furthermore, these higher levels are maintained throughout the entire study and though the magnitude of change that occurs just after the learning task is proportionally the same for the two age groups, the prolongation of the rise in the aged suggests that the autonomic reactivity is sustained for a longer period of time. These physiological response characteristics would indicate that the aged individual, rather than being uninvolved in the task (or inattentive), is quite involved and therefore experiencing a greater degree of internal activation.

In conjunction with the behavior during learning, these physiological observations suggest that the response inhibition of the aged may be secondary to a heightened level of autonomic arousal in the old. This arousal, which may serve to inhibit verbal responsivity, results in a poorer performance and an apparent decline in verbal learning.

It is certainly possible, though not necessary, that the physiological state may be perceived by the S and result in greater subjective anxiety. Other possible correlates of this interaction are that the aged are more upset by the prospect of having to learn and therefore approach the task with heightened anxiety, or that the response inhibition itself in the face of stimulation or self-perception of failure generates the autonomic response.

In the experiment under discussion, physiological measures other than FFA were taken. To accomplish this, each S was required to wear a lightweight cloth harness with electrocardiogram (EKG) electrodes pasted onto his chest wall. In addition, a beltlike pneumograph was worn around the abdomen. In this experimental situation we noted for the first time that no significant improvement in learning was seen during the longer exposure time. Since improvement from 4 to 10 sec had been repeatedly observed during conditions under which no blood sampling, needle puncturing, or physiological recording was involved, it raised the suspicion that anxiety generated by the laboratory situation was in some way interacting with anxiety generated by the learning situation to impair performance under the longer interval. It has already been suggested that task anxiety is maximized under conditions of 4-sec stimulus presentation and minimized under the 10-sec pace condition; in consequence, an increase in situational anxiety might be expected to exert its most apparent inhibitory influence on learning at the 10-sec interval. In operational terms, if elevation of the arousal process in the aged beyond moderate levels contributes to an increase in response inhibition, then it might be expected that this effect is maximal at the 4-sec interval and that additional stress brought into the situation with equal intensity across both pacing intervals should result in behavioral change at the slower (10-sec) pace, since other sources of stress (e.g., effects of rapid pacing) are minimal. To restate this proposition, it has been contended herein that the pace of the learning task results in response inhibition at 4-sec and is minimized at 10 sec. A stress brought to bear at both pacing speeds should therefore have little effect at 4 sec, where response inhibition is already maximal; however, a noticeable effect should appear at 10 sec, where the inhibitory effects of the pace are minimal. It was also hypothesized that such generalized situational anxiety would be reduced by familiarizing Ss with the experimental situation, and that the effects of the familiarization would be reflected in improved learning at the 10-sec exposure condition through a reduction in omission errors.

E. Experiment V: Effects of Exposure Time and Situational Familiarity on Learning Performance by the Aged

To test these hypotheses, two additional groups of aged Ss were studied. Twenty men were obtained from Duke University Medical Center hospitals who were essentially the same as the Ss studied in experiment IV. These two groups of 10 each were brought to the laboratory on two successive days. On day 1, they were treated the same way as the Ss in Experiment IV, except that a continuous performance task was substituted for the learning task. This continuous performance (vigilance) task involved the pressing of a telegraph key in response to a two-unit sequence of letters appearing on a memory drum. The speed of the task on day 1 was set to coincide with the learning task to be given the same S on day 2. Blood samples were obtained at the same intervals as during the learning task. On the second day, the Ss returned to the laboratory. One group was presented the 4-sec learning task while the other completed the 10-sec learning task as described earlier.

The data were compared with those obtained with one day's study involving physiological examination [condition II] and with the learning without

TABLE III

MEAN TOTAL ERRORS

| Condition | Exposure time (sec) | | | |
| | 4 | | 10 | |
	Mean	SD	Mean	SD
I	84.3	19.9	31.9	18.4
II	82.0	26.0	63.2	33.2
III	77.1	17.3	57.4	20.7

physiological study [condition I, see Expt. I]. Table III summarizes the results. The hypothesis that learning errors are always greatest at the 4-sec condition is again confirmed. It should be recalled that under the condition of physiological measurement with a 1-day laboratory experience (II), no significant improvement in performance occurred with increasing stimulus exposure time. In accordance with the hypothesis, however, with adaptation to the laboratory and a two-day experience, the change at longer exposure intervals is significant ($t = 2.31, p < .05$). Comparison of condition II (1 day) and the adaptation condition (III) confirms the hypothesis that the observable effects of induced anxiety, i.e., response inhibition, would be maximized at the 10-sec pacing but modifiable by familiarizing the S with a laboratory situation. Table IV shows the changes in omission and commission errors for the various conditions.

No changes in commission errors were observed with increased exposure time under any of the conditions, whereas omission errors again accounted for the change in performance. In summary, this study involved learning under three experimental conditions and two pacing speeds for a group of aged men. It was hypothesized that the arousal and response inhibition generated by the speed of pacing was maximal at the fastest speed (4-sec interval) and that the arousal produced by a noxious experimental situation would therefore be maximally apparent at the point where the other sources

TABLE IV

MEAN OMISSION AND MEAN COMMISSION ERRORS

| Condition | Omission errors | | Commission errors | |
	4 sec	10 sec	4 sec	10 sec
I	61.7	18.4	22.7	13.4
II	67.1	43.1	14.9	20.1
III	56.5	37.8	20.6	19.6

of arousal were minimal, i.e., the 10-sec pace. Further, it was felt that the arousal-producing properties of the experimental situation might be modified by familiarizing Ss with the conditions of the experiment prior to the learning. The results supported these hypotheses. There were no differences in learning at 4 sec between any of the conditions. At the 10-sec pace, the conditions of physiological recording without adaptation were effective in inhibiting learning with a greater tendency on the part of those Ss who withhold responses. When the Ss were given the opportunity to adapt to the situation, improvement at the 10-sec interval was observed.

It should be noted that the improvement in learning at 10 sec may be a function of the difference in variance between the two conditions of physiological measurement. The effects of the adaptation as seen in Condition III appear to have reduced the wider individual reactions to the stressful events of physiological measurement seen in condition II (Troyer, Eisdorfer, Bogdonoff, & Wilkie, 1967). The data can be interpreted to indicate that the techniques for obtaining quantifiable physiological data also serve as stimuli that interact with other sources of anxiety to affect learning and performance. They may be further interpreted to support the seemingly obvious hypothesis that internal arousal plays a significant role in the learning behavior of older subjects. It must be pointed out again, however, that arousal is generated not only by the conditions of physiological measurement but also by the learning task itself. In this context the work of Powell *et al.* (1964) may be interpreted as indicating that older Ss show a higher level of arousal during the learning situation and tend to manifest persistent elevations during and following a learning situation. That is, older Ss seem to have a less efficient cutoff mechanism than that found in the young, who show a decrease in plasma FFA following their first peak arousal to learning. It may be that this heightened level brought by older Ss to the learning situation is sufficient to make learning more difficult, thus setting off a vicious cycle of increased upset and increased relative task complexity. The physiological measures that were obtained during the two-day study included plasma FFA and heart rate response. The FFA levels for the two days of the study are shown in Figs. 10 and 11. The striking finding here is that for day 2 (learning), there is a significant interaction effect between the 4-sec and the 10-sec groups. The postlearning FFA levels of the 10-sec group persist, whereas those of the 4-sec group return to a resting level. The results would suggest that FFA level is related to work levels rather than to the level of arousal generated by the pace of the task. It may thus reflect sustained interest on the part of the 10-sec group while interest and involvement have waned in the 4-sec groups. If the task is perceived as too difficult, diminished involvement might be expected to occur with subjective withdrawal from task involvement as a valuable stabilizing mechanism.

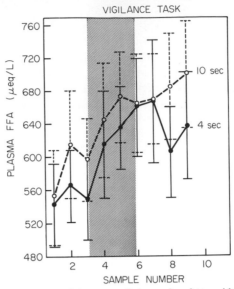

Fig. 10. Mean and standard error of the mean of plasma free fatty acid levels in both groups of Ss in response to a vigilance task on the first day in the laboratory with either 4-sec or 10-sec stimulus exposure time.

The heart rate data were analyzed for change from day 1 to day 2 and showed significantly greater variation the second day on the 10-sec than on the 4-sec trials. Again, the data may be reflecting the greater arousal seen at the 10-sec condition. The suggestion that the diminished FFA mobilization and greater cardiac stability noted at the 4-sec task may reflect withdrawal from a too difficult situation seems reasonable, although further work will have to be done to substantiate this point.

F.   Experiment VI: Effect of Task Simplification on Fast-Paced
     Learning Performance by Young and Old Ss

In an attempt to examine further the hypothesis that task difficulty at 4 sec is responsible for the greater number of errors made by old and young, we attempted to reduce the relative task complexity. One would expect that because of ability or experience, aged Ss of higher than normal intelligence would find learning tasks easier. Seventeen men ranging in age from 67 to 83 (mean 74.6) years and 19 men ranging in age from 23 to 48 (mean 33.8) years with WAIS vocabulary scores of 13 or higher were Ss in the verbal rote learning paradigm. The older Ss were volunteers from a retirement community in Florida and all led relatively independent and quite active lives. The younger men were recruited from individuals with higher education in the local community but excluded faculty members from local universities.

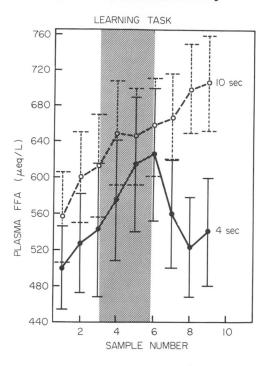

Fig. 11. Mean and standard error of the mean of plasma free fatty acid levels in both groups of *S*s in response to the learning task on the second day in the laboratory with either 4-sec or 10-sec stimulus exposure time.

The *S*s were again divided into the fast (4-sec) and slow (10-sec) exposure groups and learned by using the serial method employed in Experiment I.

The performance of the high-IQ groups was compared with that previously obtained from old and young *S*s with an average IQ. Figure 12 shows the mean total number of errors made by the young and old, average and high-IQ *S*s as a function of exposure conditions. A two-by-two analysis of variance for the faster pacing showed that age, IQ, and their interaction were all significant ($p < .01$); *t* test indicated that at the faster time (4 sec), the higher-IQ older *S*s performed better than their normal age peers, and not differently from normal young men, but not as well as high-IQ young men. Figure 13 shows that omission errors followed the same pattern as total errors, whereas commission errors were different only between the high-IQ young and average-IQ old *S*s. At the slower rate (10 sec), the high-IQ old group performed less well than the younger group but not differently from the average-IQ old *S*s. At this slower speed, the high-IQ older *S*s showed a pattern of omission errors that was not different from the average-IQ young but they made more errors than the high-IQ young. Another interesting finding was

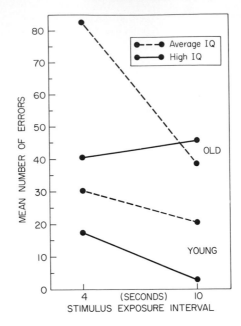

Fig. 12. Mean total number of errors as a function of age and exposure time for high and average intelligence groups.

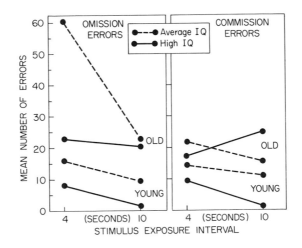

Fig. 13. Mean number of omission and commission errors as a function of age and exposure time for high and average intelligence groups.

that at the slower speed there was a significant age and interaction effect for commission errors, indicating that the high-IQ old made more errors than their young counterparts.

When the analysis was restricted to the high-IQ Ss, it was found again that the old were less capable learners than the young, even at this higher verbal IQ level. Of greater significance, perhaps, for our theoretical framework was the pattern of errors and the finding that the high-IQ old Ss do not show the high rate of omission errors at the faster pacing. Thus, the hypothesis that if the task were made relatively more simple to the aged S, there would result a reduction in response inhibition, characterized by fewer omission errors with resulting improved performance, seems to be confirmed. In this respect our highly intelligent aged Ss performed qualitatively like normal young adults.

These data suggest that older persons with a higher verbal IQ have a propensity for heightened verbal responsivity. Thus, in selecting for high verbal IQ, we may be selecting those persons most likely to give us a verbal response under any condition. There probably exists a postmaturity age-related propensity for suppressing responses. Botwinick (1966) has suggested that the aged need greater assurance of success before they attempt a response. Our data support this contention that as the task becomes easier, responses and apparent learning increase. Perhaps a key variable is the expectation of success on the part of our high-IQ Ss, in contrast with a fear of failure that may characterize our normal aged. This difference in approach to the task may be the basis of many of the observed differences between the aged and young and between the average-IQ and high-IQ Ss.

G. Experiment VII: Relation of Intervening Strategy to Learning Performance by the Aged

The final set of issues that have been subjected to investigation through these studies involves the intervening strategy in learning. Korchin and Basowitz (1956) contended that the aged are primarily S-R learners and that the improvement of the older S with more time available would be secondary to the reinforcement of S-R units. The data are not entirely consistent with this thesis in that no increase in commission errors was made at the slower pace and therefore there was no opportunity to "learn from their mistakes" as was predicted by Korchin and Basowitz. The increase in total number of responses made by the older Ss as they went from 4 sec to 10 sec of exposure time was virtually identical with the increased number of correct responses. Thus, it would almost appear that the improvement reported was a function of the release of responses learned through some cognitive or positional identification and previously inhibited by some intervening state (e.g., arousal generated by the situation or the rapid pace of the task, or both).

It has been suggested elsewhere (Eisdorfer, 1966) that this extremely high proportion of correct responses elicited as pacing is slowed from 4 to 10 sec might be a reflection of a cognitive component of the learning at the slower, more relaxed, pace.

In attempting to study the relationship between the cognitive and S-R components of learning, the following paradigm was developed, based in large measure on the work of Ebenholtz (1961, 1963). Ss for the study were 51 men, 60–80 years of age, in the domiciliary unit of the Bay Pines Veterans Administration Hospital. All were screened, using the vocabulary subtest of the WAIS, and all scored within the scaled score 7–12. Ss were then placed in one of eight experimental groups for a two-day study. The study involved the serial rote learning procedure described earlier. Approximately half of the Ss received a 4-sec exposure and half the 10-sec pace with a 1-sec inter-stimulus interval. Ss in each of the two pacing conditions were assigned to one of four subgroups on the first day. The procedure on the second day, the day immediately following the initial learning was as follows.

a. Condition I: Control ($N = 6$ at 4 sec, 6 at 10 sec). This involved repetition of the learning task under the same conditions as on day 1.

b. Condition II: Substituted-Scrambled ($N = 6$ at 4 sec, 6 at 10 sec). On day 2 four words were removed from the original list (learned the previous day) and an additional four words, having similar structure, frequency, and associative properties, were substituted. The words eliminated were in the second, fourth, sixth, and eighth positions on the day-1 list for the given S. The eight words were rerandomized and presented to the S on day 2 in the manner previously described. The exposure intervals were the same on both days.

c. Condition III: Substituted-Same Position ($N = 7$ at 4 sec, 7 at 10 sec). On day 2 the words at the first, third, fifth, and seventh positions of the day-1 list for each S were replaced by the new words. In this instance, the four old words were retained in their original position. The revised word list was then relearned by Ss, using the same technique and speed as on day 1.

d. Condition IV: Circular ($N = 7$ at 4 sec, 6 at 10 sec). For this condition on day 2, the words were the same as on day 1, but on the initial trial they were presented in the order 1, 2, 3, 4, 5, 6, 7, 8, 1; for the second trial, the words were ordered 2, 3, 4, 5, 6, 7, 8, 1, 2; third trial, 3, 4, 5, 6, 7, 8, 1, 2, 3, and so on, to complete the fifteen trials. Under this condition, each succeeding trial begins with the next word in the series and a given word is always preceded and followed by its adjacent word. On successive trials, however, the position (i.e., first, second,..., last) of the words varied.

These conditions were selected to serve a number of purposes. Condition I gives an estimate of comparative savings in relearning from day 1 to day 2. Condition II provided a test in relearning under the two paces with lists having four stimuli in common on both days but where no S-R or cognitive elements would carry over. Condition III maximized the opportunity for a positional (cognitive) carry-over. Half of the words remained in the same position on both days, but the S-R component was diminished since the adjacent words were always changed, as were the words two units away. The circular sequence (condition IV) maintained the S-R relationship while minimizing the positional elements of the learning task.

The results of the data analysis indicated no differences among the eight subgroups in age or vocabulary level. *Ss* ranged in age from 69.67 to 75.83 (mean 72.23) and the subgroup vocabulary scores varied from 9.1 to 10.3 (mean 9.7). Table V shows the results of the analysis for percentage of total errors in learning made by the eight subgroups for both pacing conditions. In the control group there was a significant improvement in the relearning situation (day 1 to day 2). The faster group improved from a mean of 58.6% to 30.7% errors, the slow group from 37.6% to 0% errors. Condition II, involving the substituted words scrambled, showed that there was essentially no difference in learning between the two days. There was thus no saving, or perhaps whatever savings might have occurred were offset by the interference effects of rerandomization of the list using the four old words. Under Condition III (same position) a significant improvement was noted at both the 4-sec and the 10-sec pacing. At the faster speed, reduction of approximately 24% errors was noted (63.2 to 39.4), whereas there was a reduction of approximately 15% (46.6 to 31.8) from day 1 to day 2 at the slower speed. Clearly, then, a significant change in relearning was associated with retaining half the words in their original position. The effect, however, was equal for both the fast and slow groups. The results of using the circular paradigm (Condition IV) showed that at the faster pace there was no difference between the original learning and circular learning, whereas at the slower-paced condition there was considerable improvement, indicating savings from the contiguity of the stimulus words, despite their shifting position.

TABLE V

MEAN PERCENTAGE OF TOTAL ERRORS AT EACH EXPOSURE TIME IN EXPERIMENT VII

	4 sec			10 sec		
Condition	Day 1	Day 2	t^a	Day 1	Day 2	t^a
Same position (III)	63.21	39.40	4.070^b	46.55	31.78	2.525^c
Scrambled (II)	49.30	48.20	0.174	28.89	35.28	1.011
Circular (IV)	63.69	65.50	0.309	40.56	20.00	3.253^b
Control (I)	58.61	30.70	4.416^b	37.64	0.003	5.955^b

$^a df = 43.$
$^b p < .01.$
$^c p < .05.$

Improvement of the control group (Condition I) was of course expected. The finding that with new words substituted at the 1, 3, 5, and 7 position (Condition III), Ss show significant savings in relearning on day 2 in contrast to no savings when the words were rerandomized (Condition II) is strongly suggestive of a positional component in learning strategy. For Condition III, the adjacent S-Rs are changed so that while there may be an S-R saving from more distant S-R association, the major effects are modified and the stimulus complex of the S-R unit is compromised. It would appear, then, that a positional (cognitive) component is responsible for the savings during the learning situation and the aged seem to profit from this element at both learning speeds.

For the circular relearning (Condition IV) the immediate and distant stimuli leading to a given response are held relatively intact while the position of a given word from onset of the series varies. A strategy based upon simple S-R bonds would predict savings under this condition. The results suggest that this only holds for the slower-paced condition. The group at 10 sec (slower pacing does show significant improvement on relearning, whereas the 4-sec group does not. It is surprising that at 4 sec the S-R bonds, which are presumed to be the principal component in learning in the aged, do not appear to yield any savings. Thus, the thesis that learning in the aged is simply a function of the acquisition of S-R bonds, particularly at the 4-sec pace, must be questioned.

As indicated earlier, the data from Condition III (substituted-same position) reveal significant savings in relearning at the rapid pace. Since the contiguous S-R bonds are disrupted for this condition, such results might be described as based on a positional strategy. We are left, then, with the conclusions that a cognitive approach to learning is present at fast pacing and that the improvement at the slower pace is a function of increased cognitive or S-R elements. The "circular" condition emphasizes the S-R component. Although the data from earlier studies run counter to a hypothesis of explicit S-R reinforcements, the possibility remains of implicit S-R reinforcements at the slower pace. If these results hold up, we must entertain the possibility that with a reduction in level of arousal, which might occur with slower pacing, there is an increase in the number of implicit S-R responses made by the aged S. Given some idiosyncratic number of implicit (rehearsal) responses, affected no doubt by his situation, the aged S will then produce an overt response with what may now (at the slower pace) be a higher response accuracy.

II. Conclusions

The current status of these studies would indicate that performance factors play a significant role in the learning of the aged, and that response inhibition secondary to task or situational factors is a variable of particular importance. The relatively greater value of a slower pace for older Ss, giving them as it does the opportunity for implicit S-R learning and the production of responses, requires greater emphasis in attempts at defining the apparent age-related deficit in learning. The relationship between learning and performance on the one hand and arousal on the other suggests that a curvilinear (inverted U-shaped) relationship between performance and arousal is a reasonable model. Such a hypothetical model, with performance on the ordinate and arousal on the abscissa, is not novel. It has been implicitly assumed, however, that the aged are at a resting state of low internal arousal and sustain a low drive state. Our contention is that the aged may not be at low state of arousal. Once aroused autonomically, perhaps because of a faulty ability to suppress end organ response or because of an altered feedback system, aged Ss appear to function as if in states of high levels of autonomic activity. Perhaps aged persons are less capable of tolerating heightened arousal. In any event, increasing anxiety or further exogenous stimulation has a detrimental effect on performance, as opposed to the incremental effect that we would anticipate from an organism stimulated at lower levels of arousal. It would be predicted, then, that where arousal or anxiety is diminished by experimental manipulation, older persons should improve their performance.

ACKNOWLEDGMENTS

The author is indebted to many colleagues whose help and stimulation were essential to the execution of these studies. To Mrs. Frances L. Wilkie, Mrs. Cornelia Service, Miss Linda Riggs, and Doctors M. D. Bogdonoff and W. G. Troyer I owe a special debt of gratitude. The studies cited were supported in part by grants from the United States Public Health Service (HD-00668) to the Center for the Study of Aging and Human Development at Duke University; the American Heart Association (64-G-159); and the National Heart Institute (HE 08571). The author was supported by a special fellowship from the National Institute of Mental Health (MSP 18 193) while some of these investigations were being undertaken.

REFERENCES

Bogdonoff, M. D., Estes, E. H., Jr., Friedberg, S. J., & Klein, R. F. Fat mobilization in man. *Ann. int. Med.*, 1961, **55**, 328–338.

Bogdonoff, M. D., Estes, E. H., Jr., Harlan, W. R., Trout, D. L., & Kirschner, N. Metabolic and cardiovascular changes during a state of acute central nervous system arousal. *J. clin. Endocr. Metab.*, 1960, **20**, 1333–1340.

Bogdonoff, M. D., Weissler, A. M., & Merritt, F. L. Effect of autonomic ganglionic blockade upon serum free fatty acid levels in man. *J. clin. Invest.*, 1960, **39**, 959–965.

Botwinick, J. Cautiousness in advanced age. *J. Geront.*, 1966, **21**, 347–353.

Caird, W. K. Memory disorder and psychological test performance in aged psychiatric patients. *Dis. nerv. Syst.*, 1965, **26**, 499–505.

Cumming, E., & Henry, W. *Growing old: the process of disengagement.* New York: Basic Books, 1961.

Doppelt, J. E., & Wallace, W. L. Standardization of the Wechsler Adult Intelligence Scale for older persons. *J. abnorm. soc. Psychol.*, 1955, **51**, 312–330.

Ebenholtz, S. M. The relative roles of position learning and sequential association in the serial learning process. Unpublished doctoral dissertation, New School for Social Research, 1961.

Ebenholtz, S. M. Serial learning: Position learning and sequential associations. *J. exp. Psychol.*, 1963, **66**, 353–362.

Eisdorfer, C. The effects of increasing exposure interval on verbal (rote) learning in the aged: Studies II and III. *Excerpta Med.* (Int. Congr. Ser.), 1963, **57**, 139–140.

Eisdorfer, C. A tentative theory on the psychophysiologic aspects of adult learning. *Proc. Nat. Conf. Manpower Training and the Older Worker*, Nat. Council on Aging, 1966, pp. 406–419.

Eisdorfer, C., Axelrod, S., & Wilkie, F. L. Stimulus exposure time as a factor in serial learning in an aged sample. *J. abnorm. soc. Psychol.*, 1963, **67**, 594–600.

Eisdorfer, C., & Cohen, L. D. The generality of the WAIS standardization for the aged: A regional comparison. *J. abnorm. soc. Psychol.*, 1961, **62**, 520–527.

Hulicka, Irene M., & Rust, L. D. Age-related retention deficit as a function of learning. *J. Amer. geriat. Soc.*, 1964, **12**, 1061–1065.

Inglis, J. Influence of motivation, perception and attention on age-related changes in short term memory. *Nature*, 1964, **204**, 103–104.

Inglis, J., & Ankus, Mary N. Effects of age on short-term storage and serial rote learning. *Brit. J. Psychol.*, 1965, **56**, 183–195.

Korchin, S. J., & Basowitz, H. The judgment of ambiguous stimuli as an index of cognitive functioning in aging. *J. Pers.*, 1965, **25**, 81–95.

Korchin, S. J., & Basowitz, H. Age differences in verbal learning. *J. abnorm. soc. Psychol.*, 1957, **54**, 64–69.

Lindquist, E. F. *Design and analysis of experiments in psychology and education.* Boston: Houghton Mifflin, 1953.

Powell, A. H., Eisdorfer, C., & Bogdonoff, M. D. Physiologic response patterns observed in a learning task. *Arch. gen. Psychiat.*, 1964, **10**, 192–195.

Ruch, F. L. Adult learning. *Psychol. Bull.*, 1933, **30**, 387–414.

Ruch, F. L. The differentiative effects of age upon learning. *J. gen. Psychol.*, 1934, **11**, 261–286.

Sorenson, H. Adult ages as a factor in learning. *J. educ. Psychol.*, 1930, **21**, 451–459.

Shock, N. W. The physiology of aging. *Sci. Amer.*, 1962, **206**, 100–110.

Taylor, J. D. The meaningfulness of three hundred and twenty words and paralogs. Unpublished doctoral dissertation, Duke University, 1959.

Thorndike, E. L., Bregman, E. O., Tilton, J. W., & Woodward, E. *Adult learning.* New York: Macmillan, 1928.

Thorndike, E. L., & Lorge, I. *The teacher's word book of 30,000 words.* New York: Teach. Coll., Columbia Univer., Bur. of Publ., 1944.

Trout, D. L., Estes, E. H., Jr., & Friedberg, S. J., Titration of free fatty acids of plasma: A study of current methods and a new modification. *J. lip. Res.*, 1960, **1**, 199–202.

Troyer, W. G., Jr., Eisdorfer, C., Bogdonoff, M. D. & Wilkie, F. Experimental stress and learning in the aged. *J. abnorm. Psychol.*, 1967, **72**, 65–70.

Wechsler, D. *Manual for the Wechsler Adult Intelligence Scale.* New York: Psychol. Corp., 1955.

Welford, A. T. *Skill and age: an experimental approach.* London & New York: Oxford Univer. Press, 1951.

Welford, A. T. *Ageing and human skill.* London & New York: Oxford Univer. Press, 1958.

Age Differences in Paced Inspection Tasks

D. R. DAVIES
Department of Psychology
University of Leicester,
Leicester, England

I. Age and Paced Inspection Performance

A. Aging and Paced Performance

There appears to be general agreement that there is a decline with age in the ability to receive and transmit information and that the decline in this ability reflects a genuine loss in capacity that has important implications for the maintenance of complex skills (Welford, 1959, 1962; Griew, 1963; Szafran, 1965). This loss in capacity is reflected in a slowing of response that appears to be central rather than peripheral in origin (Birren, 1965). In addition, and it is not clear to what extent the two phenomena are related, older people seem to be more cautious about responding and more likely to withhold responses when given the opportunity to do so (Craik, 1962; Silverman, 1963). Further, in unpaced tasks, older people work at a slower rate but tend to be more accurate than younger Ss (Botwinick & Shock, 1952) and in general they appear to attach more importance to accuracy than to speed of response. This bias in favor of accuracy may reflect a compensation for declining response speed or it may be independent of it.

217

Because of their marked slowing of response in situations where speed is important, older *S*s are very vulnerable to performance impairment on paced tasks (Welford, 1959), tasks in which stimuli are presented at a fixed rate that is determined not by *S* but by *E*. An experiment by Brown (see Welford 1958, pp. 109 ff.) in which a plotting task was used provides a very clear demonstration of this point. Under unpaced conditions it was found that performance showed relatively little change with age up to and including the fifties, but began to deteriorate in the sixties and seventies. Under paced conditions, however, *S*s in their fifties performed very much worse than *S*s in their twenties, thirties, and forties. *S*s in their sixties also showed a marked decline compared with those in their fifties.

There are at least four components of the task situation contributing to performance on paced tasks. The first is stimulus duration: how long *S* is given to take in the stimulus; the second is the signal-to-noise ratio: how easy the stimulus is to distinguish from its background; the third is the interstimulus interval: how long *S* is given to make a decision about the nature of the stimulus and to formulate an appropriate response; and the fourth is the number of responses required per unit of time. In this latter case particularly there is considerable overlap between paced and unpaced tasks. Paced tasks such as the Continuous Performance Test, or CPT (Rosvold, Mirsky, Sarason, Bransome, & Beck, 1956), which lasts for 10 or 20 minutes and in which *S* is instructed to detect a sequence of letters (e.g., X followed by A), or just one (e.g., X alone), usually require a response rate of about twelve responses per minute. On the other hand, some unpaced tasks, such as the unpaced version of the five-choice serial task (Leonard, 1959), demand much higher rates of responding, about 80–85 responses per minute. However, paced tasks such as the Mackworth Clock Test and unpaced tasks such as the Digit Symbol Substitution Task in general demand considerably lower rates of responding than does the CPT.

Whether a high rate of responding is required or not, impairment of paced performance shows itself principally in periodic, brief interruptions in otherwise efficient performance. This results in omission errors, although incorrect responses may also occur. In unpaced tasks requiring a high rate of responding, impairment of performance results in an increase in the number of long response times (in the unpaced five-choice serial reaction task a long response is defined as one of 1.5 sec or longer). Here again, however, impairment of performance can also show itself in an increase in the number of wrong responses.

In this chapter our concern is with the performance of older and younger *S*s on paced inspection tasks. This term is used instead of "vigilance tasks" since many of the findings that will be considered are from tasks that last for short periods of time and there is some doubt about whether they qualify as vigilance tasks (McGrath, 1963). The tasks that will be discussed are paced in the sense that the stimuli to which *S*s are instructed to respond do not remain present until a response is made, as in the unpaced five-choice serial reaction situation. In extended paced inspection tasks, however, there are usually very few stimuli that require a response and responses are not, at least from S's point of view, required to be produced in a given time interval, although in fact E may employ a cutoff point to distinguish borderline correct detections from other responses that may either be discarded or classed as commission errors.

First, some recent evidence on the general effects of pacing on the performance of older Ss will be briefly discussed, following which evidence from short and extended paced inspection tasks will be reviewed. Finally in this section, some experiments on age, discrimination reaction time, and false reactions will be considered.

Eisdorfer, Axelrod, and Wilkie (1963) found that increasing the stimulus duration in a verbal learning situation resulted in a relatively greater improvement for older Ss as compared with younger. This improvement was found to be associated with an increased number of responses emitted by older Ss. Eisdorfer (1963) found that older Ss improved their performance monotonically as the exposure time was increased from 4 to 10 sec with a 1-sec interstimulus interval. Increasing the interstimulus interval from 1 to 7 sec also resulted in a greater tendency for older Ss to make a response. (Eisdorfer, 1965).

Eisdorfer found that older Ss could in fact respond fairly rapidly when they had more time available to them, but when this time was reduced, they were less likely to respond at all. He suggested that this is not entirely the result of an inability to respond within the time available, but also of a decreased propensity to do so. He further pointed out that this decreased probability of response might be associated with increased anxiety, related to perceived task difficulty, on the part of older Ss. Eisdorfer, Troyer, and Bogdonoff (1966) found that the increased number of omission errors made by older Ss in the faster-paced condition was not accompanied by any significant change in heart rate as compared with a baseline day, but in the more slowly paced condition, where older Ss were responding more frequently, a significant change in heart rate took place. Plasma free fatty acid levels were also taken and were found to return more rapidly to the baseline level in the faster-paced condition; in the more slowly paced condition, on the other hand, this measure showed a continuous rise. Eisdorfer, Troyer, and Bogdonoff suggest that in the faster-paced condition older Ss tended to disengage themselves from the task and that learning is more arousing for the old than for the young.

B. Age Differences in Short Paced Tasks

Canestrari (1962, 1963) found that on a version of the CPT in which Ss were required to detect the presence of an X or a T older Ss detected significantly fewer signals than did younger Ss and made significantly more commission errors during the 10 min of the task. In a task where Ss were required to detect an A followed by an X older Ss made significantly more omission errors but did not make significantly more commission errors. On neither task was there a significant difference in long latency errors, defined as a response to a signal that took place 0.70 sec after its onset.

The major difference between the two situations, one of which produced a significantly greater number of commission errors from older Ss than the other, appears to be the type of signal for which the Ss were searching on the one hand and the duration of the signal on the other. It is possible that older Ss experienced more difficulty in remembering to search for two types of signal rather than one, although evidence to be reviewed later suggests that this explanation is unlikely.

Canestrari (1963) also compared the effects of pacing and self-pacing on the paired-associate learning of older and younger Ss. Older Ss benefitted much more from the self-paced condition than did younger Ss. Canestrari suggested that anxiety brings about a disruption of performance at the CPT and found that when the effects of anxiety were controlled to some extent, a high positive correlation emerged between the performance of older Ss on the CPT and on the paced paired-associate learning task. He hypothesized that the common characteristic underlying performance at both tasks was readiness to respond.

Thompson, Opton, and Cohen (1963) presented the monosyllabic numbers 1, 2, 3, 4, 5, 6, 8, and 10, one at a time, to older and younger Ss. There were two versions of the task, a visual one, in which the numbers were presented on a memory drum, and an auditory one in which they were presented on a tape recording. S was required to detect either two successive even numbers or two successive odd numbers. In both the visual and auditory tasks, each of which lasted for 5 min, the numbers were presented at three different speeds, the interval between numbers being 4 sec, 2 sec, and 1 sec. In the visual task the signal duration for the 4-, 2-, and 1-sec intervals was 2, 1, and 1 sec, respectively; for the auditory task it was presumably the same for the three interstimulus intervals. The number of signals presented at the 4-, 2-, and 1-sec intervals was 15, 25, and 40, while the number of responses required per minute was 3, 5, and 8.

The results of this experiment indicated that the performance of older Ss (all male) was more adversely affected than was that of younger Ss by the 1-sec presentation speed. The percentage of correct detections in the auditory task dropped from 82.4% at the 4-sec presentation speed to 35.4% at the 1-sec presentation speed for older Ss, and from 79.6% to 48%, for younger Ss. A similar drop in the percentage of correct detections occurred for both age groups in the visual task, but it was less steep.

This study clearly indicates that increasing speed of presentation by reducing the length of the interstimulus interval exerts a more marked effect on the performance of older Ss. The authors suggested that as presentation speed was increased the "vigilance" aspect of the task became less important. Support for this point of view was provided by the demonstration that, for the Ss used in the experiment just described, the positive product-moment correlation obtained between performance at the odd-even task and the Wechsler Adult Intelligence Scale (WAIS) Digit Symbol Scale (a test that has a high loading on a perceptual-motor speed factor) increased as speed of presentation increased. This was true of both age groups.

If only omission errors are taken into account, then this study would appear to provide support for the suggestion that as the rate of pacing is increased in a task, older Ss tend to make fewer responses and can thus be thought of, to some extent, as disengaging themselves from the task situation. It becomes important, therefore, to investigate what happens to commission errors in such a situation. If omission errors made by older Ss increase as presentation speed increases but commission errors do not, then this would provide support for the view that older Ss, as pacing increases, disengage themselves from the task either because they are unable or because they are unwilling to sustain the demands made upon their declining perceptual-motor speed. In other words, can an increase in commission errors made by older Ss under conditions of increasing presentation speed be accounted for in terms of declining response speed?

In a preliminary attempt to investigate this question a small pilot study was carried out in which the experiment of Thompson et al. (1963) was partially repeated. Two 5-minute versions of the odd-even task were used. In the first, a 4-sec interstimulus interval was employed and in the second, a 1-sec interval. In both tasks, which were recorded on tape, the numbers 1, 2, 3, 4, 5, 6, 8, and 10 were used, the signal duration being 1 sec. The 4-sec task contained 60 numbers and 15 signals; the 1-sec task contained 150 numbers and 40 signals. The task was relayed to Ss via headphones and E monitored the task in an adjoining room through a separate pair of earphones. Whenever S thought he had detected a signal, he pressed a key connected to a buzzer system and E marked S's response on a copy of the task at an appropriate point. As in Thompson, Opton, and Cohen's experiment, the 4-sec task always preceded the 1-sec task. The instructions for the 1-sec task, which were the same as those for the 4-sec task, were repeated on the tape recording. Ss were not informed of the change of presentation speed. No practice on either task was given; before the 4-sec task commenced, E gave S the instructions and answered questions about the nature of the task S was required to perform. Twelve younger Ss (age range 17–31), who were either students or laboratory technicians, and 12 older Ss (age range 56–67), who were either retired professional men or laboratory technicians, took part.

The results are shown in Table I. Wilcoxon t tests were performed on both the percentage of correct detections and the number of commission errors made by older and younger Ss under the two speed conditions. Mann-Whitney U tests were performed on the same scores across age groups for the two conditions. The results show that for both age groups omission and commission errors increased at the faster presentation speed and that the percentage of correct detections made by older Ss was significantly less than the percentage made by younger Ss in the faster-paced condition but not in the more slowly paced condition. The number of commission errors made by older Ss in the faster-paced condition was greater than the number made by younger Ss, but the difference was significant only at the 10% level. In view of the small number of errors of both kinds made in this experiment it was not considered worthwhile to run correlations between the two sets of scores, although inspection of the data did indicate that there was a tendency for Ss who made more omission errors to make more commission errors as well.

The results of this study seem to indicate that as the presentation speed is increased, Ss are liable not only to make more omission errors but also more commission errors, and that older Ss are more likely to make both kinds of error than are younger Ss. It appears, then, that the effects of making increasing demands on response speed are not only to cause correct responses to drop out, but also to make it more probable that incorrect responses will be included.

It is perhaps worth mentioning at this stage that in short paced tasks of the kind described there appears to be little differential effect of stimulus

TABLE I

PERCENTAGE OF CORRECT DETECTIONS AND MEAN NUMBER OF COMMISSION ERRORS

	Task 1	Task 2	Wilcoxon[a]
Correct detections			
Younger Ss [b]	100%	94.88%	$p < .01$
Older Ss [b]	100%	89.16%	$p < .01$
Mann-Whitney U test [c]	NS[d]	$p < .05$	
Commission errors			
Younger Ss [b]	0.25	1.16	$p < .01$
Older Ss [b]	0.16	2.25	$p < .01$
Mann-Whitney U test [c]	NS[d]	$p < .10$	

[a] Two-tailed; task 1 versus task 2.
[b] $N = 12$ in each case.
[c] Two-tailed; older Ss versus younger Ss.
[d] NS = not significant.

duration on the performance of different age groups. In the studies mentioned the stimulus duration was usually 1 sec. The nature of the stimulus to be detected, the interstimulus interval, and the number of responses required per unit of time do, however, appear to be important. Stimulus duration and the nature of the stimulus to be detected could perhaps be regarded as being more on the "input" side than on the "output" side and, as will be discussed further in a later section, the age deficit in short paced inspection tasks would appear to result primarily from a failure to mobilize responses rather than a failure to "perceive" stimuli, insofar as a division of this kind can be made at all.

C.   Age Differences in Extended Paced Inspection Tasks

Extended paced inspection tasks differ from brief tasks of the same kind mainly in terms of the number of responses required per unit of time and, of course, in terms of the length of the task. In the majority of such tasks, then, few responses are required, usually not more than one per minute and frequently considerably less.

In general, older Ss perform as well as younger ones on extended paced inspection tasks. In a 40-min task containing 44 signals (three odd numbers, all of which were different) the percentage of correct detections made by older Ss was 68% and that made by younger Ss, 69% (Griew & Davies, 1962, Experiment III). When a similar task was extended to 75 min and the number of signals reduced to 30, the percentage of correct detections became 57% for older Ss and 61% for younger Ss (Davies & Griew, 1963). In the first study the mean commission error score for older Ss was 5.3 and for younger Ss, 3.3. In the second study the means were 0.9 and 1.8, respectively. Thus, extending the task duration and reducing the number of signals diminished the percentage of correct detections and the number of commission errors to a greater extent for older Ss than for younger ones. In neither study, however, was there a significant difference in either the number of correct detections or the number of commission errors made by older and younger Ss.

In addition, in a 40-min task containing 44 signals where older and younger Ss were required to notice discrepancies between a printed list of numbers, both older and younger Ss performed equally well, the percentage of correct detections made by older Ss being 82% and by younger Ss 83% (Griew & Davies, 1962, Experiment II). There was no age difference in commission errors on this task, the mean number for both age groups being 3.80. Changing the characteristics of the signal also appears to exert no significant differential effect on the efficiency of older and younger Ss. If, instead of being required to detect three successive odd digits that are all different, Ss are required to detect three successive numbers that are either successive increments of two (e.g., 246, 468, 135, 357, 579, or 024) or successive decrements of two, that is, the same numbers in reverse (e.g., 642, etc.), performance on this task is generally inferior to performance on the odd-odd-odd task. Table II shows data from a small-scale study in which eight younger Ss (age range 19–26 years) and six older Ss (age range 55–61 years) took part. The 40-min task contained 40 signals, 10 in each 10-min subperiod.

It can be seen that although older Ss detect fewer signals, the difference between their performance and that of younger Ss is not significant. However, the difference in commission error scores is significant at the 10% level, a difference that would appear to warrant further investigation. A criticism of this study, apart from the small number of Ss used, is that the age range is limited, a point made by Surwillo and Quilter (1964) with reference to the experiment by Davies and Griew (1963). It is possible, as Talland (1966) has suggested, that age deficits on these types of task do not really emerge until the middle or late sixties. Finally, York (1962) also found no age difference in correct detections in a sensory vigilance task in which Ss were required to detect a double flash of light interspersed among a series of single flashes.

There are, however, some exceptions to these findings. The first is that if the task involves a short-term memory loading, then older Ss perform significantly less well than do younger Ss (Griew & Davies, 1962, Experiment I). In this study, instead of pressing a button to report the detection of a signal, Ss were required to write down the three digits that constituted the signal. In this case the percentage of correct detections made by older Ss was 44% and by younger Ss, 59%. The mean number of commission errors made by older Ss, 5.1, was not significantly different from the mean number made by younger Ss, 7.4, however.

Second, Surwillo and Quilter (1964), using the Mackworth Clock Test,

TABLE II

PERCENTAGE OF CORRECT DETECTIONS AND MEAN NUMBER OF COMMISSION ERRORS

	Younger Ss $(N = 8)$	Older Ss $(N = 6)$	
Correct detections	57	51	NS
Commission errors	3.10	5.75	$p < .10$ $(U = 18)^a$

[a] Two-tailed.

found that older Ss detected significantly fewer signals in the last quarter hour of an hour-long task. This finding has been confirmed in subsequent studies (Surwillo & Quilter, 1965; Surwillo, 1966). Here the additional factor of scanning involved in locating a signal around the clock face may have been important. Talland (1966) has suggested that this factor may affect older Ss more adversely than younger ones. Also, Wallis and Samuel (1961) have suggested that more variability in performance is found among Ss engaged in prolonged visual tasks than in Ss engaged in prolonged auditory tasks, since the added factor of signal location contributes to a decline in performance, and operators looking for faint signals scan visual displays with varying degrees of skill, a factor that may be relatively independent of their level of vigilance.

Third, a recent experiment by Tune (1966), using a forced-choice vigilance task, has produced some interesting findings. Tune required his Ss to listen to a tape recording of groups of ten digits (the numbers 1 to 9 inclusive were used in a quasi-random order), each group being followed by 10 sec of silence. The task was to identify three consecutive odd digits that were all different and that might or might not be embedded in the group of ten digits, occurring at neither the beginning nor end of such a group. Ss were required to listen to each group of ten digits and in the 10 sec that followed to place a tick in one of two columns on a prepared answer sheet. The columns were headed "No" (meaning that a "wanted" combination of numbers did not occur) and "Yes" (meaning that it did). In the latter case Ss were encouraged to write down the numbers constituting the signal, although the instructions given emphasized that this was unimportant and in the scoring of results transcription errors were not counted against Ss. Scores were assessed entirely in terms of the number of "Yes" responses. The total number of signals in the task was 27.

In addition to being divided into two age groups, Ss were also further subdivided into equal groups of introverts and extroverts in terms of their scores on Part 2 of the Heron Inventory (Heron, 1956). The results of this experiment showed, in the first place, that Ss performed very well on the task, in terms of correct detections. The percentage of correct detections (calculated from the data given by Tune) was 89.2% for older Ss and 92.2% for younger Ss, the Spearman rank correlation between age and correct detections being virtually zero. The mean commission error score, on the other hand, was 21.05 for older Ss and 2.40 for younger Ss. The rank correlation, age by commission errors, was thus highly significant. The majority of commission errors made by older Ss were contributed by the extroverts (325 out of a total of 421).

This result was interpreted in terms of arousal theory. Tune tentatively suggested that older Ss are less aroused; that less aroused Ss are more likely to seek information about the task they are performing; and that commission errors can be regarded as an index of need for information. Such an interpretation rests on two main assumptions: first, that older Ss are less aroused; and second, that commission errors can be regarded as an index of need for information. It is also questionable whether less aroused Ss are more likely to seek information about the task they are performing. It could be argued that they are less likely to do so because they are less aroused and therefore less efficient at distinguishing between signals and nonsignals. It is also possible that older Ss, when faced with a choice between saying "Yes" or "No" in a signal-detection situation, are more likely to say "Yes," this being in some way different from a situation in which they report the presence or absence of a signal by either pressing a button or refraining from response altogether. In Tune's situation, unlike most vigilance tasks, older Ss were unable to refrain from responding, a factor that may be important, in view of the general failure to obtain age differences in commission errors on similar tasks in which Ss could respond at will.

It is possible that instructing Ss to respond more frequently than they would otherwise introduces a form of "response pacing" that increases the probability of commission errors on the part of older Ss. There are at least two ways of testing this hypothesis. The first is to reduce the interval allowed for response and see whether commission errors made by older Ss increase disproportionately. The second is to compare two groups of older Ss and two groups of younger Ss on both the 10-sec interval, as used by Tune, and a situation in which the task is identical but Ss are not forced to respond following each group of ten digits. The free-response situation might be expected to bring about a significant reduction in the number of commission errors made by older Ss.

In summary of recent work on extended inspection tasks, it appears again that neither the nature of the stimulus to be detected nor the stimulus duration has a greater effect on older Ss than on younger ones in terms of correct detection scores. The principal factor contributing to age differences in tasks where scanning factors are not involved would seem to be the response requirements of the task. If these are either such that a load on short-term memory is added or such that S is forced to make a response where in normal conditions he would not, then significant age differences in either correct detections or commission errors emerge.

D.   Age, Discrimination Reaction Time, and False Reactions

The final group of tasks to be considered are those in which S is required to make a response to one kind of stimulus but to withhold response to another kind. When the stimulus to which a response is to be withheld occurs infrequently, the task resembles a vigilance situation in which response to the signal has to be withheld.

Arnhoff (1959) used a discrimination reaction time task in which older and younger Ss were required to respond to one stimulus, but not to others that differed in spatial location from the first. In such a task, as Canestrari (1965) has pointed out, the instructions have to make it clear that Ss must respond rapidly, otherwise an insufficient number of false reactions is obtained to permit age differences to be investigated. Arnhoff found that older Ss made significantly fewer false reactions but their reaction times were also slower and the difference on the first measure could thus be attributed to differences in speed of response rather than to differences in spatial-stimulus generalization, the topic under investigation. Canestrari (1965) thus employed a probability learning situation in a successful attempt to establish age differences in spatial-stimulus generalization.

However, tasks similar to that used by Arnhoff have been used by Lacey and Lacey (1958) in studies of background autonomic activity in relation to certain hyperkinetic-impulsive aspects of behavior. They were able to demonstrate that the amount of nonspecific activity in both cardiac and sudomotor measures derived from a group of college students was positively related to the number of false reactions in a task essentially the same as that used by Arnhoff. In addition, labiles (that is, Ss exhibiting relatively large amounts of resting nonspecific activity) tended to have faster reaction times than stabiles (Ss showing a low incidence of nonspecific activity). Stabiles tended to differentiate themselves from labiles by being more capable of slowing their reaction times to conform with experimentally imposed requirements for wariness and caution.

There have been some failures to confirm these findings, failures that can perhaps be accounted for by differences in experimental design or procedure. With this qualification, it appears that labiles tend both to have faster reaction times and to be more impulsive; that is, they make more false reactions. This suggests that older Ss, who tend to have slower choice reaction times than younger Ss (Welford, 1959) and who also seem to be more autonomically stabile (Malmo & Shagass, 1949; Surwillo & Quilter, 1965), should also make fewer false reactions on this type of task.

Davies and Treacher (1966) attempted to examine the relation between age and cardiac lability and the relation among age, reaction time, and errors. In one experiment 12 men between 19 and 28 years of age, who were mainly laboratory technicians, although a few were students, and 12 men between 55 and 65, who were laboratory technicians and maintenance men of the university, took part. All Ss were paid for their services and older and younger Ss were balanced with respect to the time of day at which they were tested.

Heart rate was recorded during the last 5 min of a 10-min pretask rest period. In order to obtain cardiac lability scores, heart rate measurements were collected by reading off the interval between each heartbeat (R-R interval), from the records by means of a millimeter ruler. These were then converted into beats per minute by means of a table. The 5-min rest period was then scored for consecutive peak-to-trough differences, a peak being the fastest beat before deceleration again occurs and a trough being the slowest beat before acceleration again occurs. Peak-to-trough differences were obtained by subtracting each trough from the preceding peak.

Three measures of lability were used. First, frequency of changes, that is, the number of peak-to-trough differences per S, ignoring size, over the 5-min rest period; second, the mean peak-to-trough difference for each S over the 5-min rest period, and third, the median of the peak-to-trough differences for each S. The first two measures differentiated between older and younger Ss at the 5% level of significance (Mann-Whitney U test, one-tailed), while the third measure just failed to differentiate between the groups at this level. On all three measures older Ss were more stabile than younger ones; that is, the frequency of peak-to-trough differences was less and the mean and (nonsignificantly) the median peak-to-trough differences were smaller.

Following the recording of heart rate, Ss performed the task. Seven white lights were arranged in a semicircle, the center light being at eye level 4 feet from S, who was seated in an adjustable chair. Three inches above the center white light was a green warning light; the interval between the warning light and the onset of a white light could be varied, giving foreperiods of 2, 3, and 4 sec. Ss were instructed to press a key when the warning light came on and to release it only when the center light followed the green warning light, ignoring the onset of other peripheral lights.

The task comprised four blocks of trials, in fixed order, the whole sequence of lights being programmed on punched tape. Blocks 1 and 3 each consisted of 27 trials in which each foreperiod was used nine times and the center light only was presented for response. Blocks 2 and 4 each consisted of 36 trials in which the center light was presented 28 times and a peripheral light 8 times; only the two inner peripheral lights were used, since it appeared from pilot studies that lights farther out on the periphery seldom produced errors. Again, each foreperiod was equally represented. There was no interval between blocks and Ss were informed that any light, central or peripheral, might follow the green warning light at any time. False reactions were, of course, recorded only from blocks 2 and 4, the maximum false reaction score for each block being eight. Reaction times were analyzed only from blocks 1 and 3, since it was found that the occurrence of a false reaction commonly disrupted reaction time for one or two subsequent trials and therefore produced atypical readings. It should be stressed that although measurements of false reactions and reaction time are thus technically based on different sections of the data, these sections are not psychologically distinct for Ss.

Neither the differences in reaction times with different foreperiods nor the difference in reaction times between older and younger Ss reached statistical significance, although younger Ss (mean reaction time 531 msec) responded slightly faster than did older Ss (mean reaction time 542 msec) and the 3-sec foreperiod tended to produce shorter reaction times than either of the others. The mean false reaction score for older Ss was 2.88 and for younger Ss, 4.16. On a Mann-Whitney U test (one-tailed) this difference fails to reach the 5% level of significance. Thus, in summary, there was a tendency for older Ss to make fewer false reactions and to have slower reaction times, but neither tendency was significant. Finally, Spearman rank correlations were run on mean reaction times and the mean number of false reactions. This did reach an acceptable level of significance ($p = -0.52$, $p < .01$), suggesting that those Ss who responded faster to the center light also tended to make more false reactions.

It is suggested that false reactions in this kind of discrimination reaction time situation bear a resemblance to commission errors in paced inspection tasks, particularly visual ones such as the CPT. Underlying both is a state of readiness to respond. This will be discussed further in the next section, where some explanations of age differences in the performance of paced inspection tasks will be considered.

II. Some Explanations of Age Differences in the Performance of Paced Inspection Tasks

In this section, the applicability of three kinds of processes to age differences in the performance of paced inspection tasks will be discussed. Such age differences, when they occur, could be attributed to failures of short-term memory or of attention, or to failures to mobilize a response sufficiently quickly. This last kind of failure could have two variants. First, it could be argued that in some paced tasks older Ss are simply unable to formulate a response sufficiently quickly, and second, it is possible that they are un-willing to mobilize a response quickly, so that responses that would have been correct, had they been made, are suppressed.

A. Failures of Short-Term Memory

It has been suggested that the deterioration with age in the performance of paced sequential tasks can be attributed to failures in short-term memory (Kirchner, 1958; Welford, 1962). Kirchner used a task in which Ss sat facing a row of twelve light bulbs, with a telegraph key placed under each bulb; in the simplest condition of this task, the "no-back" condition, Ss were required, on the lighting of a bulb, to press the appropriate telegraph key. Lights changed every 2 sec. There was no difference in the percentage of correct responses achieved by older and younger Ss on this task. A difference appeared in two further conditions, however; the task was changed so that the lights still came on in a random order at 2-sec intervals, but Ss were required to press the key under the light that had just gone off rather than the one that had just come on. This condition, the "one-back" condition, produced an age difference that became much greater when Ss were required to work in a "two-back" condition. When faced with a "three-back" condition, the older Ss, aged 64–78 years, did not attempt it. In the two-back condition some of the older Ss were unable to do the task at all, owing to failures to understand the instructions, and those who did fully understand made about half the number of correct responses made by younger Ss. Welford (1958) characterizes this task as one in which there is "a continual alternation between intake of information and use of it in responding action. It would seem that some process involved in responding exerts a serious interfering effect upon the information stored in short-term memory" (pp. 250–251).

What implications does this finding have for age differences in paced inspection performance? It would seem that such tasks rarely possess features that place heavy demands on short-term memory, unless this concept is somewhat expanded to include the forgetting of task instructions, that is, what constitutes a signal. In Canestrari's (1962) task, where Ss had to remember to search for two kinds of signal, an X or a T, it is possible that the load on short-term memory is greater than in tasks where only one kind of signal has to be detected, but evidence on this point is lacking.

In any event, Talland (1966) found that an impairment in accuracy in a continuous visual detection task presented at a fast rate occurred in older Ss, even though the task did not demand the retention of information from previous displays. This impairment remained when the time allowed for a response was doubled, but diminished when a slower rate of display change was used. The crucial factor in the decreased accuracy of older Ss appeared to be the fast rate of display change, which demanded both quicker decisions and a more rapid formulation of response.

B.   Failures of Attention

A second possibility is that the age deficit in paced inspection tasks, where it occurs, arises because older Ss need more time to appreciate the nature of each stimulus, that is, to perceive and classify it. Alternatively, momentary failures to take in information might be more likely to occur in older Ss. Either hypothesis implies that any observed age differences would be accentuated if the stimulus were made less easy to perceive while stimulus duration were unchanged, that is, if the signal-to-noise ratio were reduced; or if stimulus duration were reduced while signal-to-noise ratio remained comparatively high. Evidence for the first assumption is not clear-cut, although the evidence reviewed does suggest that reducing the signal-to-noise ratio, even though it does not differentially affect omission errors of older and younger Ss, does produce a change in commission errors (older Ss making more); the change, however, is not significant. It is possible that changes in both omission and commission errors made by older Ss would occur in sensory vigilance tasks, where lights or tones are used as stimuli, rather than in cognitive ones, where letters or numbers are used. This might also be the case for stimulus duration; the lowest signal duration employed in studies of the performance of older Ss on cognitive vigilance tasks has been 1 sec, although signal duration itself has not been extensively studied. Both variables would appear to need more study in relation to age differences in paced performance.

Failures of attention should be distinguished from failures of response, and because of the well-documented decline in response speed with age, such a distinction is not easy to make. However, when differences in the performance of a paced inspection task emerge where there is no reason to suspect differences in speed of response as a contributing factor, there are some grounds for assuming that failures of attention are responsible. Such evidence comes from studies of individual differences unrelated to age in paced inspection tasks.

For instance, in a recent experiment Davies and Hockey (1966) compared the performance of introverts and extroverts in a 32-min task where Ss were required to look for discrepancies between a series of digits presented via closed-circuit television, with a stimulus duration of 1 sec, and a series of digits on typescript. Each discrepancy constituted a signal. Ss performed the task under one of two conditions of signal frequency, high or low, and in either noise (95 db) or quiet (70 db). The number of correct detections made by extroverts declined steadily in quiet at both levels of signal frequency, whereas the number made by introverts did not. Noise removed the decline in performance shown by extroverts at both signal frequency levels and significantly increased the number of correct detections under the low signal frequency condition. Introverts made significantly more commission errors in quiet than in noise, while extroverts made significantly more in noise than in quiet. The result appeared to be due to the fact that in noise extroverts made more responses, without increasing their probability of being correct when they did respond. (In connection with age differences, however, it should be noted that preliminary results from a study investigating the effects of noise on the performance of older and younger Ss indicate that older Ss make more commission and omission errors in noise than in quiet.)

In terms of free-response speed, extroverts and introverts do not differ; if anything, extroverts tend to respond more quickly (Farley, 1966). Any interpretation of the results in terms of response speed is therefore unlikely. Failure of attention may represent a more likely explanation; on the other hand, attention may itself be subsumed under readiness to respond.

C. Failures of Response Mobilization

Failures of response mobilization will be considered under two headings: brief consideration will be given to the possibility, first, that older Ss are unable to respond quickly enough in the type of paced inspection tasks that have been discussed; and second, that the effect of pacing is to bring about suppression of response to a greater extent in older than in younger Ss.

From the previously mentioned studies by Eisdorfer, it would appear that older Ss are capable of producing, under unpaced conditions, response times shorter than the interstimulus intervals used in the paced versions of the task. As Eisdorfer implied, failures to respond under paced conditions appear, at least in part, to be attributable to response suppression rather than to the inability to formulate a response. Some evidence for this has been provided by Opton (1964).

Opton investigated the electroencephalographic concomitants of performance at an auditory version of the odd-even task in old and young Ss. He hypothesized that the reduction or absence of "normal" electroencephalogram (EEG) desynchronization would accompany transient performance lapses on the task. He further hypothesized that the combination of omission errors and reduced EEG desynchronization would occur more often in old than in young Ss. In this experiment, summated EEG amplitude, an index of EEG desynchronization, was measured for 1 sec before and for 1 sec after correct responses, omission errors, and nonsignal stimuli during performance of the odd-even task. Control and resting conditions were also monitored.

Old Ss made 14% fewer correct detections than did the young Ss, a difference significant at the 10% level; EEG amplitude declined from before to after the stimulus when correct detections were made and rose when omission errors were made. There was no change in EEG amplitude from before to after neutral stimuli, or in control conditions. No age difference emerged in EEG amplitude, although the trend was for older Ss to show greater desynchronization with correct responses but also a greater increase in EEG amplitude with omission errors. The transient nature of the increase in EEG amplitude suggested to Opton an explanation in terms of inhibition and he pointed out that many earlier studies have indicated that a variety of types of behavioral inhibition is accompanied by augmentation of EEG amplitude.

Finally, a brief redescription of older Ss' performance in paced inspection tasks will be given. It would seem that the performance of Ss in paced inspection tasks can be described in terms of their readiness to respond. This readiness is affected by task characteristics such as the nature and duration of the stimulus, the interstimulus interval duration, and the frequency with which responses are required. In addition, older Ss are less ready to respond than younger ones, although in many paced inspection tasks the pacing is not severe enough to bring about age differences in performance. When the rate of pacing does become severe, and here some critical level is assumed, older Ss have two very broad strategies available to them; either they can withdraw from the task situation wholly or in part, which tends to result in their making many omission errors but few commission errors, or they can speed up their rate of decision making so that a response is made on the basis of less evidence than would be the case if the task were unpaced. This results in an increase in commission errors and an increase in omission errors, compared to younger Ss.

Whether or not the way in which older Ss approach paced situations masks an attentional or a response speed deficit, or both, remains to be fully investigated. In such an investigation the use of unpaced inspection tasks could clearly be useful. It is worth noting that Wilkinson (1961), using younger Ss, found that signals were just as likely to be missed in an unpaced inspection situation as in a paced one. In Section III, the difference between short and extended paced inspection tasks will be further discussed in relation to performance decrement over time.

III. Performance Decrement and Arousal Theory

It seems reasonable to regard the gradual decline in performance at many extended paced inspection tasks as being associated with a progressive decrease in the level of arousal. Experiments using physiological measures such as skin conductance (Dardano, 1962; Davies & Krkovic, 1965; Ross, Dardano, & Hackman, 1959), heart rate (Eason, Beardshall, & Jaffee, 1965; Griew, Davies, & Treacher, 1963), and EEG alpha activity (Davies & Krkovic, 1965) seem to support this notion. However, many paced inspection tasks do not produce a performance decrement, and arousal may be a major contributing factor only when the task is performed under extremely unstimulating conditions, for example, in situations where reports of drowsiness are common or where Ss actually fall asleep.

The decline in performance may also be associated wih greater caution (Broadbent & Gregory, 1963). Both these possibilities imply that the number of responses emitted, whether correct detections or commission errors, will decline with time on task, and this appears to be the case in the majority of experiments in which a vigilance decrement has been reported. However, performance decrements can also occur under highly stimulating task conditions; examples are discussed by Broadbent (1963).

Broadbent argued that it is difficult to reconcile the deterioration in performance sometimes found under conditions of high-intensity noise with the view that performance is worse under low levels of stimulation. He nevertheless reconciles the two sets of findings by suggesting that if the effects of high arousal are due to an increase of competing but incorrect responses, then it is not unreasonable to assume that these effects should show themselves only after the situation has continued for some time. The competing responses would perhaps fail to show themselves at first, since the correct responses would be predominant. After working for some time at a task, however, the incidence of occasional competing responses, presumably in this context either commission errors of failures to respond at all, might increase in keeping with the various phenomena suggested by such concepts as reactive inhibition or stimulus satiation. On this view it might be expected that the number of commission errors would increase under noise conditions during the second half of an extended task, but the evidence on this point is equivocal.

There appears to be only one experiment in which physiological measures have been taken from older Ss during the performance of an extended inspection task in which their performance, assessed in terms of correct detections, is known to deteriorate with time. In order to test the hypothesis that differences in autonomic activity are associated with age differences in the rate at which vigilance deteriorates, Surwillo (1966) recorded heart rate, palmar skin temperature, and palmar skin potential during performance of the clock test. He found that in the final 45 min of the hour-long task, heart rate declined and skin potential increased progressively, but the slopes of the regression lines that described these changes did not differ significantly with age. Skin temperature, on the other hand, declined progressively with time on task in the older group but not in the younger group, and the slopes in this case did differ significantly. The latter finding was consistent with the hypothesis that differences in autonomic activity are associated with the more rapid decline of vigilance in old than in young Ss. As Surwillo points out, however, declines in skin temperature are not uncommon over time periods of the order of 1 hour, and the differences observed in this study, although correlated with time and age, may be independent of vigilance performance. But it is interesting to note that heart rate and skin temperature, although virtually identical for the two age groups during the first minute of the task, differed significantly at the end of the task. In contrast, skin potential showed differences across the entire 1-hour period.

These results can perhaps be taken as tentative support for the notion that there are age-related changes in arousal during extended tasks. Whether or not similar inferences can be drawn from studies that do not make use of physiological measures remains to be seen.

IV. Summary and Conclusions

In this chapter the results of experiments comparing the performance of older and younger Ss at both short and extended paced inspection tasks and in related task situations have been reviewed. In some situations age differences occur, in most they do not. In general, analysis of results has been confined to correct detections, and age differences on this measure occur mainly in brief inspection tasks, for example, the CPT and the odd-even task. However, age differences in commission errors occur both in brief and extended tasks.

Age differences in omission errors increase when the interstimulus interval is reduced, that is, when Ss are given less time to mobilize a response. Older Ss might also be at a disadvantage if the stimulus duration were reduced, but this hypothesis has not been tested. Age differences in omission errors also appear on the CPT, in which both the interstimulus interval and the stimulus duration are shorter than is generally the case. However, when the CPT has been used in the context of age differences, Ss have been required to search for more than one signal, for example, both an A and an X, and this extra load may have contributed to the reported age differences, confounding the effects of interstimulus interval and stimulus duration.

Age differences in commission errors also begin to appear when the interstimulus interval is reduced or when the signal is made less easy to distinguish from its background. Significant age differences in commission errors have been reported using the CPT in one experiment (but not in another), and in a forced-choice task in which Ss were required to make a yes or no response following each presentation of a stimulus series in which a signal could have been embedded.

Response latencies have been rarely recorded during paced inspection task performance. Where they have been, the mean reaction time of older Ss, although longer, has not been significantly different from that of younger Ss (Surwillo & Quilter, 1964). In this experiment the failure to obtain a significant difference in reaction time was not attributable to differences in the variance of the response latencies of the two age groups. In addition, a highly significant negative correlation was found between reaction time and correct detections. The magnitude of the response latencies obtained in this study was considerably in excess of that obtained in conventional reaction time situations, presumably reflecting, as Surwillo and Quilter suggested, the greater difficulty of the task.

Studies on age, discrimination time, and false reactions indicate that older Ss respond more slowly, significantly so in one experiment but not in another, and also make fewer false reactions, again, significantly in only one study. However, both studies found a significant negative correlation between the number of false reactions and mean reaction time, but the amount of the variance left unaccounted for was comparatively large, and Arnhoff (1959) considered that the relationship between reaction time and false reactions was not age related, in view of his finding that the correlations between the two measures for each age group were not significantly different from each other.

In discussing these results and in attempting to account for age differences where they occur, failures of short-term memory and of attention are perhaps given less consideration than they deserve, and emphasis is placed on failures of response mobilization.

It is generally assumed that the efficiency of the central nervous system decreases with age, and this might well result in information at the senses being less reliably transmitted to points deep within the nervous system, especially in situations where critical stimuli are present for brief periods of time or are in other ways made difficult to detect. In unpaced tasks, one way of compensating for this decreased efficiency of information transmission is for Ss to allow themselves more time to respond. In paced tasks this is not possible. An alternative strategy would be to adopt a more risky criterion for responding, that is, to respond on the basis of less internal evidence, because all the evidence has not yet been fully assembled. The evidence reviewed here does not, on the whole, tend to support the view that older Ss are more cautious. Greater caution would presumably be reflected either in much longer reactions or in failures to respond. Although there are indications that in some Ss this may be happening (Opton, 1964), comparisons of the total number of responses (correct detections + commission errors) emitted by younger and older Ss in paced inspection tasks suggest that older Ss make as many responses as, if not more than, younger Ss. As already indicated, there also appears to be no significant difference in reaction times between age groups. Further studies, using measures derived from signal detection theory, are in progress, and it is hoped that these will provide evidence about the criterion for responding adopted by older Ss in paced inspection situations.

REFERENCES

Arnhoff, F. N. Adult age differences in performance on a visual spatial task of stimulus generalization. *J. educ. Psychol.*, 1959, **50**, 259–265.

Birren, J. E. Age changes in speed of behavior: its central nature and physiological correlates. In A. T. Welford & J. E. Birren (Eds.), *Behavior, aging and the nervous system.* Springfield, Ill.: Charles C. Thomas, 1965. Pp. 191–216.

Botwinick, J., & Shock, N. W. Age differences in performance decrement with continuous work. *J. Geront.*, 1952, **7**, 41–46.

Broadbent, D. E. Possibilities and difficulties in the concept of arousal. In D. N. Buckner & J. J. McGrath (Eds.), *Vigilance: a symposium.* New York: McGraw-Hill, 1963. Pp. 184–198.

Broadbent, D. E., & Gregory, M. Vigilance considered as a statistical decision. *Brit. J. Psychol.*, 1963, **54**, 309–323.

Canestrari, R. E., Jr. The effects of aging on vigilance performance. Paper presented at a meeting of the Geront. Soc., Miami, 1962.

Canestrari, R. E., Jr. The relationship of vigilance to paced and self-paced learning in young and elderly adults. *Dissertation Abstr.*, 1963, **24**, 2130–2131.

Canestrari, R. E., Jr. Age differences in spatial stimulus generalization. *J. genet. Psychol.*, 1965, **106**, 129–135.

Craik, F. I. M. The effects of age and the experimental situation on confidence behaviour. *Bull. Brit. psychol. Soc.*, 1962, **47**, 21. (Abstract).

Dardano, J. F. Relationships of intermittent noise, intersignal interval and skin conductance to vigilance behavior. *J. appl. Psychol.*, 1962, **46**, 106–114.

Davies, D. R., & Griew, S. A further note on the effect of aging on auditory vigilance performance: the effect of low signal frequency. *J. Geront.*, 1963, **18**, 370–371.

Davies, D. R., & Hockey, G. R. J. The effects of noise and doubling the signal frequency on individual differences in visual vigilance performance. *Brit. J. Psychol.*, 1966, **57**, 381–389.

Davies, D. R., & Krkovic, A. Alpha activity, skin conductance and vigilance. *Amer. J. Psychol.*, 1965, **78**, 304–306.

Davies, D. R., & Treacher, A. C. C. An experimental study of impulsivity and autonomic lability in older and younger subjects. Paper presented at the 7th int. Congr. Geront., Vienna, 1966.

Eason, R. G., Beardshall, A., & Jaffee, S. Performance and physiological indicants of activation in a vigilance situation. *Percept. mot. Skills*, 1965, **20**, 3–13.

Eisdorfer, C. The effects of increasing exposure interval on verbal (rote) learning in the aged: Studies II and III. *Excerpta Med. (Int. Congr. Ser.)*, 1963, **57**, 139–140.

Eisdorfer, C. Verbal learning and response time in the aged. *J. genet. Psychol.*, 1965, **107**, 15–22.

Eisdorfer, C., Axelrod, S., & Wilkie, F. L. Stimulus exposure time as a factor in serial learning in an aged sample. *J. abnorm soc. Psychol.*, 1963, **67**, 594–600.

Eisdorfer, C., Troyer, W. G., Jr., & Bogdonoff, M. D. The effect of the pace of the task upon autonomic responses to learning in the aged. Paper presented at the 7th int. Congr. Geront., Vienna, 1966.

Farley, F. H. Individual differences in free response speed. *Percept. mot. Skills*, 1966, **22**, 557–558.

Griew, S. Information transmission and age. In R. H. Williams, C. Tibbitts, & W. Donahue (Eds.), *Processes of aging*, Vol. 1, *Social and psychological perspectives*. New York: Atherton Press, 1963. Pp. 63–79.

Griew, S., & Davies, D. R. The effect of aging on auditory vigilance performance. *J. Geront.*, 1962, **17**, 88–90.

Griew, S., Davies, D. R., & Treacher, A. C. C. Heart rate during auditory vigilance performance. *Nature*, 1963, **200**, 1026.

Heron, A. A two-part personality inventory for use as a research criterion. *Brit. J. Psychol.*, 1956, **47**, 243–251.

Kirchner, W. K. Age differences in short-term retention of rapidly changing information. *J. exp. Psychol.*, 1958, **55**, 352–358.

Lacey, J. I., & Lacey, B. C. The relationship of resting autonomic activity to motor impulsivity. *Res. Publ. Assoc. Res. nerv. ment. Dis.*, 1958, **36**, 144–209.

Leonard, J. A. Five-choice serial reaction apparatus. *Med. Res. Council appl. Psychol. Res. Unit Rept.*, 1959, No. 326/59.

McGrath, J. J. Some problems of definition and criteria in the study of vigilance performance. In D. N. Buckner & J. J. McGrath (Eds.), *Vigilance: a symposium*. New York: McGraw-Hill, 1963. Pp. 227–246.

Malmo, R. B., & Shagass, C. Variability of heart rate in relation to age, sex and stress. *J. appl. Physiol.*, 1949, **2**, 181–184.

Opton, E. M., Jr. Electroencephalographic correlates of performance lapses on an attention task in old and young men. *Dissertation Abstr.*, 1964, **25**, 3115–3116.

Ross, S., Dardano, J. F., & Hackman, R. C. Conductance levels during vigilance task performance. *J. appl. Psychol.*, 1959, **43**, 65–69.

Rosvold, H. E., Mirsky, A. F., Sarason, I., Bransome, E. D., Jr., & Beck, L. H. A continuous performance test of brain damage. *J. consult. Psychol.*, 1956, **20**, 343–350.

Silverman, I. Age and the tendency to withhold response. *J. Geront.*, 1963, **17**, 372–375.

Surwillo, W. W. The relation of autonomic activity to age differences in vigilance. *J. Geront.*, 1966, **21**, 257–260.

Surwillo, W. W., & Quilter, R. E. Vigilance, age and response time. *Amer. J. Psychol.*, 1964, **77**, 614–620.

Surwillo, W. W., & Quilter, R. E. The relation of frequency of spontaneous skin potential responses to vigilance and age. *Psychophysiology*, 1965, **1**, 272–276.

Szafran, J. Decision processes and aging. In A. T. Welford & J. E. Birren (Eds.), *Behavior, aging and the nervous system*. Springfield, Ill.: Charles C Thomas, 1965. Pp. 21–34.

Talland, G. A. Visual signal detection as a function of age, input rate and signal frequency. *J. Psychol.*, 1966, **63**, 105–115.

Thompson, L. W., Opton, E. M., Jr., & Cohen, L. D. Effects of age, presentation speed and sensory modality on performance of a "vigilance" task. *J. Geront.*, 1963, **18**, 366–369.

Tune, G. S. Errors of commission as a function of age and temperament in a type of vigilance task. *Quart. J. exp. Psychol.*, 1966, **18**, 358–361.

Wallis, D., & Samuel, J. A. Some experimental studies of radar operating. *Ergonomics*, 1961, **4**, 155–168.

Welford, A. T. *Ageing and human skill*. London & New York: Oxford Univer. Press, 1958.

Welford, A. T. Psychomotor performance. In J. E. Birren (Ed.), *Handbook of aging*. Chicago, Ill.: Univer. of Chicago Press, 1959. Pp. 562–613.

Welford, A. T. Changes in the speed of performance with age and their industrial significance. *Ergonomics*, 1962, **5**, 139–145.

Wilkinson, R. T. Comparison of paced, unpaced, irregular and continuous display in watch-keeping. *Ergonomics*, 1961, **4**, 259–267.

York, C. M. Behavioral efficiency in a monitoring task as a function of signal rate and observer age. *Percept. mot. Skills*, 1962, **15**, 404.

Changes in Psycholinguistic Performances with Age*

KLAUS F. RIEGEL

Department of Psychology
University of Michigan
Ann Arbor, Michigan

I. Introduction

Off and on in its short history, experimental psychology has been criticized for its blind commitment to the conceptual systems and methods of the natural sciences; occasionally it has been argued that experimental psychology has been too strongly oriented toward the scientific scheme of *classical* physics and chemistry, without being seriously affected by the reorientation that led to the development of *modern* natural sciences. In this paper it will be demonstrated how the viewpoints of modern natural sciences can

*This report was prepared while the author was on a sabbatical leave at the Harvard Florence Research Project (Florence, Italy), director Dr. H. Boutourline Young. The research reported has been aided by the grants No. 55–139 and 61–237 from the Foundation's Fund for Research in Psychiatry. Hew Haven, Connecticut, and the grant HD 01368 from the United States Public Health Service.

be applied in the study of psychological processes and their changes during the life-span. The topic to be discussed, psycholinguistic performances, is especially suited for such treatment because psycholinguistic material is relatively easy to quantify and large samples of data are usually available. In order to describe some differences between the classical and modern approaches, it is necessary to discuss a simple model of verbal behavior proposed by Bousfield and Sedgewick (1944).

The model to be described represents some kind of mental container (black box) in which incoming elements are being stored for future releases. Since different elements may arrive simultaneously or after short successive delays, they may become associated and, instead of a mere conglomerate of isolated units, the notion of a primitive internal organization may be advanced.

Bousfield and Sedgewick's model is a statistical output model and, thus, differs from the stimulus-response models of classical experimental psychology. It has been devised to describe the function and—possibly—the underlying psychological mechanisms that determine the outflow of elements such as words, when, for instance, Ss are asked to produce all the words that come into their minds, or all words beginning with a certain letter, all names of animals, and so on. At variance with traditional experiments, inquiries are not necessarily made into the one-to-one relationship between items, such as the stimulus and response terms in studies of word associations or paired associates, but the general states of the performing system are studied as a function of time and the internal (such as the variability and strength of Ss' verbal habits) and external conditions (such as the size of word classes and the distributions of their elements). Assuming a constant rate of outflow, i.e., a fixed relationship between the items to be emitted per time unit and those still left in the repertoire, Bousfield and Sedgewick have succeeded in predicting the outflow with a high degree of accuracy.

The model described can be extended to cover the information input. All that need be done for this purpose is to consider E as a kind of secondary S who receives the output produced by the real S. Of course, such an analysis would also require an exploration of how much of the input S is able to retain over how long a period of time, and in order to do this one would have to rely again on the output S is able to produce. Thus, our example emphasizes the close interaction between input, output, and various storage phases. The performing system also interacts with other systems (and with itself through its own feedback) and changes continuously, but in all these considerations the fate of any single item (such as a particular word) is of little interest. Only the overall growth and its dependency on internal and external conditions are being analyzed.

Nowadays few experimental psychologists are interested in the study of the fate and "hookup" of individual elements. Most psychologists have compromised and apply lists of, for instance, 100 words in word-association studies or lists of eight or twelve paired associates. This compromise seems similar to the one that has led to the notion of difference limens as statistical rather than ideal concepts (Müller, 1878). Some psychologists, however, claim that psychological laws ought to be derived from the observation of single events provided that the E has created ideal experimental conditions, i.e., has isolated beforehand all the significant factors influencing these events. Lewin (1927), for instance, maintains that classical physics derives its laws in this manner, and recommends this approach for the study of behavior, abandoning notions that were to become essential for modern experimental designs in psychology, i.e., the notion of allowing variations in order to detect significant variables and their interactions rather than of deciding on some fixed values beforehand (Riegel, 1958a).

In contrast to Lewin's attempt, the notion of Ss as psychological systems whose changes over time and under the influence of internal and external statistical contingencies are to be analyzed has attracted continued interest. For instance, studies in which data are analyzed in terms of information measures generally imply these notions. More particularly, Brunswik (1949) has directed our attention toward the impact of external physical contingencies for the analysis of perceptual and cognitive processes, whereas Barker and Wright (1949) have introduced similar ideas into developmental psychology.

Though developmental psychologists like Barker or Wright will agree that an individual attains his particular intellectual and cognitive status only because of continuing stimulation, learning, and reactions, single events that lead to the acquisition (hookup) of particular items are of little interest for their analyses. All that is important are physical (for our purpose linguistic) contingencies to which an individual (for our purpose, a growing and aging individual) is being subjected and which produce changes in the states of the organism (psychological habits) due to the accumulation of experiences over time.

In the following section, we will describe the most primitive conditions of such a changing psycholinguistic system. The body of this chapter will consist of attempts to substantiate these interpretations with psychological data and of a general outline of how to look at developmental and aging processes.

II. Distributional Properties

Let us imagine that a complete record were available of all the words spoken to an individual during his entire life-span, and that, moreover, the occurrence of each item had a time marking. Such a record would allow us to analyze changes with time in the amount of linguistic input, i.e., in the total number of words given, and in the amount of linguistic information, i.e., in the number of different words given.

Unfortunately, only crude approximations of such records are available; thus we are left to guess what kind of changes are taking place. Possibly, the amount of spoken input given per day reaches its maximum during adolescence and early maturity, with a severe decline during the later years of life. In comparison to speech, written input may reach its peak at a later age and the subsequent reduction may be less marked. Indeed, the evidence available on this point, namely, a sample survey on the time spent in daily reading (Link & Hopf, 1946), indicates a high degree of stability between 15 and 70 years. Hence, let us assume that the amount of linguistic input is constant over days. The accumulated amount of input will thus increase linearly with age.

On the basis of our record it would also be feasible to determine changes in the number of different words (linguistic information) as a function of the total number of words occurring in the linguistic environment of our S (linguistic input). Generally, this relation, the type-token ratio, reflects the richness of the linguistic stimulation and thus should vary between social situations. However, it also changes with sample size. Assuming, again for simplicity, that there were no variations in the quality of the linguistic input either from situation to situation or from day to day, i.e., that the number of different words given per average day were constant (see Fig. 1A), the cumulative number of different words would approach an upper limit in the form of a negatively accelerated growth function (see Fig. 1B).

The relationship between the number of different words and the total number of words has been analyzed in various statistical studies of literature and writings (see Herdan, 1960). Generally, these studies have shown that by increasing the total number of words considered (as happens when we progress from the first to the last page of our ideal record) the relative number of different words decreases. For instance, if we take the first five words of the record, all of them are likely to be different from one another, and thus the type-token ratio will be 1.0. If we consider the first fifty words, the type-token ratio will be smaller than 1.0, since we will encounter numerous repetitions, especially of articles, prepositions, conjunctions, pronouns, auxiliaries, and other frequently used words.

The foregoing example illustrates the well-known fact that small samples are poor representations of a statistical universe. The distribution of words in a sample of five is likely to be rectangular. Only large samples approximate sufficiently well the standard distribution of English words, the standard curve of English described by Zipf (1949). For the present purpose we are especially interested in determining how increases in the total number of words given, i.e., increases concurrent with the growth of an individual,

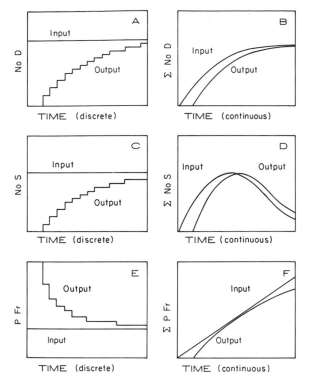

Fig. 1. Hypothetical age trends of the number and accumulated number of different (A, B), single (C, D), and primary (E, F) words given (input) or produced (output).

will affect increases in the number of different words and how fast the distributional properties of the target languages will be approximated.

A. Response Variability

The linguistic contingencies that impinge upon an individual provide absolute upper limits for this performance but do not inform us about his abilities to make efficient use of these opportunities, i.e., to perceive, store, retrieve, and reproduce selectively the linguistic stimulation given. In contrast to the analysis of linguistic input, empirical evidence on the growth of the active vocabulary during the life-span is available.

Several complete records of the words used by children up to the ages of 2 or 3 years have been reported in the literature. In most cases a positively accelerated increase has been observed up to the age of 2 years. Thereafter the vocabulary increases linearly at a very high rate. For the periods of later childhood and adolescence, estimates have been derived from speech or writing samples and with the aid of vocabulary or association tests. All estimates indicate a continuing rise in the number of different words used. Only during the late teens does the rate of growth decrease (see McCarthy, 1954).

Data on young and old adults have been obtained with the same methods (see Riegel, 1958b) and a continued, but diminishing, increase in vocabulary scores up to an age of 30–35 years has been observed. Thereafter the vocabulary remains highly stable or increases only slightly. Similar results have been reported by Smith (1955, 1957) in a longitudinal analysis of letters written by some elderly Ss during the last 40 years of their lives. The following study of word associations supplements these findings.

A 120-item free word-association test was administered to 500 Ss in northern Germany (Riegel & Riegel, 1964). Groups of 76 Ss each, equally divided by sex, represented the age levels of 55–59, 60–64, 65–69, 70–74, and over 75. When checked against census data on seven criteria, these samples were found to match closely the population in their home area. A group of 120 young Ss aged 16–20, equally divided by sex, was also tested. This sample was checked on four criteria against census data and in IQ against the corresponding standardization groups of the Wechsler Adult Intelligence Scale (1956). This group, too, could be regarded as representative of the corresponding population. Results will be reported separately for the young Ss (Y) and for the old Ss below (I) or above (II) the age of 65, respectively.

The test was given individually in an oral form. The list of stimuli consisted of 47 concrete nouns (CN), 31 abstract nouns (AN), 24 verbs (VE), and 18 adjectives or adverbs (AD). Stimuli also varied in the frequency of their occurrence in the German language. According to Kaeding (1898), 19 stimuli occurred more than 1000 times (hi), 72 occurred more than 10 but less than 1000 times (me), and 29 occurred less than 10 times (lo) among the eleven million words counted.

The responses to each stimulus were listed separately for the three age groups. Limiting our discussion for the present to the first cross-sectional comparisons (see columns with subscript A in Table I), the proportions of single responses (responses occurring only once to each stimulus in each age group) increased significantly with age ($p < .05$). The proportions of primary responses (responses most commonly given to each stimulus in each age group) decreased with age but not significantly. The type-token ratios (not shown in Table I) increased significantly with age ($p < .005$). Thus all these measures indicate quite consistently an increase in response variability with age and confirm the findings on the continued growth of the active vocabulary.

The average proportions ($\bar{p}$) of single and primary responses account for only 53% of all responses to concrete noun stimuli, whereas for the other stimulus classes single and primary responses account for 66%–69% of all responses, respectively. Thus concrete nouns elicit a great many nonsingle and nonprimary responses of intermediate strengths.

The variations in these percentages become more pronounced when the stimuli are classified by their frequency of occurrence. For this reason a more detailed inquiry was desirable. In it the stimuli were subdivided into eight frequency classes (instead of the three shown in Table I) and more sensitive measures of the response distributions, instead of the enumerations of single and primary responses, were applied. For the analysis of the distributions the measure of "relative uncertainty" was used. This measure attains its maximum value of 1.0 when all Ss give single responses, and its minimum value of 0.0 when only the primary response is elicited.

As shown in Fig. 2, the highest degree of response uniformity is found for stimuli of intermediate frequency, namely, for words that occur between 100 and 309 times (log 2.0 to log 2.5) according to Kaeding's count. Although it is not surprising to find greater idiosyncrasy below this level, for stimuli of higher frequencies the range of common experiences might have become too large to evoke any particular response common to different Ss. Old Ss, being always more idiosyncratic, seem to reveal this curvilinear trend more clearly than the young, and the second older group slightly more than the first.

As shown in the lower portion of Table I, there are further differences and, in particular, changes with age in the proportions of primary responses. Disregarding these changes for a moment, all findings indicate a continuing increase in response variability with age. Because of the congruence between these results and the inferences derived from our linguistic input model,

TABLE I

PERCENTAGES OF SINGLE AND PRIMARY ASSOCIATIONS
AS A FUNCTION OF AGE, STIMULUS CLASS, AND RESEARCH DESIGN[a]

Stimulus class	Single responses						Primary responses					
	Y_A	I_A	I_B	II_A	II_B	$\bar{p}$	Y_A	I_A	I_B	II_A	II_B	$\bar{p}$
Concrete nouns	26	32	32	35	34	32	21	19	22	20	21	21
Abstract nouns	54	54	51	53	52	51	15	14	18	14	15	15
Verbs	46	52	51	52	52	51	17	14	19	13	18	16
Adjectives	51	62	61	61	60	59	12	12	12	9	13	10
High frequency	30	39	41	40	41	38	18	15	17	14	15	16
Medium frequency	36	42	41	45	43	41	19	17	20	17	19	18
Low frequency	48	63	60	58	58	57	13	14	18	13	18	15
Average ($\bar{p}$)	38	44	44	46	45	43	17	16	19	15	18	17

[a]A = first testing; B = second testing. Young Ss, Y; old Ss below 65, I; old Ss over 65, II.

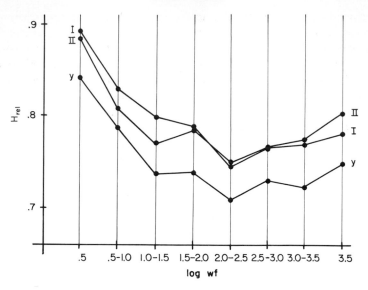

Fig. 2. Response uncertainty (H_{rel}) as a function of stimulus frequency (log wf).

it is tempting to extend this model in order to account for changes in linguistic output.

For such an extention we have to realize that the linguistic input given to each S is cumulative, whereas, his output will depend at any instant on the size of repertoire attained, but is a singular event for the S. Thus, continuing verbal stimulation will produce genuine longitudinal increases of his repertoire; his output, however, will represent cross sections taken at different points during the life-span and will not have a cumulative effect, except for the external records produced and perhaps through the feedback S provides to himself. For the present purpose, we are only concerned with the accumulation within the S.

Consequently, the associative responses analyzed in the present study have to be predicted from the three graphs at the left in Fig. 1, which represent the discrete conditions per average time unit, for instance, per day. For the analysis of the input, however, the left-hand graphs represent merely the assumed conditions (in lieu of available evidence) from which the continuous changes over time—shown in the three graphs at the right—have been deduced. It must also be mentioned that the amounts of input and output depicted in Fig. 1 are not comparable in an absolute sense. Only the relative changes are of importance. Presumably the absolute amount of input will by far exceed the output produced.

As previously stated, the number of different words occurring in the linguistic environment per average day is assumed to be constant (see Fig.

1A). Consequently, the number of single words (see Fig. 1C) and the frequency of the primary word (see Fig. 1E) will be constant as well.

The very first output in each S's life consists only of one word, repeatedly produced on the average day. Thus the number of different words equals 1; the number of single words equals 0; and the strength of the primary word is at its maximum. As more words are used, their frequencies begin to diverge; some may be used only once during a single day, others very often. As both the number of different words and the number of single words increase, the frequency of the primary word is bound to decline (see Fig. 1A, C, E). Ultimately, the number of different words produced may exceed those provided on an average day, but this is not a necessary conclusion and depends on S's ability to store and retrieve the input given to him.

In comparison to the discrete input and output conditions, the accumulated number of different words given as input increases with age in the form of a negatively accelerated growth function (see Fig. 1B), the precise shape of which has been described previously (Riegel, 1966). The accumulated number of single words changes in the form of a complex curve whose precise shape is not known. As the total amount of input increases with time, the number of single words will increase as well. But words will progressively reappear and thus cease to be single words. At a certain point in time, the number of single words will be at its peak. Thereafter their number will decline and approximate zero (see Fig. 1D). In contrast, the frequency of the primary word will increase linearly with age (see Fig. 1F).

As stated before, the curves of the accumulated output are of less interest for our purpose than those of the accumulated input. Thus it is noteworthy only that—language being a social phenomenon—the onset of all output curves ought to be delayed and that the initial growth in output will be steeper than that of the input.

Finally, we need to ask, more specifically, how an individual uses the linguistic information acquired. As previously suggested, contingencies in the linguistic environment will ultimately be matched by the distributions of elements in the psycholinguistic system of the language user. In regard to his linguistic output we have to ask whether his performance, too, depends on these internalized distributions or, as an alternate model, merely on the range of different elements available.

It should be emphasized at this point that the present studies do not allow for a decision between these alternatives but only for an evaluation of the major assumption made in the first model. One version of the first model (see Riegel, 1966) has been based on an analysis by Zipf (1949) in which he plotted the logarithms of the frequencies of words occurring in connected discourse against the logarithms of their ranks and observed a straight-line relationship. In the present context we will show that a modified form of Zipf's law holds for the distributions of associative responses of old and young Ss (see also Skinner, 1937; Howes, 1957) and thus seems to provide an adequate basis for the development of a psycholinguistic output model.

The second model, derived by Bousfield and Sedgewick (1944), relies on information on the number of different elements only, not on their relative frequencies. No supportive evidence for this model will be provided in the present paper. It ought to be mentioned, however, that Riegel and Birren (1966) were able to predict the performance of old and young Ss in a task of discrete syllable associations with greater success when only the range of available responses was considered than when their relative frequencies were also taken into account. In a similar task of continuous associations, however, and in particular for responses given late in the trials, prediction was more successful when the relative frequencies of the responses were also considered. Thus, depending on the type of task, both models seem to be useful. When there is time stress, as in the task of discrete associations and for the first responses of the continuous associations, the Bousfield-Sedgewick model seems most appropriate. The continuing responses, however, are better predicted by a model based on Zipf's law.

B.   Rank-Frequency Distribution

The response distributions were summed over stimuli and the total number of single responses given to the 120 stimuli, the total number of responses that occurred twice, three times, and so on were enumerated separately for the three frequency classes of the stimuli and the three age groups. Repetitions of responses when given to different stimuli were disregarded. A rank of 1 was assigned to the single responses, a rank of 2 to the responses occurring twice, and so on, and the ranks were plotted on log-log paper against the number of different single, double, triple, etc., responses. The regression lines of the logarithms of the frequencies on the logarithms of the ranks and the goodness of fit of the linear regression lines were determined. In Table II, the major results are given separately for the three age groups and the three frequency classes of the stimuli.

The reported analysis differs from that of Zipf (1949), who assigned a rank of 1 to the word most frequently occurring, a rank of 2 to the word next highest in frequency, etc. The modification of the method was necessary because the highest frequencies of words in our sample are far below those observed by Zipf. Those high-frequency words represent, primarily, interstitial words (i.e., articles, pronouns, prepositions, conjunctions, auxiliaries, etc.), whose chief function is to connect other words in continuous discourse. Such words are completely absent from the lists of word associations.

As shown in Table II, the slopes for the three age groups are almost

TABLE II

REGRESSION CONSTANTS (a), REGRESSION WEIGHTS (b), AND COEFFICIENTS
OF DETERMINATION (r^2) FOR THE RANK-FREQUENCY DISTRIBUTIONS
OF THREE AGE GROUPS AND THREE CLASSES OF STIMULUS FREQUENCIES[a]

	Age group			Frequency		
	Y	I	II	High	Medium	Low
a	3.46	3.42	3.40	3.24	3.73	3.23
b	− 2.10	− 2.17	− 2.22	− 2.05	− 2.16	− 2.25
r^2	.96	.94	.94	.92	94	.94

[a] First cross-sectional data; young Ss. Y; Ss under 65, I; Ss over 65, II.

perfectly matched by the slopes for the three frequency classes of the stimuli. Thus young Ss seem to react as a person of average adult age reacts to high-frequency stimuli; old Ss react as a person of average adult age reacts to medium- or low-frequency stimuli.

The differences between the age levels had to be expected because, as shown in Table I, young Ss produce lower proportions of single, and higher proportions of primary, responses than elderly Ss. Furthermore, single and primary responses account for only 55% of all responses produced by young Ss, but for 60% and 61%, respectively, of those produced by the old. (The differences between the young and either one of the old groups were significant; $p < .01$.) Thus the percentage of medium-strength responses is larger for young than old Ss. The summed percentages of single and primary responses vary even more markedly between the frequency classes of the stimuli than between the age groups, being lowest (54%) for high-frequency stimuli and highest (72%) for low-frequency stimuli. (The difference between the two classes was significant; $p < .01$.)

Comparing the differences in the slopes of the regression lines with our predictions presented in Fig. 1, the following changes in the input-output relation are conceivable and have to be explained by differences in the associations between elements. Young Ss tie a smaller number of different responses to a set of stimuli than old Ss, but the strength of these ties is higher; for old Ss the input-output matrix is more equalized and the strengths of the ties are lower.

The number or strength, or both, of interconnections between elements may also explain the differences in the slopes between the response distributions of the three frequency classes of stimuli. High-frequency stimuli produce (much like young Ss) a response distribution with a modest slope. Since the number of different words is restricted in the early parts of the output (see Fig. 1A) and since high-frequency words are likely to occur early in samples (which is also the reason why they have occurred to young Ss), they can form connections with fewer other responses than low-frequency words. Being fewer in number, however, the connections for high-frequency words will be stronger than those for low-frequency words or those that an old person has to handle.

C.   Response Stability

Our previous discussion has been based on at least two gross assumptions. First, we regarded the person as a perfectly efficient language-handling system: *All* the information provided was perceived, stored, and if necessary, retrieved and selectively produced by him. Second, we regarded the linguistic input (and subsequently the output) as completely homogeneous, with no variation in quality or type, as conceivable under varying social conditions. Undoubtedly, modifications and extensions of the model will become necessary, and its rigidity will have to be reduced in the subsequent sections. One of these extensions has already been mentioned in the preceding paragraphs and concerns variations with age in the number or strength, or both, of interconnections of the items stored.

For the present purpose it is important to determine what effects the increase in the number of different responses will have on the stability of the responses between successive tests. If stability were primarily due to high-ranking responses, we should expect a decrease in stability with age; if it were based on low-ranking responses, we should expect an increase in stability with age. Thus, we have to analyze the dependency of the stability on the commonality of the associations as well as on the age of Ss. The proposed analysis is complicated by the unequal distances between adjacent age groups and because single responses had to be excluded for technical reasons. The analysis is primarily based on retest data of the elderly Ss.

Five years after the initial testing all available old Ss were asked to cooperate in a second test. Two hundred two Ss participated again; 62 had died during the intervening period; 32 were too sick at the time of the second test; 84 refused to be retested. Ss retested differed significantly on a number of variables from the total original sample as well as from Ss *not* retested. Generally, they were found to be more intelligent, less rigid, and less dogmatic, and to have a more positive attitude toward life and a wider range of interests. As described in earlier reports (Riegel, Riegel & Meyer, 1967a, b) samples from successive age groups thus are bound to become increasingly biased. For the present context it is uncertain, however, and will not be analyzed, whether this bias influences the results on response stability.

Table III lists the percentages of identical responses between adjacent

TABLE III

PERCENTAGES OF IDENTICAL RESPONSES AS A FUNCTION OF AGE, STIMULUS CLASSES, AND RESEARCH DESIGN[a]

Stimulus class	Cross-sectional data			Longitudinal data	
	$Y_A - I_A$	$I_A - II_A$	$I_B - II_A$	$I_A - I_B$	$II_A - II_B$
Concrete nouns	56 51	58 51	58 48	51 58	48 59
Abstract nouns	30 29	33 35	37 26	27 33	28 35
Verbs	31 28	34 33	36 28	30 36	29 35
Adjectives	24 23	26 19	27 19	22 24	21 31
High frequency	51 42	49 44	48 41	42 47	42 45
Medium frequency	43 40	45 43	47 38	40 47	38 48
Low frequency	23 25	28 24	28 22	28 25	25 32
Averages	39 39	44 40	44 36	38 45	36 44

[a] A = first testing; B = second testing. Two figures are given for each comparison: the first refers to the frequency of the identical responses observed for the first (younger) groups of the comparisons, the second to the second (older) groups of the comparisons.

age levels for both cross-sectional and longitudinal comparisons. Responses given only once within each age group (single responses) have been left out of consideration. The percentages of nonidentical responses can be derived by subtracting from 100 the percentages of single and of identical responses, given in Tables I and III, respectively. For example, young Ss gave on the average 38% single responses, and 39% of their responses (excepting singles) are identical with those of the first elderly group. Thus, the average percentage of nonidentical responses is 23.

Two percentages are given for all comparisons because the identical responses may have been used at different frequencies in the two groups, i.e., may differ in their associative strengths. The number of different identical responses for two groups of comparison remains, of course, the same.

Starting at the bottom of Table III, and with the cross-sectional comparisons, the following conclusions can be drawn. The percentages of identical responses decline only slightly with increasing age distances between two groups. Thus there is less average agreement between the young adults and the first elderly group (39% and 39%) than between the first and second elderly groups (44% and 40%). (The difference between 39% and 44% is significant; $p < .01$.) In the former case, the age distance is about 42 years and in the latter, 13 years. Because one age group remains the same in both comparisons it seems less reasonable to attribute the observed difference in percentages to the chronological ages of Ss (see Riegel, 1965a).

In the transition from the young adults to the first elderly group both percentages are of the same magnitude (39%). At the higher age levels, however, there is a decrease from the first to the second percentage, both when the first and second elderly groups are compared (44% and 40%; age distance 13 years) and when the retest results of the first group are compared with the original results of the second elderly group (44% and 36%; age distance 8 years). Accordingly, identical responses are used at relatively lower frequencies by the second than by the first groups of the comparisons and, thus, by the older than by the younger groups of the comparisons. This result parallels the decrease in primary association strength with age and, generally, the increasing slope of the rank-frequency distributions (see Table II).

The percentages of identical responses obtained for the longitudinal data are comparable to the cross-sectional results in magnitude. However, the percentages of the longitudinal analysis are always higher for the second than the first groups of the comparisons. This result indicates a relatively greater use of the identical responses at the second time of testing, but is not surprising, since at the time of the first testing our groups were "diluted" by Ss who did not participate in the retesting. Thus, their first percentages of identical responses ought to be equal, or (because of random fluctuations) slightly below the percentages of the cross-sectional comparisons. The second percentages, however, being obtained only from Ss who participated in both tests, ought to be higher than the diluted percentages.

The percentages of identical responses are a positive function of stimulus familiarity. High-frequency stimuli produce markedly larger percentages of identical responses than uncommon words. The form classes of the stimuli have a yet more marked effect. Concrete noun stimuli produce by far the highest agreements; the percentages are of intermediate range for abstract nouns and verb stimuli and are lowest for adjectives. It should be noted, however, that both the form and frequency classes interact. Concrete nouns have generally higher frequencies of occurrence than adjectives.

III. Performance Speed

Thus far we have been concerned with distributional characteristics of psycholinguistic data. In our interpretation, we considered the elements of psycholinguistic performance, the words, as entering and being emitted by the language-handling system in an all or none fashion. Only their presence or absence has been regarded as of significance and has been recorded in the form of distributional charts whose differences between age groups have been analyzed. We are now ready to explore this system further by considering differences in efficiency with which input is received and output is produced. Possibly, such differences depend again on distributional properties in that, for instance, elements that have been received frequently might be faster incorported and more readily produced than new items.

There can be little doubt that one reads faster than one is able to write. According to the few data available (Riegel, 1965b, 1966), persons between 15 and 40 years of age read slightly more than ten times as fast as those between 11 and 35 years of age are able to write. On the average these groups read about 250 words per minute and write about 23 words per minute. During the subsequent periods of life there is a more marked decline in writing than in reading speed. This finding is congruent with other results on the differential decline of sensory and psychomotor functions, and implies that an imbalance may develop in the input-output relation.

Even without considering this interaction, however, the decline in reading speed, taken alone, has some important implications for our interpretations. Based on the limited evidence available on the time spent in daily readings, we had assumed that the amount of linguistic input remains about constant during the adult life-span. If reading speed declines, this assumption cannot be maintained, and the amount of linguistic information acquired will be more drastically reduced than predicted from the model. It thus seems important to look into this matter more carefully.

A. Reading Time

Forty words were sampled from the 120 stimuli of the word-association tests described earlier and were tachistoscopically presented to 24 young Ss; 22 of these 40 words were presented to 16 old Ss. The age of the groups, equally divided by sex, ranged from 15.5 to 17.3 and from 61.8 to 78.6 years, respectively. The thresholds obtained were used to derive multiple regression equations based on objective characteristics of the words. Of about forty different parameters tested, the following four proved to be significant predictors in the regression equations for the young and old Ss.

$$\text{Young:} \quad Y = 13.29C + 8.04P - 4.98W + 0.87L - 2.08$$
$$\text{Old:} \quad O = 170.53C + 267.06P - 95.95W + 45.46L - 70.09$$

where C = concrete nouns versus other words (concrete nouns received a score of 2, the others of 3); P = prefix versus no prefix (words with a prefix received a score of 3, the others of 2); W = logarithms of word frequencies as determined from Kaeding's count (1898) (a constant of 3.00 was added to all scores; when no frequency was reported logarithms of $2.00 = -1.00 + 3.00$ were assigned to the words); L = number of letters per word.

The results indicated very large age differences in thresholds favoring young Ss (Riegel, Riegel & Wendt, 1962). The predictors of the thresholds as well as the order in which they entered into the multiple regression equations were precisely the same for the two age groups. However, the relative weights of the predictors varied markedly between the age groups. If we divide each regression weight by the sum of all four weights and express the ratios as percentages, we obtain the following results.

Whether the stimulus was a concrete noun or not contributed 49% to the predicted threshold for young Ss but only 29% for the old. Previously we have argued (Riegel & Riegel, 1961) that concrete nouns are easier to recognize because S's perception is facilitated by his familiarity with not only the denoting word but also the denoted object. This interpretation was based on the increased significance of the parameter of word frequency when counts of children's rather than of adults' language are applied. The language of children and, in particular, of very young ones is dominated by descriptions of concrete situations. Thus, if one obtains—as we did—higher correlations between thresholds of adults and word frequencies of children than between thresholds of adults and word frequencies of adults, this result indicates the significance of the denoted object for the recognition of the denoting word as much as it indicates the significance of word frequency itself. According to our present results the significance of the denoted objects for the recognition of the denoting words is reduced if we move upward on the age scale beyond the level of our young Ss.

In comparison to the first parameter, words beginning with a prefix affected the recognition speed of old Ss more seriously than that of young Ss. This parameter contributed 46% and 29% to the predicted thresholds, respectively. The age differences of word frequency in the prediction of recognition thresholds were only slight. Old Ss were somewhat less affected (16%) than young (18%), while the length of the word—being generally of minor importance—was more critical for old (8%) than young Ss (3%). This result supplements the finding that an added prefix makes the recognition harder, especially for old Ss.

Recognition time of the stimuli contributed only about 1/20 to the reaction time of the word-association test. Nevertheless, when by the equations given earlier the thresholds for all 120 words of that test were predicted, recognition and reaction time were found to correlate highly. The correlation increased slightly between the three successive age groups from 0.57 to 0.60 and 0.62. Furthermore, recognition times correlated about equally with various indices of the response variability (proportions of single responses, proportions of primary responses, and relative uncertainty of the response distributions), indicating more complex interactions that call for further explorations.

B. Reaction Time

Reaction times were obtained for all 120 stimuli and for the whole sample of 500 young and old Ss rather than for the limited numbers of stimuli and Ss used in the recognition experiment. Since recognition time correlated highly with reaction time, we are able to generalize some of the previous findings, or at least to generate promising hypotheses. For such generalization it ought to be emphasized that recognition time refers to that portion of the internal transmission process during which the information is encoded (taken in, perceived). Reaction (more precisely, 19/20 of it) refers to the selection of items linked to the stimulus and includes also the production of the motor response. The correlation between both time measures suggests that the recognition of the stimulus may already imply the arousal and to some extent, perhaps, the identification of items related to the item to be recognized. Consequently, factors determining recognition time, such as the four parameters discussed in the preceding subsection, may also determine the arousal of associative connections and their readout. With this expectation in mind the data on the reaction times will be analyzed.

Estimates of Ss' reaction times were obtained in units of half-seconds by using stopwatches. After a stimulus had been pronounced, the stopwatch was activated. The onset of S's response represents the end point of the reaction time interval. Measures were obtained from all Ss at the time of the first and second testing, and thus cross-sectional as well as longitudinal comparisons can be made. In the analysis of the results, average reaction times are plotted either for all responses, single responses, or primary responses against either stimulus classes or—in the next section—against the size of the response classes.

As shown in Fig. 3, average reaction time was lowest for the first elderly group at the time of the first testing. The reaction time was but slightly higher for the young adults, but increased steadily and markedly after the age of 60. When the average total reaction times were considered, the cross-sectional comparisons were almost perfectly matched by the longitudinal data.

Cross-sectional and longitudinal results diverged rather markedly and systematically when the reaction times for single and primary responses were considered separately. Both cross-sectional comparisons (at either the first or second testing) revealed increases closely parallel to one another, the increase for single responses being steeper than for the primaries. However, the longitudinal comparisons of the two elderly groups indicated much larger increases in reaction times for single responses than would be expected from the cross-sectional data. Longitudinal comparisons of the primary responses, on the other hand, pointed to a marked drop

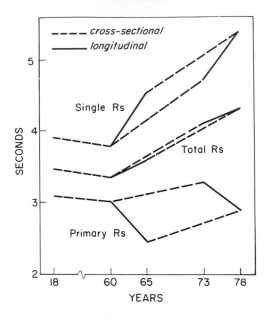

Fig. 3. Associative reaction time for all, single, and primary responses as a function of age and research design.

rather than to an increase in reaction times with age. Thus, the longitudinal comparisons indicated increasing differentiations of the reaction time: the older a person is, the more sensitive are his reactions; if he gives a common response, he will react very swiftly; if he gives an unique response, his reaction will be unusually slow.

The increase in the variability of the reaction times with age may have to be attributed to the selective dropout of Ss during the intertest interval (Riegel, Riegel & Meyer, 1967a, b). Possibly because of their higher intelligence and better adjustments, the Ss retested reacted more discriminatively than the original group when giving either primary or single responses in a word-association experiment.

Grouping the stimuli by their frequencies, we observed only small differences in reaction time. As shown in Fig. 4, reaction times to medium-frequency stimuli were slightly longer than to high-frequency stimuli. At the second testing, this relation was reversed. Reaction times to rare stimuli were always highest. The increases in reaction times from the first to the second testing equaled those expected for Ss that have advanced 5 years in age. These increases were not confounded with stimulus frequency. Thus, the greater differentiation of the reaction times observed among the retested Ss when giving either primary or single responses (see Fig. 3) was not a function of the frequency of the stimuli.

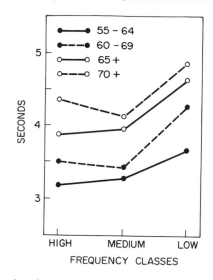

Fig. 4. Associative reaction time to high-, medium-, and low-frequency stimuli for different age groups. (Solid lines represent data from the first test; the dashed lines represent retest data.)

Categorizing the stimuli in terms of their form classes, as shown in Fig. 5, led to different results. Reaction times to concrete noun stimuli, being lowest on the average, were stable or decreased slightly when analysed in longitudinal comparisons. Thus they are comparable to those observed for the

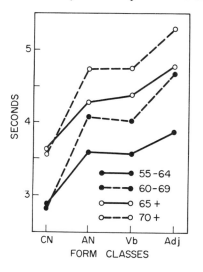

Fig. 5. Associative reaction time to concrete nouns (CN), abstract nouns (AN), verbs (Vb), and adjectives (Adj) for different age groups. (Solid lines represent data from the first test; dashed lines, retest data.)

primary responses, shown in Fig. 3. Reaction times to adjective stimuli, and to a lesser extent to abstract nouns and verbs, showed a greater increase from the first to the second testing than would be expected for Ss who had aged 5 years. Thus, they are comparable to those observed for the single responses, shown in Fig. 3, This correlation between the reaction times to concrete noun stimuli and for primary associations, on the one hand, and to adjective stimuli and for single associations, on the other hand, received some direct support from the frequency tabulations of Table I Concrete noun stimuli elicited stronger primary responses and a lower percentage of single responses than adjective stimuli.

The last finding also explains the high correlation between recognition and reaction times. In both cases the time of processing information was considerably reduced when stimuli were concrete nouns, i.e., denoted perceivable objects. Variations in stimulus frequencies influenced Ss' speed less markedly than previously emphasized (Howes & Solomon, 1951). In particular, reaction times seemed to be curvilinearly related to the frequency of the stimuli, being shortest at the medium- but longer at the high-frequency level (see Fig. 4). This curvilinear relationship has been most clearly observed in our analysis of stimulus frequency and response dispersion (see Fig. 2) rather than of stimulus frequency and reaction times and will require a more detailed discussion in the following section.

C.   Distributional Properties and Reaction Times

In Fig. 6 responses have been grouped by their strength, irrespective of the stimuli by which they were elicited. The groupings are in terms of logarithmic

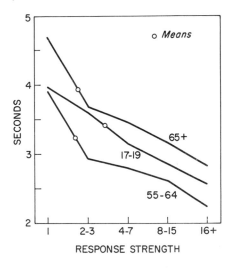

Fig. 6. Associative reaction time as a function of response strength and age.

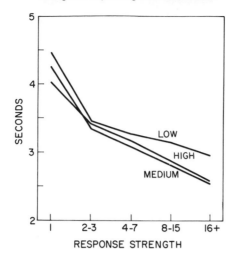

Fig. 7. Associative reaction time as a function of response strength and stimulus frequency.

units allowing about equal numbers of responses to fall into each category. Thus, all single responses have been placed in the first category, responses with frequencies of two or three in the second, responses with frequencies between four and seven in the third, and so on. The average reaction times of the three age groups have been plotted against these categories.

Generally, the data shown in Fig. 6 confirm the Thumb-Marbe law (1901) on the negative relationship between reaction time and associative strength. As observed in a previous study (Riegel & Birren, 1965), the Thumb-Marbe law holds for elderly Ss as much as for the young adults commonly tested. In the present study there is, however, a notable deviation from the straight-line relationship. The reaction times of both elderly groups increase disproportionally in case of the single response category.

In particular, the decrease in reaction times between the young adults and the first elderly group has to be attributed entirely to the nonsingular responses. The marked increase after the age of 65, on the other hand, affects responses of all frequencies about equally, i.e., a fixed constant of about 0.7 sec is added to the reaction times of the first elderly group, irrespective of the strength of the responses.

Disregarding differences in the age of Ss, the changes in reaction times as a function of the frequency classes of the stimuli are shown in Fig. 7. Even though the differences are not very large, they allow for valid conclusions since they are based on more than 40,000 measurements. The relationship between reaction time and the strength of responses given to common stimuli was closely linear. The curvilinearity of the relation is strongest for low-frequency stimuli, for which, moreover, the differences in reaction times between all nonsingular responses are relatively small, i.e., the slope of this portion of the curve is flat.

As for the rank-frequency distributions, there seems to be some similarity between the curves for the three frequency classes and for the three age groups. Young adults react similarly to the way in which a person of average adult age would react to high-frequency stimuli. The curve for the first elderly group resembles that for the medium-frequency stimuli, and the curve for the second elderly group resembles that for the rare stimuli. According to some of our previous results, associations to low-frequency stimuli have lower strength than those to common words. Similarly, responses given by elderly Ss show lower strength than those of young adults. Thus, the foregoing proposition extends the previous findings on the similarity of the effects of stimulus frequency and age of Ss to the analysis of the reaction times. This extension is congruent with the Thumb-Marbe law on the negative relationship between reaction time and strength of responses.

As shown in Fig. 8, the relationship between reaction time and response strength has been separately analyzed for the four form classes of the stimuli. Here, reactions to abstract nouns and verbs show the closest approximations to a straight line, whereas those to adjectives reveal a curvilinear relation similar to that of the low-frequency stimuli. The trend of the reaction times to concrete noun stimuli, being the lowest of all, resembles that of the common stimuli. Again the similarity between adjectives and low-frequency stimuli, on the one hand, and concrete nouns and high-frequency stimuli, on the other, is not superficial, but is implied in the response distributions shown in Table 1.

IV. Linguistic Structures

According to the preceding results, high-frequency stimuli elicit a medium-large range of responses at fast speed, whereas medium-frequency stimuli elicit a small range at fast speed and thus are connected with fewer responses; low-frequency stimuli elicit many different responses at low speed. The effect of stimulus frequency parallels that of age. Young Ss react (both in terms of their response variability and speed) in a manner similar to that in which a person of average adult age would react to high-frequency stimuli; old Ss react in a manner similar to that in which an average adult would react to low-frequency stimuli.

The observed relationships were equally, and sometimes even more, pronounced when the stimuli were categorized by their form classes rather than by their frequencies. In particular, the confounded category of concrete nouns—confounded in terms of grammatical, semantic (concrete nouns denote objects), and frequency classes (concrete nouns have high frequencies

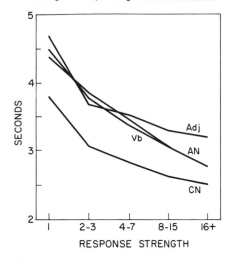

Fig. 8. Associative reaction time to concrete nouns (CN), abstract nouns (AN), verbs (Vb), and adjectives (Adj) as a function of response strength and form class of the stimuli.

of occurrence)—produced by far the smallest number of different responses and the fastest reactions. This holds for word associations as well as for the recognition of words.

The results just presented indicate differences in interword connections. The number and strength of these connections vary with the familiarity and, even more, with the grammatical and semantic classes of the stimuli. Since they also vary with age of *S*s, our results paved the way for a more comprehensive analysis of changes in psycholinguistic structures.

In the following subsection three types of classifications will be applied to both the stimuli and the responses in order to analyze these structures. In the preceding sections such classifications have been applied either to the stimuli or the responses alone, but seldom to both of them simultaneously. Again, we will use classifications by frequency classes (here, the response class will be restricted to the class of most commonly used words, namely, the primary responses), form classes, and as an extension, semantic stimulus response relations.

A. Commonality Structure

In order to gain insight into the cross-sectional and longitudinal changes, it would be conceivable to evaluate the content of the 40,000 responses from the first and 20,000 responses from the second test. Such an analysis, however, would require extensive classifications of the responses by a number of judges, and thus would not only be exceedingly time consuming but would introduce ambiguity. For this reason we restricted our analysis to the primary responses, which will be studied in terms of their strength and agreement among the age groups. Turning first to agreement in primary responses among the three cross-sectional groups of the first testing, the following results were obtained.

Agreement in primary associations, i.e., the percentage of identical primary responses, is greater according as the age distance between the comparison groups is smaller. Forty-two percent of the primary responses are the same and 12% are different for all three age groups. The remaining 46% represent agreements between any two of the three groups, among which 69% are taken up by the agreements between the two elderly groups, 19% between the young adults and the first elderly group, and 12% between the young adults and the second elderly group.

As shown in Table IV, these results clearly depend on the frequency classes of the stimuli. The triple agreements in primary associations increase markedly and the lack of agreements decreases with increasing stimulus frequency. Double agreements attain their highest values at the medium level of stimulus frequencies. This result has to be attributed to the two elderly groups, in particular, whose reaction to the medium-frequency stimuli (39%, compared with 16% to high-frequency, and 26% to low-frequency stimuli) show this cirvilinear relation more clearly than young *S*s. In turn, this result is dependent on the nonlinear interaction between stimulus frequency and strength of associations shown in Table I and Fig. 2.

As reported previously, and congruent with the foregoing results, high-frequency stimuli do not elicit primary responses with highest associative strength. Primary association strength attains its highest value at the medium level of stimulus frequency and is markedly reduced at the low-frequency level. This nonlinear interaction holds for all age groups and may be explained by the effectiveness of strong competing responses, in the case of high-frequency stimuli, that prevent any one of them from attaining

TABLE IV

PERCENTAGES OF TRIPLE, DOUBLE, OR NO AGREEMENTS IN
PRIMARY RESPONSES AMONG THREE AGE GROUPS AS A
FUNCTION OF STIMULUS FREQUENCY[a]

Stimulus frequency	Triple	Double	No agreement
High	63	37	0
Medium	40	51	9
Low	32	42	26
Averages	42	46	12

[a] First cross-sectional data.

an exceptionally high level of strength. Not as many strongly competing responses may be available for medium-frequency, and very few for low-frequency, stimuli.

As a further step in our analysis we determined the extent to which the strength of primary associations determines the agreement in primary associations among age groups. For this purpose we turn to the longitudinal data of Table V. As shown by the last four percentages in the last line, the average strength of those primary responses, which are the same at both testing sessions, is about twice as high as the strength of nonidentical primaries. Again, medium-frequency stimuli yield the strongest primaries in the case of both identical and nonidentical responses. In extension of our previous finding (Table I), however, identical primaries given to low-frequency stimuli are as strong as or even stronger than those given to high-frequency stimuli. Thus, identical primaries occur to low-frequency stimuli only when their strength is exceptionally high. Finally, the age differences in the percentages of identical primaries (shown in the first two columns of Table V) are negligible. The second elderly group however, produces disproportionally more identical primaries to high-frequency stimuli and disproportionally fewer to low-frequency stimuli, thus indicating a greater sensitivity to stimulus frequency.

Returning to Table I, the strength of primary associations is highest for concrete noun stimuli and lowest for adjectives and declines rather

TABLE V

PERCENTAGES OF IDENTICAL PRIMARY ASSOCIATIONS AND STRENGTH OF IDENTICAL AND NONIDENTICAL PRIMARY ASSOCIATIONS AS A FUNCTION OF AGE AND STIMULUS CLASSES[a]

| | Percentages | | Primary associative strength | | | |
| | | | Identical Rs. | | Nonidentical Rs. | |
Stimulus class	I	II	I	II	I	II
Concrete nouns	68	76	22	22	14	11
Abstract nouns	52	57	18	17	10	9
Verbs	52	48	16	17	9	8
Adjectives	61	44	14	11	9	8
High frequency	68	79	16	14	11	9
Medium frequency	60	62	21	21	11	10
Low frequency	62	55	16	17	9	7
Averages	62	63	19	19	11	9

[a]Data are longitudinal.

steadily with age. The percentages of identical primaries observed in the longitudinal analysis of the two elderly groups (first two columns of Table V) show similar results, except that these percentages are disproportionally high for the second elderly group when the stimuli are concrete nouns, and disproportionally low when the stimuli are adjectives. This age effect parallels the one between high-frequency and low-frequency stimuli, since many of our concrete nouns are common and many of the adjectives are rare words of the language.

In Table VI the primary responses are classified into the same four form classes that have been used for the stimuli. Here a rather steady decline with age in the percentages of concrete and abstract noun responses can be noted. The percentages of adjective and, in particular, of verb responses, increase with age. A detailed analysis, taking into account the form classes of the stimuli as well as of the responses, will be discussed in the next subsection.

B. Grammatical Structure

On different occasions we have classified our stimuli. Of these, the preceding classification into frequency classes is clearly consistent with the proposed model, which is based on such notions as word variability, frequency distributions, and strength of associations. In classifying the responses in terms of their frequencies of occurrence as well, we were able to analyze parts of the transmission process intervening between stimulus input and response output.

In the present section we will apply our grammatical classification to both the stimuli and responses and thus we will learn something about Ss' specific conceptual sequences and their possible origins. For instance, if our Ss frequently selected their responses from form classes other than those of the stimuli, we could infer that their associations are formed on the basis of general experiences with linguistic discourse (syntagmatic associations), because here, too, form classes are likely to alternate from word to

TABLE VI

PERCENTAGES OF PRIMARY RESPONSES FALLING INTO DIFFERENT
FORM CLASSES AS A FUNCTION OF AGE[a]

Response class	Y	I	II
Concrete nouns	43	38	38
Abstract nouns	25	18	18
Verbs	16	26	25
Adjectives	16	18	19

[a]Cross-sectional data.

word. If, on the other hand, most of the responses were of the same form classes as the stimuli, Ss would be likely to enumerate coordinates or substitutes of the stimuli (paradigmatic associations). These associations may have originated with Ss, experiences in the general physical environment, where different objects co-occur, rather than in the linguistic environment, where such co-occurrences seem to be less common.

The application of such classifications implies further deviation from our original model, namely, the notion that associative processes occur at different conceptual levels. At the lowest level, the original elements, the words, are connected. At the higher levels and at a time when Ss have developed some rudimentary notions of classes, elements occur as members of these classes and classes are connected. Thus, if a S hears stimuli like "the table," "boys," or "liberty," he will at the same time receive them as nouns, if for no other reasons than that they were preceded by an article or had particular suffixes. Consequently, if Ss' associative processes follow paradigmatic patterns, they will produce other nouns as responses; if their associative processes follow syntagmatic patterns, they will produce form classes other than that of the stimuli.

Such an interpretation, to be sure, raises numerous problems, of which only a few explorations have been made in the past. This interpretation will help to explain grammatical performance, which is known to be acquired early in life at a very rapid pace and is highly stable during the life-span. Viewed in this manner, grammatical performance implies that S has acquired some notions about grammatical class membership and about the sequential arrangements of these classes in proper speech. His performance proceeds on at least two levels. At the more abstract level, the order of word classes is determined, and at the lower level, selections of specific words are made from among the members of the appropriate classes.

The rapid pace of learning and the high stability of grammatical performance during the life-span are not the only arguments supporting the notion of such multilevel associative processes. Language itself is highly organized and any sequence of input is syntactically (and semantically) structured. Thus S's performance would be poor indeed if he were to adopt the strategies of some experimental psychologists and attend to isolated words (or nonsense syllables) and their hookup only. If S does not simultaneously view the message as a sequence of items representing particular word classes, his acquisition of grammatical rules for proper speech would require extra efforts and additional time. Moreover, the structure of the linguistic input provides that there will be no surplus abilities involved in Ss' grammatical performances. In most cases Ss merely reproduce what the natural language has provided to them, even though they have leeway in selecting various (and even original) combinations of elements from the grammatical classes.

As shown in Fig. 9, Ss quite frequently use the form class of the stimuli for their responses, and thus prefer paradigmatic over syntagmatic responses. This holds most strongly for the concrete nouns and least for the abstract nouns. There are also some age differences. Old Ss show a greater degree of alternation and thus rely relatively more on syntactic habits than the young. In particular, old Ss shift toward a greater use of verbs in the case of concrete-noun stimuli; toward concrete nouns in case of adjective stimuli; and toward either adjectives or abstract nouns in case of verb stimuli. Because verb responses to concrete nouns most likely indicate the usage or functions of the stimulus object, the differences between the age groups also indicate a greater preference for meaningful semantic responses on part of old Ss. On the other hand, concrete nouns given to adjective stimuli seem to denote the objects that have the qualities indicated by the stimulus. The same might be true when adverbial responses qualify verb stimuli.

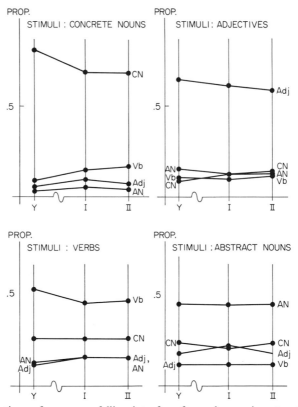

Fig. 9. Proportions of responses falling into four form classes given to stimuli grouped into the same four form classes as a function of age: Concrete nouns: CN; abstract nouns, AN; verbs, Vb; adjectives, Adj.

Finally, we applied a measure of information transmission to estimate the overall correlations between the stimulus and the response classes. This measure varies between 0 and 1 and indicated a higher agreement in form classes, i.e., a lower degree of alternation, and a greater preference for paradigmatic responses on the part of the young than the old Ss. The scores were .45 for the young and .32 for each of the elderly groups. Thus, our earlier results on the greater randomness of the response repertoires of elderly Ss were confirmed. Previously, we were only able to study the response distribution independently of the stimulus distribution. With our last analysis we have shed some light on the process intervening between the stimulus perception and response production.

C.   Semantic Structure

The discussion in the last subsection has moved us still further away from the statistical notions proposed at the beginning of our paper. Instead of regarding the linguistic environment as a statistical universe from which random samples of input are drawn, we have come to emphasize the organization of this universe in terms of grammatical classes and class sequences. This modification also implies that the information-transmitting individual is going to learn the structural properties of the linguistic universe. Figuratively speaking, he will not simply drop words or word pairs into his black box like marbles into an urn, but will assign them to particular sections of his psycholinguistic system and will learn how to relate these sections to one another.

The grammatical classes discussed represent some of the largest and most general categories of language. They safeguard the proper order of words for communication purposes but do not reduce the ambiguity of messages sufficiently. In the present subsection we shall discuss a larger set of narrower classes, the semantic classes, which, even though less well defined and analyzed, reduce further the indeterminacy of messages.

Relying on an example used by Chomsky (1957), grammatical classes taken alone would allow us to form grammatically correct but meaningless sentences, such as *Colorless green ideas sleep furiously.*

The additional constraint imposed by semantic classes will further reduce the ambiguities, but, as emphasized by Miller (1964), some ambiguity will remain or can be removed only in reference to the wider context of the linguistic material or the social situation in which it occurs. Thus, different persons may derive different interpretations, as in this example provided by Lenneberg (1965): *They are shooting psychologists.*

In contrast to syntax, semantic structure does not necessarily emphasize the sequential order of items, but may be regarded as a coordinated structure providing "semantic fields" for the individual words. (For this reason, most semantic classes are subsets of the class of paradigmatic associations mentioned before.) Because the semantic fields are interconnected, sentences like the following become interpretable: *The banks are overflowing with customers.*

Here, the semantic fields of "banks" and "overflowing" may share responses such as "river," "water," or "sand," and this may at first suggest an interpretation of "banks" in terms of "river banks." However, the succeeding word (customers) will share responses like "money," "credit," or "counter" with "banks," and thus will change the interpretation to that of "monetary institution." "Overflowing" and "customers" will share only a few responses, such as "mass" or "plenty," but will be interpreted on the basis of connections between the other stimuli that will blend the interpretation of "overflowing" in a noncustomary manner.

At present little is known about semantic classes and their interactions. For this reason we are confined to a procedure that has been applied by the present author (1965c) in an analysis of denotative aspects of word meaning. In these studies various restricted or controlled associations were obtained, and the response distributions and overlaps between different types of restrictions were analyzed. For the present purpose, some of these word lists will be used for classifying the stimulus-response relations of the free word associations obtained from our samples of young and old Ss.

1.   Language Production

In order to reduce the ambiguity of the semantic classification, nine judges gave, under five different instructions, two restricted associations to each of our 120 stimuli. They were asked to find synonyms (SY), antonyms (AN), superordinates (SU), coordinates (CO), and parts (PA). The five tasks as well as the 120 stimuli were randomized each time.

According to the results, the restricted associations to many stimuli are not independent but the same responses may be given under different instructions. Using the percentages of overlap between the response distributions, we determined the main dimensions of our classification system. As discussed elsewhere (Riegel & Riegel, 1963), three independent dimensions have been obtained, represented by the tasks (1) superordinates-coordinates, (2) parts, and (3) antonyms. The synonyms have relatively high loading on both the first and the third dimensions.

Figure 10 indicates the proportional use of the five response classes by the three groups of Ss in their free associations. Generally, many more responses are synonyms, coordinates, or denote parts, than are superordinates or antonyms. The age differences in the proportions on both the last two types of responses remind us of our earlier findings. Superordinates follow a trend similar to the single responses and antonyms a trend similar

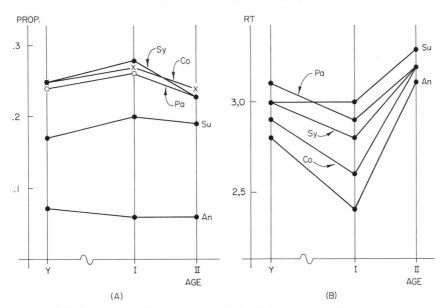

Fig. 10. (A) Proportions of five groups of classifiable responses for three age groups. (B) Associative reaction time (RT) in second for five groups of classifiable responses and three age groups. Because of the overlap between the groups, responses may be repeatedly listed and thus the sum of the proportions may exceed 1.0. Superordinates, Su; coordinates, Co; synonyms, Sy; antonyms, An; parts, Pa.

to the primary responses. The same is true for the reaction times. Ss are slowest in associating superordinates to the stimuli and fastest in associating antonyms. The reaction times for the other three types of associations are of intermediate magnitude.

In applying our frequency classification of the stimuli, it was found that the first elderly group made particular efforts to give classifiable responses to rare stimuli, i.e., when they found a challenge and an opportunity to exhibit their knowledge and experience. They seemed to regard the task as an achievement test rather than a free-association test in its proper sense. To a lesser extent this was also true for the medium-frequency stimuli, but here the first elderly group did not differ as markedly from the other two groups of Ss as they did in the case of the low-frequency stimuli.

To extend these findings it remains to be shown on what particular types of stimuli the first elderly group exceeded both the younger and the older Ss in their classifiable responses. For this purpose we enumerated separately the proportions of synonyms, coordinates, superordinates, parts, and antonyms given as responses in the free-association task. Figure 11 indicates no age differences for the antonym responses but a strong dependency of the proportions on stimulus frequency. Both coordinates and parts are used slightly more often by the first elderly group, provided that the stimulus is

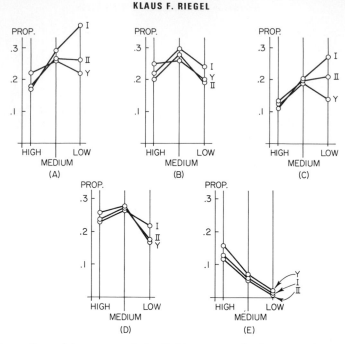

Fig. 11. Proportions of five groups of classifiable responses by frequency classes of stimuli and age: (A) synonyms; (B) coordinates; (C) superordinates; (D) parts; (E) antonyms.

a low-frequency word. This difference is much more pronounced for synonyms and superordinates to low-frequency stimuli, both of which thus become the preferred modes of responding for the first elderly group. To a lesser extent this result holds for the second elderly group too, but not at all for young *S*s.

These last findings raise the question why the very old *S*s shift from classifiable to less meaningful responses. Our observations during the testing sessions suggest that the very old *S*s tried equally hard to give such responses but lacked the ability to respond in reasonable time. Generally, it was exceedingly difficult to administer the free associations to old persons; the test did not seem to make enough sense to them, and consequently they tried to impose their own thought structure on the test and testing situation. This led to an increase in classifiable meaningful responses among *S*s of the first elderly group. The very old, however, did not always succeed and gave up. This is indicated by a sharp increase in reaction time and in the proportion of *subjective* responses, to be discussed next.

A count of all subjective evaluations, personal statements, expressions of feelings, attitudes, and stereotypes was made. In most cases such a classification was unambiguous and difficulties arose only when the stimulus itself had evaluative attributes, as in the case of the adjective *avaricious*. The percentage of agreement in the classifications made independently by two judges was 89.

Subjective responses increased markedly with advancing age. Comparing the frequency classes of the stimuli, a differential increase was observed. *S*s of the first elderly group emitted very few subjective responses to low-frequency stimuli, but—as noted earlier—many classifiable responses (particularly superordinates and synonyms). For *S*s of the second elderly group, the proportion of subjective responses to rare stimuli increased and almost reached the levels for medium- and high-frequency words. Consequently, the proportion of classifiable responses (particularly of superordinates and synonyms) dropped and, most likely, classifiable responses were substituted for by subjective evaluations.

According to the results just presented, there are further age differences in the types of responses and presumably in the types of cognitive systems intervening and connecting stimuli and responses. As a person ages, he increases not only his proportion of syntagmatic associations (i.e., those that could have originated from experience with linguistic context and are, so to say, telegraphic versions of sentences), but also—at least up to the age of about 65—his proportion of paradigmatic associations.

Since the classes of syntagmatic and paradigmatic associations are mutually exclusive, these findings seem contradictory at first. However, not all paradigmatic responses (determined on the basis of form-class agreements between stimuli and responses) could be further classified with the aid of our criterion lists of restricted associations. Some had to be left as unclassifiable. Thus, the foregoing results supplement one another: Young *S*s emit a relatively large proportion of syntagmatic responses, but the proportion of their paradigmatic responses is still larger; some responses are unclassifiable. At the age level of the first elderly group, almost all responses are accounted for; the proportion of syntagmatic responses has dropped and that of paradigmatic associations has increased. For the second elderly group, both proportions have dropped and many of the remaining associations have become subjective and evaluative in content.

2. Language Comprehension

In the previous sections we have emphasized language production exclusively. We shall now deal with its perception and comprehension. Since language is a social phenomenon, its comprehension is bound to precede its production, but this topic, being more elusive than language production, has hardly come under investigation. The following exploration, therefore, will demonstrate only some of the most obvious problems and, once more, will lead us into a general discussion of semantics and to further possible modifications of our model.

In the present study the techniques of restricted word associations were applied in a reversed manner, i.e., sets of responses were selected from previously obtained restricted association norms (Riegel, 1965c) and presented to Ss with the appropriate explanations of the type of restrictions used. Under varying conditions, Ss were requested to identify the original stimuli (target words) that had produced the responses that were now administered as stimuli (clue words). For example, according to the norms, the response *animal* is the primary superordinate to *zebra*. In the present experiment, *animal* was presented to Ss with the instruction to guess what the original stimulus had been. Four types of restrictions were used, either singly or in pairs, under the following instructions.

I am looking for something that:

is an	*animal*	(superordinates);
is like a	*horse*	(similars);
has	*stripes*	(parts);
can be found in	*Africa*	(locations).

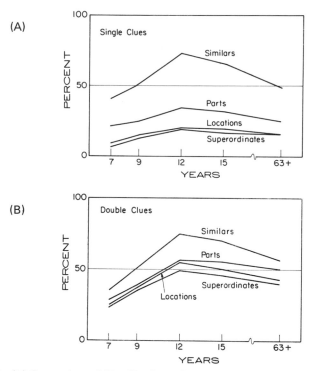

Fig. 12. (A) Proportions of identifications of target words by five age groups when single clues are given. (B) Proportions of identifications of target words by five age groups when double clues are given.

A total number of 64 single and 96 double clues were given, including all combinations of the four types of restrictions equally often, namely, 16 times. The items were presented in different random orders.

Old Ss were twelve men and women, each over the age of 63, coming from a middle-class background and living in an apartment building administered through a local older citizens' club in Ann Arbor, Michigan. Young Ss were recruited from elementary and high schools in the same neighborhood area. Each group included twelve boys and twelve girls, with mean ages of 6.8, 8.8, 11.8, and 14.8 years, respectively.

As shown in Fig. 12, double clues produced on the average more identifications of the target words (46%) than single clues (28%). Similars were by far the most efficient single clue (56%) and also contributed much when used in combination with any of the other three clues (58%). Indeed, supplementing similars with these other clues added on the average very little to the identification of the target words (2%). Locations and superordinates were very poor single clues (15% and 14%, respectively), but the percentages for both types were only sightly below the general average when each was used in combination with any of the other three clues (42% and 39%, respectively). Parts, both when used as single or double clues, matched the general averages almost perfectly (28% and 47%, respectively).

Generally, these results imply that definitions by types, as for example in "a *zebra* is like a horse," are more efficient for the identification of (and possibly the explanation of new) concepts than classical generic definitions, as for example in: "a *zebra* is an amimal with stripes," even though in the latter case two informative clues, i.e., superordinate plus part (or attribute) rather than one, i.e., similar, are given. Indeed, hardly any other condition excels single similars (56%), whereas the classical superordinate–part combination provides on the average for only 34% of the identifications.

Under all conditions performance increased rather markedly after the age of 6.8 years but had already reached its peak at 11.8 years. Thereafter, at first a slight, and later on an accelerated, decline was observed. The decline in performance between the 11.8-year-old and the aged Ss amounted on the average to 10% for the single and 12% for the double clues, being most marked for similars, namely, 26% for similars as singles and 18% for similars as one of the double clues. The smallest amount of decline occurred with superordinates when given singly (3%) and with parts when used in combination with any of the other three clues (6%), perhaps indicating the lesser usefulness of superordinates (the maximum is but 19%) and the greater usefulness of parts for all age levels (the maximum is 56%).

A more comprehensive interpretation of age changes in the identification of words or concepts can be obtained by comparing logical with infralogical clues. The former imply conceptual abstractions, as for instance clues of superordinates and similars; the latter ask for abstractions of certain properties of the objects or events denoted by the words, as for instance clues of location and parts. Grouping the clues in this manner provides five classes: double logical clues (superordinates plus similars), double infralogical clues (locations plus parts), mixed clues (superordinates plus locations, superordinates plus parts, similars plus locations, similars plus parts), single logical clues (superordinates, similars), single infralogical clues (locations, parts).

The average decline in performance being about 11%, both single and double logical clues show larger age deficits (14% and 17%, respectively), while both single and double infralogical clues produce less marked declines (6% and 4%, respectively). For the mixed clues the decline equals about that of the general average, namely 12%. These results are congruent with some of the findings on language production discussed in the preceding section, as well as with those by Riegel and Birren (1967). They imply a specific lack of capacity on the part of old Ss to deal with the more abstract (logical) relations and a preference for concrete (infralogical) forms of conceptualization.

Apart from these specific results the findings just presented lead us once more to a discussion of some general problems of semantic theories, which in turn may suggest further modifications of the proposed model on changes in psycholinguistic performance with age. Sufficient data on word-identification tasks like the one discussed could enable us to quantify the meaning of words. For such a quantification we would have to describe a set of semantic relations (possibly somewhat larger than the one applied in the foregoing) that would allow an average person to identify the target item with a specified degree of success, let us say 90 times out of 100. Such a set of semantic relations could be said to exhaust the meaning of a word by locating it with a sufficient degree of precision within a framework of associative connections.

The meaning of a word thus conceived consists of a set of interrelated connections, and the interpretation of the language-handling system based on such a notion would be at variance with the previous one, in which words were considered as elements entering the systems in almost the same manner as, for instance, particles of an ideal gas enter a container. If, as we assumed, input is constant over time, the main determinants of the state of the substance in the container are the relative frequencies of the elements and their distributions as prevailing in the physical surrounding. Using such a simple statistical model, most of the observations reported could be uniformly interpreted.

On various occasions, however, an alternative model was envisaged that would require additional assumptions, on the one hand, but would simplify the interpretations on the other. In particular, such a modification became suggestive when the co-occurrence of items in the linguistic and general physical environments was stressed in order to explain the development of associative bonds. In its simplest form such a modification merely requires that we consider elements in pairs rather than in isolation. Taking into account all possible combinations of elements (words), many of which are bound to have exceedingly low or zero probabilities, we did not extend our interpretation markedly.

Some conclusions to be drawn from our study on language comprehension suggest farther-reaching modifications, however; namely, that the relations between items, the associations, rather than the items to be related, need to be emphasized. Accordingly, elements such as words are depicted as the intersecting points of the many interrelations (represented, for instance, by lines or vectors) that make up a complex network, whereas in our former interpretation the system was viewed as a display of points from which the interconnecting lines could be derived.

Of course, points and connecting lines are mutually dependent in such a system, but the emphasis on one or the other may alternate: lines can be defined by points, or points can be defined by lines. Traditionally, the emphasis on points, the particle theory, has dominated the study of language, if for no other reason than that words (or smaller units such as phonemes) remain the most solid building blocks and the units most readily analyzed. However, if we consider the following two sentences: *Colorless green ideas sleep furiously* and *Colorful green leaves move gently*, we realize that the words taken separately do not allow for an interpretation of the sentences, even though in both cases syntactic constraint has been imposed. Interpretation depends on the appropriateness of some other relations between the words. Although it is difficult to specify what kinds of relations are involved, the additional constraint that they impose make possible the interpretation of the second sentence.

The problems connected with the two alternative conceptualizations are not new but have led in the past to the development of different schools of thought in psychology and linguistics as well as in the natural sciences. In early psychology these two views have been represented by "elementarists" like Wundt, on the one hand, who studied the basic psychological particles of sensation, perception, and emotions, and by the act-psychologists like Brentano, on the other hand; Brentano used an unsuccessful method in his attempt to study the processes of sensing, perceiving, and feeling. In linguistics the alternative interpretations have been elaborated by Pike (1959), and in the natural sciences they are represented by the attempts to analyze events in terms of mass and matter, or in terms of energy and movements. Modern physicists maintain that these two aspects are not mutually exclusive but rather mutually elusive. Thus, if you try to measure one, the analysis of the other aspect will be distorted. The same difficulties seem to arise in the study of psycholinguistic events.

Throughout our discussion we have stressed the particle theory of psycho-linguistic functions. A relational interpretation, however—even though more burdening for our thoughts and imaginations—provides some definite advantages. Thus it is not surprising that most of the recent advances in linguistics have added more to our understanding of linguistic relations than of linguistic elements. While this holds for Chomsky (1965) and his associates, the linguistic theory proposed by Lamb (1966) deserves at least equal attention because it represents psycholinguistic processes in a manner similar to those used in computer programming as well as in neurophysiology. Undoubtedly, if we search for neurophysiological counterparts of psycholinguistic processes, it will be inappropriate to locate or project particular elements into the neurophysiological structure, but it may be quite reasonable to search for representations of networks of interconnections.

V. Summary

In our analysis of changes in psycholinguistic performances with age, Ss were viewed as information-handling systems whose performances are dependent on the cumulative amount of linguistic stimulation given. Little attention was directed toward traditional forms of experimentation, in which the fate of single elements (though averaged over a few trials) has been analyzed. Assuming that the total amount of stimulation increases linearly with age, predictions were made on how much of the information provided may have been received by Ss at various age levels and how much they may have been able to use for their output.

This simplified statistical model of a psycholinguistic black box was successively refined. First, the notion of psycholinguistic elements was supplemented by an emphasis on associative connections that enabled us to analyze age difference in simple probability structures. Second, the notion of stimulus and response classes, such as the grammatical classes, was emphasized. Third, class relations, particularly semantic relations, were analyzed.

Generally, the data supported the statistical model and its modifications. Response variability increased with the accumulated amount of linguistic input. Consequently, old Ss connected a greater number of different responses with any given stimulus. In particular, their behavior resembled that of the average person when reacting to low-frequency stimuli. Here, the response variability was large. Response stability decreased with age as well as with decreasing stimulus frequencies. It was highest for common nouns denoting objects.

On the basis of the Thumb-Marbe law on the inverse relationship between response strength and reaction time, our model was extended to predict changes in reaction times with age. Generally, the higher reaction times of elderly *S*s had to be attributed to their markedly delayed reactions when singular responses were given. Their speed was less affected for higher-ranking common responses. This result was confirmed in the retest analysis. Retested *S*s increased their speed from session to session in the case of common responses, but their speed of reaction was further reduced when singular responses were given. Thus, the variability in reaction times was higher in the second than in the first testing.

At all age levels associative reaction time was highly correlated with the recognition times for the stimuli. Thus, perceptual and associative processes seem closely interconnected and responses may already be activated when the stimuli are being identified. The speeds of recognition and reaction were lowest when the stimuli denoted common concrete objects. The frequency of the words themselves was of secondary importance only. This effect was less significant for old *S*s, whose recognition speed is more strongly influenced by the length of the words than that of young *S*s.

The structures intervening between stimuli and responses were responsible for most of the modifications suggested for the model; these structures were analyzed in terms of commonality and of grammatical and semantic properties. At all age levels, medium-frequency stimuli produced the lowest, high-frequency stimuli higher, and low-frequency stimuli by far the highest response variability. This effect was slightly more pronounced for old than young *S*s.

Old *S*s were more inclined to produce associative responses of a form class other than the stimuli (syntagmatic associations); young *S*s produced relatively more responses that can function as substitutes for the stimuli (paradigmatic associations). This result confirmed the greater uncertainty of the intervening (in this case, grammatical) structures of old *S*s.

*S*s between 55 and 65 years of age showed a strong tendency to produce meaningful responses, especially when the stimuli were rare words. At the higher age level this tendency was partially substituted by the production of emotional and evaluative statements. In their language comprehension, old *S*s make less efficient use of logical than of concrete infralogical relations.

Generally, these last explorations led us to question the usefulness of linguistic elements (such as words) as building blocks of a psycholinguistic theory. Instead, a psycholinguistic analysis should equally emphasize the significance of relations, which will enable us to explore problems of meaning and the more complex forms of psycholinguistic performances. Similarities between such a reorientation and recent advances in linguistics, neurophysiology, computer theories, and modern physics were mentioned.

REFERENCES

Barker, R. G., & Wright, H. F. Psychological ecology and the problem of psychosocial development. *Child Develpm.*, 1949, **20**, 131–143.

Bousfield, W. A., & Sedgewick, C. H. W. An analysis of sequences of restricted associative responses. *J. genet. Psychol.*, 1944, **30**, 149–165.

Brunswik, E. *Systematic and representative design of psychological experiments.* Berkeley: Univer. of California Press, 1949.

Chomsky, N. *Syntactic structures.* The Hague: Mouton, 1957.

Chomsky, N. *Aspects of the theory of syntax.* Cambridge, Mass.: MIT Press, 1965.

Howes, D. On the relation between the probability of a word as an association and in general linguistic usage. *J. abnorm. soc. Psychol.*, 1957, **54**, 75–85.

Howes, D., & Solomon, R. L. Visual duration thresholds as a function of word-probability. *J. exp. Psychol.*, 1951, **41**, 401–410.

Herdan, G. *Type-token mathematics.* The Hague: Mouton, 1960.

Kaeding, F. W. *Häufigkeitswörterbuch der Deutschen Sprache.* Berlin: Selbstverlag, 1898.

Lamb, S. M. Prolegomena to a theory of phonology. *Language*, 1966, **42**, 536–573.

Lenneberg, E. H. Summary and final comments. In K. F. Riegel (Ed.), *The development of language functions. Rept. No. 8*, USPHS Grant HD 01368, Ann Arbor, Mich.: mimeorg. rept. available from Center Human Growth and Developm., Univer. of Michigan 1965. Pp. 175–182.

Lewin, K. Gesetz und Experiment in der Psychologie. *Symposion*, 1927, **1**, 375–421.

Link, H. C., & Hopf, H. A. *People and books.* New York: Book Manuf. Inst., 1946.

McCarthy, Dorothea. Language development in children. In L. Carmichael (Ed.), *Manual of child psychology.* (2nd ed.) New York: Wiley, 1954. Pp. 492–630.

Miller, G. A. The psycholinguist. *Encounter*, 1964, **23**, 29–37.

Müller, G. E. *Zur Grundlegung der Psychophysik.* Berlin: Griefen, 1878.

Pike, K. L. Language as particle, wave, and field. *Texas Quart.*, 1959, **2**, 37–54.

Riegel, K. F. Die Bedeutung der Statistik für das psychologische Experiment. *Psychol. Beitr.*, 1958, **3**, 595–618. (a)

Riegel, K. F. Ergebnisse und Probleme der psychologischen Alternsforschung: Teil II. *Vita humana*, 1958, **1**, 204–243. (b)

Riegel, K. F. Age and cultural differences as determinants of word associations: Suggestions for their analysis. *Psychol. Rept.*, 1965, **16**, 75–78. (a)

Riegel, K. F. Speed of verbal performance as a function of age and set: A review of issues and data. In A. T. Welford & J. E. Birren (Eds.), *Behavior, aging and the nervous system.* Springfield, Ill.; Charles C Thomas, 1965. Pp. 150–190.(b)

Riegel, K. F. The Michigan restricted association norms. *Rept. No. 3*, USPHS Grant MH 07619. Ann Arbor, Mich.: available from Dept. Psychol., Univer. of Michigan mimeogr. rept. 1965. (c)

Riegel, K. F. Development of language: Suggestions for a verbal fallout model. *Human Develpm.*, 1966, **9**, 97–120.

Riegel, K. F., & Birren, J. E. Age differences in associative behavior. *J. Geront.*, 1965, **20**, 125–130.

Riegel, K. F., & Birren, J. E. Age differences in verbal associations. *J. genet. Psychol.*, 1966, **106**, 153–170.

Riegel, K. F., & Birren, J. E. Age differences in choice reaction times to verbal stimuli. *Gerontologica*, 1967, **13**, 1–13.

Riegel, K. F., & Riegel, Ruth M. Prediction of word-recognition thresholds on the basis of stimulus-parameters. *Lang. Speech*, 1961, **4**, 157–170.

Riegel, K. F., & Riegel, Ruth M. An investigation into denotative aspects of word meaning. *Lang. Speech*, 1963, **6**, 5–21.

Riegel, K. F., & Riegel, Ruth, M. Changes in associative behavior during later years of life: A cross-sectional analysis. *Vita humana.* 1964. **7**, 1–32.

Riegel, K. F., Riegel, Ruth M., & Meyer, G. A study of the drop-out rates in longitudinal research on aging and the prediction of death. *J. Pers. soc. Psychol.*, 1967, **4**, 1342–348. (a)

Riegel, K. F., Riegel, Ruth M., & Meyer, G. Socio-psychological factors of aging: A cohort-sequential analysis. *Human Develpm.*, 1967, **10**, 27–56. (b)

Riegel, K. F., Riegel, Ruth M., & Wendt, D. Perception and set: A review of the literature and a study on the effects of instructions and verbal habits on word recognition thresholds of young and old subjects. *Acta Psychol.*, 1962, **12**, 224–251.

Skinner, B. F. The distribution of associated words. *Psychol. Rec.*, 1937, **1**, 71–76.

Smith, Madorah E. Linguistic constancy in individuals when long periods of time are covered and different types of material are samples. *J. gen. Psychol.*, 1955, **53**, 109–143.

Smith, Madorah E. The application of some measures of language behavior and tension to the letters written by a woman at each decade of her life from 49 to 89 years of age. *J. gen. Psychol.*, 1957, **57**, 289–295.

Thumb, A., & Marbe, K. *Experimentelle Untersuchungen über die psychologischen Grundlagen der sprachlichen Analogiebildung.* Leipzig: Engelmann, 1901.

Wechsler, D. *Die Messung der Intelligenz Erwachsener.* Bern: Huber, 1956.

Zipf, G. K. *Human behavior and the principle of least effort.* Reading, Mass.: Addison-Wesley, 1949.

Cognitive and Personality Variables
in College Graduates of Advanced Age*

K. WARNER SCHAIE   and   CHARLES R. STROTHER
West Virginia University   *University of Washington*
Morgantown, West Virginia   *Seattle, Washington*

I. Introduction

The increase in sophistication of research methods available to students of the aging process has led to a mounting conviction that it is imperative to move from the description of phenomena to their experimental manipulation. Nevertheless, many of the false starts and indeed the scarcity of experimental studies may be attributed to the fact that descriptive work has not gone far enough and has failed to explore some of the most relevant issues that should be covered before fruitful experimentation becomes

---

*Parts of this chapter were presented at the 7th International Congress of Gerontology pre-congress colloquium on psychological functioning in the normal and senile aged and appear in the colloquium proceedings under the title "Limits of optimal functioning in superior old adults."

possible. For example, descriptive studies covering substantial portions of the adult life-span can still be cited as noteworthy exceptions whether they be of a cross-sectional or longitudinal nature, and few such studies extend far enough to generate useful data on the most advanced years. It may be fortunate, of course, that the efforts devoted to substantial studies have been relatively limited, since past major efforts can and have been attacked from the standpoint of method (Jones, 1959; Schaie, 1959, 1965).

While one-shot studies (including longitudinal studies limited to a single cohort*) cannot contribute conclusively to our understanding of lawful changes related to age, they can and do provide useful descriptive data on the state of functioning organisms at a given point in time. To serve this purpose, the investigator must consider the equivalence of sample characteristics for the different age groups included in his study. Particular concern is occasioned by the knowledge that older samples are frequently not representative of their population cohorts because they were obtained from institutional settings or other specialized sources. Moreover, it is argued that the description of older individuals on psychological measures suffers because such Ss have lower motivation, and are less familiar with and unfavorably disposed toward psychological tests. Disabilities of older Ss with respect to speeded measures also are presumed to make evidence on age differences difficult or impossible to interpret.

Problems of adequate assessment of the aged individual transcend the concern of the researcher interested in developmental changes with advancing age. Similar problems make it difficult for the practicing clinician to assess the degree of pathology in the older individual, since normative data on a representative population may yield no more than measures of typical pathology. It is generally not the objective to identify the one-eyed man who is king among the blind. Hence, a more meaningful point of reference might be sought by inquiring into the limits of optimal functioning for a population of specified age. Given such information, experimental intervention might then be addressed to the question whether specific populations can by suitable treatment approach the known limits. Knowledge of optimal limits, moreover, might permit more meaningful comparisons of the capability of populations of different ages and antecedent conditions where the comparison of certain so-called representative populations may be implicitly impossible because of the conditions under which these populations must be defined and measured.

If we are interested in defining optimal limits, it then becomes necessary to obtain information on a sample that is unusual in that it must be res-

---

*The term cohort refers to that group of persons who enter the environment at the same point in time. The point in time may be broadly defined as the extent of the interval used in the particular study.

tricted to the upper limits of the population. This approach in itself is not novel. Indeed, Sward (1945) many years ago used a population of older executives in order to demonstrate decline in intellectual functioning even under favorable conditions. The Sward study, however, is deficient in the sense that there was no adequate information that would permit the secure inference that his sample consisted of Ss who were superior for their age on the most crucial variables likely to be related to intellectual decrement.

It might well be argued that it is much more difficult to identify individuals who are well functioning than those who are burdened with specific dysfunctions. Nevertheless, criteria can be developed that will permit ready identification of a superior group of normal adults who would be suitable for a study of the upper limits of optimal behavior in our older population. It should be stressed that it would be foolish to assume that such individuals would be representative in any sense, since we must be interested in a highly specialized population. Hence, it is incumbent upon us to describe in detail, and clearly to understand, the social environment and physical status of individuals whom we consider to be a criterion group for the upper limits of the population.

It has been our good fortune to have had available an unusual group of Ss who met the foregoing strictures and on whom comprehensive data are available. The study here reported has an interesting natural history. It originated when the senior author served as executive secretary to a multidisciplinary faculty group at the University of Washington that was interested in problems of aging. This study group was approached by a group of retired professors who felt it desirable to demonstrate by intensive studies that their members retained a high level of functioning. Consequently a comprehensive survey of psychological, social, and physical functioning was designed that would permit demonstration of optimal behavior by a group of old people who perceived themselves as still most capable but whose performance was being questioned by society.

It is the purpose of this chapter to report upon data on cognitive and personality variables in a rather special population. To justify our attention to this population it must be demonstrated that it can indeed be used to qualify as a suitable vehicle for describing optimal limits of functioning under optimal assessment conditions. Hence, a much more detailed description of relevant physical and background data than would otherwise be required in a paper dealing with psychological variables will be necessary. We are therefore not directly concerned with methodological questions of measurement or theoretical questions on the nature and meaning of psychological decrement with age. Instead we will attempt to show that we have obtained a sample of individuals who should be as intact as can be found at their age, who are measured under optimal conditions, but who nevertheless show significant changes in cognitive performance from the performance seen in individuals in the prime of life.

II. Method

A. Subjects

All of our Ss were volunteers obtained from the membership of a retired university faculty group or from among retired academic or professional workers who had responded to appeals in newspapers published in the city in which the research was conducted. The public appeal indicated our interest in studying outstanding old persons over the age of 70 who, because of their physical and mental fitness, would be able to demonstrate that productive and meaningful living was possible in advanced age. The minimum requirements for initial acceptance for the study were that the prospective S be 70 years or older, have a minimum education of a bachelor's degree, have at some time during his life been employed at the professional level, not reside in an institution for the aged or infirm, and be in good enough physical shape to visit the project office without any help or assistance by a third party.

Before final acceptance for the project, each S was further interviewed intensively about his motives and expectations in regard to the proposed study. It was explained that about eight hours, spread over several days, would be required for the physical examinations, psychological tests, and interviews. At this point, every S was given an opportunity to withdraw from the study if he wished and was rejected in those instances where the screening interviewer concluded that participation would present any physical or psychological problems. All Ss were informed that feedback would generally be limited to reports on group performance and that they ought not to participate if they expected their participation to result in health or counseling services. These stringent restrictions in the selection of Ss suggest that the participating Ss were as highly motivated a group as can be obtained for the type of population being studied.

The final group of Ss consisted of 25 men and 25 women ranging in age from 70 to 88 years with a mean age of 76.5 years. Age means and standard deviations were approximately equal for male and female subgroups. Clinical and laboratory examinations (some details of which will be reported later) indicated that all members of the group were in fair to superior physical condition for their age.

B.   Procedure

Four two-hour blocks of examinations were conducted. These consisted of a physical examination block, a social history block, and two psychological testing blocks. The four blocks were randomized and procedures within each block were also randomized to avoid systematic fatigue or other order effects. The clinical medical examination was conducted by a licensed physician, and all laboratory tests and audiometry were conducted by qualified technicians. A trained social worker collected structured interview data, and the psychological testing was conducted by master's level clinical psychology graduate students.

The medical examination was begun by administering the Cornell Medical Index (CMI) (Brodman, 1953). A physical examination included assessment of the cardiovascular, respiratory, and nervous system. Superficial examination of the abdomen, skin, eyes, ears, nose, and throat, and skeletal areas was also made. Laboratory studies included a chest X ray, audiometric examination, urinalysis, and blood counts.

Social history and background data included structured interviews covering the material in the survey on activities and attitudes by Burgess, Cavan, and Havighurst (1948), a housing survey (Cohen, 1954), and a recreational fact-finding inventory (Kunde, 1954).

The psychological test battery included the Thurstone Primary Mental Abilities Test, Intermediate Form (Thurstone & Thurstone, 1947), the Wechsler Memory Scale (Wechsler, 1945), and the Symbol-Gestalt Test (Stein, 1961) as measures of intellectual functions. The Edwards Personality Preference Schedule (EPPS) (Edwards, 1954) and the Test of Behavioral Rigidity (Schaie, 1955, 1960) were used to assess personality dimensions thought to be relevant. Although some of these tests are group procedures, all were administered individually to assure that no spurious low performance was reported as a function of improperly understood instructions or of any of the other hazards of group testing.

The purpose of our batteries was not only to measure the performance of a superior group of old people on psychological variables, but also to demonstrate that this group had the social and physical characteristics that would permit us to conclude reasonably that we were indeed measuring the optimal limits of psychological functioning in old age. In the following sections, we shall therefore first describe the qualifying characteristics of our sample. Next we shall describe the comparisons of our sample on the psychological variables in relation to the performance of comparable young adults at early maturity. In all these instances we shall pay due attention to the range of behavior as well as to group characteristics.

III. Results

A.   Physical Characteristics

1. Self-Description of Physical Health

Our subjects were introduced to the medical examination by being asked to complete the Cornell Medical Index, a true-false inventory that lists a large number of possible somatic complaints and covers the areas of vision, hearing, respiratory system, cardiovascular system, musculoskeletal system, skin, nervous system, and genitourinary system. Also included were questions on fatigability and the presence of obesity. Means and standard deviations of the number of complaints for each of these systems or areas are given in Table I. In most instances, the number of complaints endorsed by our Ss was quite low even when compared with normative populations in their prime. Some typical complaints are not even restricted to advanced age, but are characteristic of adults in general, such as the almost universally endorsed item indicating that the S requires eyeglasses. The range of endorsed items was in all instances less than the possible number of complaints and 60% or more of the Ss did not endorse any complaint at all in the areas of audition, skin, musculoskeletal systems, and the complexes of fatigability and obesity. Moreover, for every region of inquiry there are at least some Ss who felt free of complaints.

The foregoing data suggest that our Ss either experienced very little

TABLE I

SELF-DESCRIPTION OF PHYSICAL HEALTH ON THE CORNELL MEDICAL INDEX[a]

Complaint area	No. of items	Mean no. of complaints			SD of complaints			Range			No. of Ss with no complaint		
		M	F	T	M	F	T	M	F	T	M	F	T
Vision	6	1.72	1.80	1.76	0.66	2.03	0.84	1–2	0–3	0–5	0	2	2
Hearing	3	0.60	0.40	0.51	0.68	0.63	0.68	0–2	0–2	0–2	13	17	30
Respiratory	18	1.64	1.48	1.56	2.26	1.67	1.65	0–7	0–5	0–7	10	11	21
Cardiovascular	13	1.72	2.08	1.90	1.18	2.46	2.07	0–5	0–8	0–8	5	10	15
Musculoskeletal	8	0.44	1.04	0.74	0.75	1.56	1.27	0–2	0–7	0–7	18	13	31
Skin	7	0.44	0.80	0.62	0.69	1.05	0.91	0–2	0–3	0–3	17	14	31
Nervous system	27	1.20	1.44	1.32	1.47	1.89	1.56	0–6	0–5	0–6	11	8	19
Genitourinary	11	2.60	3.00	2.80	1.54	2.65	2.17	0–7	0–8	0–8	1	6	5
Fatigability	8	0.48	1.24	0.86	1.09	1.72	1.47	0–5	0–6	0–6	19	14	33
Obesity	1	0.20	0.24	0.22	0.40	0.40	0.41	0–1	0–1	0–1	20	19	39

[a]Male, M; female, F; total, T.

physical discomfort or, as may be more plausible, were unwilling under the conditions of our inquiry to admit a large number of physical complaints. Indeed, it might be that the complaints endorsed, particularly since most of them came from relatively few Ss, may be more related to psychological problems than to physical difficulties. If the latter is true, one would then expect little agreement between physical complaints and objectively determined disease processes. This is indeed what was found when actual physical examinations were conducted.

2.   The Physical Examination

Every S received a complete physical examination following the format of the State of Washington disability examination. The examining physician was then asked to make a rating of clinically positive, questionable, or negative findings for each of ten diagnostic areas according to the set of criteria specified in Table II. A clinically positive finding here is considered one that involves the positive identification of pathology. The written record of the examination was independently reevaluated by a second physician, who also made ratings for the categories requiring subjective judgement. A third physician-judge finally arbitrated the few instances of disagreement.

The results of the physical examination are reported in Table III. It is of interest that most of the identified physical problems involve the peripheral sense organs, the cardiovascular system, and the finding of obesity. Nevertheless, there were three members of the group whose eyesight was normal and two who had less than a 10-dB hearing loss. Additionally, three individuals had only marginal visual loss and eight had marginal auditory loss.

A more detailed analysis of auditory loss furthermore showed significantly more severe loss at higher than lower frequencies, and more loss for the male than the female Ss. The men, however, showed significantly less loss at the lower frequencies, and performed significantly better with their right than their left ears (also see Schaie, Baltes, & Strother, 1964).

Fewer than 10% of our Ss showed positive significant findings in the respiratory, musculoskeletal, genitourinary, and nervous systems and only two questionable findings occurred for fatigability as measured by hemoglobin and hematocrit analyses.

The overall analysis showed that at least one significant physical symptom could be found for every S. By assigning a weight of 2 to a positive finding and 1 to a questionable finding, a crude overall index of physical problems can be obtained. This index ranged from 3 to 12 out of a possible 20 points, with a mean index of 8.1 for the men and 6.8 for the women. The physical examination thus showed our sample to be in generally good condition, though some sense organ impairment and cardiovascular defects were quite

TABLE II

CRITERIA FOR THE EVALUATION OF PHYSICAL EXAMINATION DATA[a]

Diagnostic area or system	Items of information used for diagnosis	Positive clinical finding	Criteria questionable	No clinical finding
Vision	Uncorrected distance vision (Snellen Chart)	20/50 or worse	20/40	20/30
Hearing	Maico audiogram (range, 256–4096) max. loss	35 dB or more	15–30 dB	10 dB or less
Respiratory	Chest X ray Clin. examination		—[a]	
Cardiovascular	Clin. examination Heart, arteries, extremities, edema liver margin		—[a]	
	Blood pressure	160/95+	150/90	145/85 or lower
	Pulse rate	90+	80–89	65–79
Musculoskeletal	Clin. examination Skeletal mineralization (X ray)		—[a]	
Nervous	Clin. impression		—[a]	
Genitourinary	Urinalysis			
	Pus cells (males only)	16+	10–15	9 or less
	Albumin	2+	1+	Trace
Skin	Clin. examination		—[a]	
Fatigability	Hemoglobin			
	Male	10.9 or less	11–11.9	12 gm or more
	Female	9.9 or less	10–10.9	11 gm or more
	Hematocrit			
	Male	39 or less	40–44	45–50
	Female	36 or less	37–39	40–45
Obesity	Abdominal examination		—[a]	
	Weight	6 lb ± normal range	Up to 5 lb ± normal range	Within normal range

[a]Where no criteria are given, clinical judgment was used in evaluating the presence or absence of pathological symptoms or conditions.

TABLE III

RESULTS OF PHYSICAL EXAMINATION[a]

Diagnostic area or system	Males			Females			All Ss		
	+	?	−	+	?	−	+	?	−
Vision	24	0	1	20	3	2	44	3	3
Hearing	22	3	0	17	5	2	39	8	2
Respiratory	3	5	17	1	4	20	4	9	37
Cardiovascular	10	10	5	16	4	5	26	14	10
Musculoskeletal	3	7	15	1	4	20	4	11	35
Skin	4	8	13	3	3	19	7	11	32
Nervous	4	1	20	1	0	24	5	1	44
Genitourinary	3	4	18	0	1	24	3	5	42
Fatigability	0	1	24	0	1	24	0	2	48
Obesity	7	3	14	10	3	12	17	6	26

[a]Frequency of positive (+), questionable (?), and negative (−) findings of pathology.

common. Subjectively, the Ss saw themselves as being in good health with relatively few complaints.

There is almost no relationship between the reported physical symptoms and findings in corresponding diagnostic areas in the actual examination. The one exception is the "honest" report of a need for wearing glasses. Biserial correlations between the presence of positive symptoms and number of CMI items endorsed all fell short of statistical significance at the 5% level.

These findings raise serious questions as to the validity of the CMI as a means of evaluating the health status of older Ss. In our sample, at least, it seems that the symptoms endorsed on the CMI are primarily of a psychological nature. Our Ss tended to report complaints in areas of physical functioning that raise apprehensions, perhaps on the basis of misunderstood superficial symptomatology. On the other hand, the S with actual physical disease who is otherwise in relatively good condition is likely to minimize or deny the presence of a physical deficit.

B.   Social and Environmental Characteristics

1.   Demographic Characteristics

The information relating to the environmental and demographic characteristics was obtained from the inventory of Burgess et al., supplemented by a housing schedule prepared by Cohen (1954). Tables IV through VII give the proportions within the sample for different types of family status, economic situation, sources of economic support, and employment status. It was found that most of the men were married and living with their wives, whereas the preponderant categories for women were single and widowed. Close to half

TABLE IV

FAMILY STATUS

Status	Male (%)	Female (%)	Total (%)
Single	4	40	22
Married	76	12	44
Married but separated	8	4	6
Widowed	12	44	28

TABLE V

PERCENTAGE BREAKDOWN ACCORDING TO EMPLOYMENT STATUS

Status	Male (%)	Female (%)	Total (%)
Working full time	4	4	4
Working part time	40	16	28
Not working	56	80	68

TABLE VI

SOURCES OF ECONOMIC SUPPORT

Source	Male (%)	Female (%)	Total (%)
Present earnings	40	16	28
Social security	12	12	12
Pension from former occupation	68	60	64
Aid from children	4	4	4
Insurance or annuities	4	36	20
Investments and savings	60	64	62

TABLE VII

ECONOMIC SITUATION

Self-description	Male (%)	Female (%)	Total (%)
Unable to make ends meet	0	0	0
Have enough to get along	28	20	24
Comfortable	52	80	66
Well-to-do	20	0	10
Wealthy	0	0	0

of the men were still employed at least part time, while only one fifth of the women were gainfully employed. Consequently a substantial minority of the males still received economic support from present earnings, even though income from investments and savings accounted for the primary source of economic support for both sexes. Only two of the Ss were supported by their children. When queried about their economic situation, all Ss indicated that they had at least enough to get along. Half of the men and four fifths of the women rated themselves as comfortably situated and one fifth of the men described themselves as well-to-do.

Special attention was given to the housing of our respondents recognizing that living arrangements may be an overriding determiner in facilitating or interfering with continuing optimal interaction with and effective participation in the community. Table VIII gives the residential location of our sample by sex and marital status. Most of our Ss lived in homes of their own in the residential area of their city, but about one fifth were apartment dwellers. Our average S occupied 5½ rooms and had lived in the same accommodations for an average of 15.5 years (range 1–44 years).

Satisfaction of our Ss with their living arrangements was also inquired into. It was found that 66% were very well satisfied and another 24% fairly well satisfied. Ss were then asked to indicate sources of dissatisfaction with their housing arrangements. The modal complaint seemed to be that the house was now too large, although a few complaints involved inconvenience due to location or physical arrangement that might interfere with optimal maintenance of environmental contacts. Since some degree of dissatisfaction seemed present, it is of interest to note the preferred, as contrasted to the actual, living arrangements of our Ss. Of our 50 Ss, only three indicated

TABLE VIII

RESIDENTIAL LOCATION[a]

District	Male					Female					Group total
	S	M	M–S	W	T	S	M	M–S	W	T	
Business	0	0	0	0	0	0	0	0	2	2	2
Rooming house	0	0	0	0	0	0	1	0	0	1	1
Apartment house	0	3	1	0	4	2	1	1	2	6	10
Small homes (less than 6 rooms)	0	5	1	2	8	4	1	0	4	9	17
Large homes (more than 6 rooms)	1	11	0	1	13	4	0	0	3	7	20
Total	1	19	2	3	25	10	3	1	11	25	50

[a]Key: S, single; M, married; M–S, married but separated; W, widowed; T, Total.

a desire to live in a residence for old people and one would have preferred to live with her children. The remaining 92% insisted on the desirability of independent living arrangements.

2. Interaction with the Environment

It has been argued that decline in performance and other psychological functions may be associated with lack of environmental interaction or of exposure to the conditions of life and cultural content that could benefit the younger *S* on certain test performance. One theoretical position (Schaie, 1962) holds that declining test performance may indeed be a function of restraints that limit the successful environmental interaction of the organism. A contrary position is, of course, taken by writers favoring the notion of disengagement (Cummings & Henry, 1961), who regard a successive and successful withdrawal from the demands of the environment as an organism-maintaining strategy. In any event, it seems incumbent upon us to present some data on environmental interaction for our sample, and Tables IX-XIV bear on this matter.

It was found that contacts with friends apparently have decreased for a majority of our respondents, but that there is a substantial minority who report increased contacts. Almost all of our *S*s maintain some contact with young people and 90% of our sample belong to at least one club or organ-

TABLE IX

CONTACT WITH FRIENDS

	Male (%)	Female (%)	Total (%)
Less than at 55	44	40	42
About same	36	24	30
More than at 55	20	36	28

TABLE X

CONTACT WITH YOUNG PEOPLE

	Male (%)	Female (%)	Total (%)
None	4	8	6
A few times a year	40	24	32
Once or twice a month	20	52	36
About once a week	20	12	16
Every day	16	4	10

TABLE XI

MEMBERSHIP IN CLUBS AND ORGANIZATIONS

No. of organizations	Male (%)	Female (%)	Total (%)
None	12	8	10
One	24	12	18
Two	12	8	10
Three	4	12	8
Four or more	48	60	54

TABLE XII

ATTENDANCE AT CLUB MEETINGS

Frequency	Male (%)	Female (%)	Total (%)
Never	24	12	18
Less than once a month	12	8	10
Once or twice a month	36	24	30
Once a week	20	32	26
Twice a week or more	8	24	16

TABLE XIII

TIME SPENT ON CLUB ACTIVITIES AS COMPARED WITH AGE 55

Amount of time	Male (%)	Female (%)	Total (%)
More	8	36	22
About same	24	32	28
Less	68	32	50

TABLE XIV

FREQUENCY OF CHURCH ATTENDANCE[a,b]

	Male			Female			Total		
	Mb	NMb	T	Mb	NMb	T	Mb	NMb	T
Never	3	9	12	3	2	5	6	11	17
Less than once a month	1	1	2	1	0	1	2	1	3
Once or twice a month	0	1	1	0	1	1	0	2	2
Once a week	8	1	9	18	0	18	1	26	27
Twice a week or more	1	0	1	0	0	0	1	0	1
Total	13	12	25	22	3	25	35	15	50

[a]All respondents were either Protestants or had no religious preference.
[b]Column-head abbreviations: Mb, church member; NMb, nonmember; T, total.

ization. Indeed more than half the sample reports membership in four or more such units. Rather active participation is indicated also by the finding that 42% of the Ss attend a meeting once a week or oftener and another 30% attend at least a meeting a month. Comparative participation with advancing age seems to be sex-linked. That is, we find almost as many women reporting increased participation as decreasing participation. On the other hand, two thirds of the men reported lessened participation, whereas only 8% reported an increase. A final index of contact is that of church membership and attendance. Here 70% of the sample (about half the men and almost all the women) indicated church membership. Only half the sample, however, attended church as frequently as once a week.

These data do not permit any direct answer to the question whether the sample's contact with the environment has increased or lessened. It seems clear, however, that most of our Ss, at least in terms of their self-report, continued to interact socially in a variety of ways, which would suggest that they had rather extensive exposure to current cultural events.

3. Use of Leisure Time

One of the criteria for successful adjustment after retirement would seem to be the effective use of leisure time and participation by the individual in meaningful nonwork-related activities. A special recreational fact-finding inventory (Kunde, 1954) was developed that surveys such areas as the amount of time spent on various types of leisure activities, specific activities engaged in, relative desirability of various kinds of recreational activities, and factors that seem to interfere with effective use of leisure time.

It soon became clear that the concept of leisure time was rather meaningless for our *S*s. Indeed, any such use had to be carefully differentiated from the notion of total use of time, which included components that, during an earlier phase in the individual's life, would be considered either work or leisure related. Table XV gives the average proportion of leisure time, by sex of respondent, devoted to the various time classifications. Both men and women spend the major portion of their time almost equally on physical activities and activities having educational value. Creative activities, social activities, and spectator sports rank next for the men, while creative, social, and devotional activities have relatively high secondary interest for the women.

Participation in specific activities (a total of 43 different activities were listed) was also tabulated. Table XVI gives the number of respondents indicating participation in specific activities listed in rank order of preference. Although the time spent in physical activities is high, this does not represent excessive participation in organized physical activity. Preference is shown rather for activities of a more passive kind, even though incidence of participation in activities involving social interaction is high. Among the reasons given for lack of recreational activity, men most frequently cited the lack of organized programs or facilities for older people, whereas women indicated physical condition as the principal source of interference. For this group an inability to finance recreation or lack of friends seems of rather low relevance.

C. Cognitive Variables

1. Measures of Intellectual Ability

The mental ability level of our *S*s was measured with the intermediate form of the Thurstone Primary Mental Abilities (PMA) Test. This instrument, although originally constructed for group testing of adolescents, has been

TABLE XV

AVERAGE PROPORTION OF LEISURE TIME SPENT ON VARIOUS TYPES OF ACTIVITY

Type of activity	Male	Female	Total
Physical	28.4	31.5	30.1
Creative	13.0	12.5	12.7
Social	8.0	10.3	9.2
Having educational value	28.7	26.9	27.7
Audience and spectator	8.3	4.0	6.0
Informal games	4.2	4.2	4.2
Civic and social services	5.2	4.4	4.8
Devotional	4.2	6.2	5.3

TABLE XVI

NUMBER OF MEMBERS OF ELDERLY GROUP PARTICIPATING IN SPECIFIC
ACTIVITIES IN ORDER OF FREQUENCY[a]

Activity	M	F	T
Reading	25	25	50
Radio Listening	24	23	47
Chores	21	25	46
Visiting	21	25	46
Attending lectures	20	22	42
Clubs	19	22	41
Dinners	18	23	41
Meetings	16	19	35
Concerts	16	18	34
Church services	14	20	34
Card games	17	16	33
Walks	15	16	31
Parties	14	15	29
Scripture reading	11	18	29
Gardening	15	12	27
Theater	15	12	27
Movies	15	12	27
Sport events	16	9	25
Discussions	11	14	25
Community work	12	11	23
Writing	12	11	23
Church work	9	14	23
Outings	12	7	19
Forums	7	11	18
Crafts	8	9	17
Television	11	3	14
Checkers	8	4	12
Lodge meetings	6	4	10
Billiards	7	0	7
Music	2	4	6
Chess	5	1	6
Prayers	4	2	6
Golf	3	0	3
Horseback riding	3	0	3
Fishing	2	1	3
Arts	2	1	3
Hymn singing	2	1	3
Croquet	1	1	2
Hunting	2	0	2
Dancing	1	1	2
Dramatics	0	1	1
Bowling	0	0	0

[a]Male, M; female, F; total, T.

shown to have adequate range of difficulty and reliability for older Ss (Schaie, Rosenthal, & Perlman, 1953). The form of the test used in this study contains the subtests of word meaning (measured by identifying the analogy of a stimulus word from a multiple-choice list); space (measured by correctly identifying rotated geometric forms); reasoning (measured by identifying the correct letter needed to complete a letter sequence); number (measured by the identification of correct or incorrect solutions for simple addition tasks), and word fluency (measured by requiring the writing of words beginning with a specified letter).

Table XVII gives the PMA raw score means and standard deviations separately by sex and for the total group, while Table XVIII provides comparison with young adults by converting the raw score means to T scores, using Thurstone's conversion table for his young adult (17 years plus) norm group. Although our Ss function well below the level they would have been expected to attain at their prime, they are still at or above the mean for the average 17-year-old in verbal and numerical abilities. On space and reasoning, however, a significant decrement is apparent, with mean values

TABLE XVII

RAW SCORE MEANS AND STANDARD DEVIATIONS ON THE PRIMARY MENTAL ABILITIES (PMA) TEST

Variable	Males		Females		Total group	
	Mean	SD	Mean	SD	Mean	SD
Verbal meaning	30.68	6.20	35.60	12.22	33.14	9.91
Space	15.20	8.06	10.80	7.64	13.00	8.09
Reasoning	8.72	4.89	11.36	5.47	10.04	5.30
Number	26.52	10.67	23.28	10.40	24.90	10.56
Word fluency	43.76	11.51	47.80	13.51	45.78	12.58

TABLE XVIII

PMA TEST MEANS CONVERTED INTO T SCORES AS COMPARED WITH A 17-YEAR-OLD NORMATIVE POPULATION

Variable	Males	Females	Total group
Verbal meaning	46	50	48
Space	40	38	39
Reasoning	42	44	43
Number	55	51	53
Word fluency	49	53	51

approximately 1 SD below the reference group. An overall estimate of mental ability, comparable to the efficiency quotient estimate obtained from standard clinical instruments, would place the mean of our group at approximately the population average for the adolescent group.

The maintenance of verbal skills in particular is further emphasized by examining the range of individual scores for those of our Ss who are in the eighties. Of sixteen such individuals, ten were still above the comparison mean for verbal meaning; nine subjects exceeded it on number and six equalled or exceeded it on word fluency. There seems to be a sex difference, shown by a greater decrement for men than for women on verbal tasks and by the reverse trend on tasks not involving verbal behavior. The men did significantly better ($p < .05$) on space, while the women exceeded the men on verbal meaning and reasoning.

Whether the PMA, developed for adolescents and young adults, should be considered suitable for our Ss is, of course, open to question. In a factor-analytically derived test, however, a pertinent bit of evidence would be the maintenance of separation between factor scores. Table XIX gives the intercorrelations among subtests. These are quite moderate except for the typically high correlation between verbal meaning and reasoning. Thus it seems that the relations among the PMA subtests are quite similar to those found in young populations.

2. Memory

The Wechsler Memory Scale (WMS) was used to determine the extent of memory deficit that might interfere with our group's effective functioning. The WMS has seven subtests: personal and current information, orientation in time and space, mental control (as measured by counting and reciting the alphabet), digit span, reproducing visual figures, reproducing the content of two short news reports, and paired-associate learning. The combined scores on these subtests yield a Memory Quotient (MQ) that is roughly comparable to the IQ derived from Wechsler's intelligence tests.

TABLE XIX

INTERCORRELATIONS AMONG THE PRIMARY MENTAL ABILITIES

	V	S	R	N	W
Verbal meaning		.35	.61	.30	.17
Space			.36	.19	.09
Reasoning				.40	.35
Number					.29
Word fluency					

The overall memory measure indicates only a mild deficit, with an MQ of 93 based on Wechsler's normative group of young adults. Of more interest, however, are specific components of memory functions. Table XX, therefore, presents the means for our group, a group of young adults, and the total number of attainable responses. Means here are based on the total group, since no significant sex differences were found. Although most of the differences between our sample and the comparison group are statistically significant, the more important issue is the absolute magnitude of the discrepancy. As expected, there was a substantial decrement in our group's ability to reproduce visual figures. But efficiency of paired-associate learning was only slightly lowered, while retention of number series and of meaningful material was still close to the young average. Orientation in time and space and mental control, as measured by counting and by listing the alphabet, were virtually unimpaired.

3. Visual-Motor Functioning

Difficulties that older people experience on tasks involving visual discrimination and response requirements involving visual mediation are at times attributed to progressive cortical decrement, particularly in the visual-motor area. Stein's (1961) Symbol-Gestalt Test was used to assess the relevant functions in our sample. Stein's test is essentially a modification of the Wechsler digit symbol subtest; his symbols have a poor gestalt and induce the S to produce closure phenomena. Table XXI gives mean scores for our group and for Stein's adult (mean age 40 years) brain-damaged and control groups.

On two of the symbol-gestalt measures our group is midway between Stein's control and brain-damaged samples. It appears that there is a lowering in both the speed of reproducing correct symbols and the rate of

TABLE XX

MEAN PERFORMANCE ON THE SUBTESTS OF THE WECHSLER MEMORY SCALE

Subtest	Total possible	Norm group (20–29 years old)	Superior old group
Current information	6.00	5.96	5.72
Orientation	5.00	5.00	4.86
Mental control	9.00	7.50	7.46
Logical memory	23.00	9.28	8.52
Digit span forward	8.00	7.04	6.86
Digit span backward	7.00	5.26	5.04
Visual reproduction	14.00	11.00	7.90
Associative learning	21.00	15.72	13.64

TABLE XXI

MEAN SCORES ON STEIN'S SYMBOL-GESTALT TEST

Scoring variable	Superior old group	Brain-damaged ($N=60$)	Controls ($N=120$)
Correct symbols in 3 minutes	42.72	29.92	50.08
No. of qualitative errors	1.68	1.62	0.63
Improvement	1.08	.45	2.16

improvement, comparing performance in the first and third minute of the test. When the number of qualitative errors is considered, our Ss are quite close to Stein's Brain-damaged group. Of course, the visual impairment shown in the medical examination may account for these results. Nevertheless it seems that, even in as well-functioning a group as ours, cortical changes as measured by visual-motor functioning are likely to have occurred.

D. Personality Characteristics

1. Behavioral Rigidity

Difficulty in optimal functioning is often related to response style as well as to intellectual ability. The construct of rigidity has been interchangeably applied in both the cognitive and personality spheres (Chown, 1959). Schaie (1955, 1960) has developed a Test of Behavioral Rigidity (TBR) that provides operational measures of the two aspects of rigidity and of the related variable of psychomotor speed. The measure of motor-cognitive rigidity is derived from a ratio of interfered to noninterfered responses. This is done by means of such tasks as having a paragraph of writing copied and then having it copied once again, substituting small letters for capital letters and capital letters for small letters. The personality-perceptual rigidity measure involves questionnaire responses regarding behaviors that require shifts in interpersonal habits and response patterns. The psychomotor speed measure is obtained by counting the number of responses elicited in simple copying and in response to overlearned antonym and synonym lists.

Table XXII gives the *T*-score means and standard deviations obtained by our sample on the TBR. The *T* scores are based on general population norms (ages 21–70). A low score is in the rigid direction. The results show a decrement in flexibility or response speed from middle adulthood, by from ½ to 1 SD, but several of our Ss were still less rigid than a comparison population in its prime. Our group was somewhat less rigid in terms of personality-perceptual rigidity than of motor-cognitive and response speed attributes, where the peripheral sense organ decrement may be particularly important. Decreased psychomotor speed is particularly significant for our male Ss.

TABLE XXII

MEANS AND STANDARD DEVIATIONS FOR FACTOR SCORES ON THE TEST OF
BEHAVIORAL RIGIDITY (GENERAL POPULATION NORMS)

	Male		Female		Total	
	Mean	SD	Mean	SD	Mean	SD
Psychomotor speed	39.16	5.51	43.64	7.50	41.40	6.90
Personality-perceptual	44.84	6.35	43.64	5.90	44.24	6.10
Motor-cognitive rigidity	44.08	6.25	42.76	7.83	43.42	7.04
Composite	42.60	4.25	43.36	5.39	42.98	4.82

2. Need Structure

The Edwards Personality Preference Schedule (EPPS), a forced-choice test
designed to measure the relative strength of fifteen needs derived from
Murray's list of manifest needs, was used to compare our group with the
status of young adults. For this analysis, a comparison group of 25 male
and 25 female graduate students with a mean age of 25 was selected to
provide close matching for academic background and vocational interest.

Table XXIII gives means for the EPPS T scores in terms of Edwards'
norms for both the young and old professional groups. Analyses of variance,
as presented in Table XXIV, showed highly significant differences between
the young and old groups on five of the fifteen needs measured by the EPPS.
In three instances (deference, order, and endurance) need scores were higher
for the older than for the younger group. The reverse was true for hetero-
sexual activity and exhibition (or attention). Marginally significant also
were differences indicating lower need for dominance and higher need for
abasement on the part of the older group.

Of particular interest are the needs with respect to which the older group
is similar to the young graduate students. One of these is the need for
achievement, which is as high in the older group as for the graduate students.
This finding may of course be a function of the fact that the older group is
composed of professional workers whose need for achievement has had a
considerable amount of reinforcement. However, our old group was also no
different from the young on need for autonomy or independence and on need
for affiliation or friendships. In the needs for nurture and succorance—the
giving and receiving of affection, sympathy, and help—old and young are
alike. The need for change or new experience is no less important to our older
than to the younger group and there is no difference between groups in the
needs of introception and aggression.

TABLE XXIII

MEAN T SCORES ON THE EPPS[a]

Need	Superior old group		Graduate students	
	Male	Female	Male	Female
Achievement	53	51	56	54
Deference	64	64	46	46
Order	63	65	48	45
Exhibition	43	41	52	47
Autonomy	51	56	55	63
Affiliation	49	51	51	49
Intraception	50	48	49	50
Succorance	45	48	48	46
Dominance	44	43	48	47
Abasement	51	50	46	45
Nurturance	49	51	48	48
Change	51	45	52	52
Endurance	62	64	51	51
Heterosexuality	31	28	50	58
Aggression	49	48	50	49

[a]Means are given in terms of Edwards's norms for both the young college group and the old group.

Table XXV gives raw score means and results of the t tests for the sex differences within the old group. The most significant such sex differences appear for heterosexuality, where males greatly exceed female Ss. The male Ss are also higher on achievement and aggression, and the female Ss on nurture, affiliation, and succorance.

One other point of interest with respect to sex differences in the need structure of our group is that on eight of the needs the sex differences are larger in the older group. Terman and Miles' (1936) data have usually been interpreted to indicate that sex differences become smaller in older groups. Our data seem to show that this is not consistently the case when needs are involved.

3. Attitudinal Variables

a. Attitudes toward Self and Environment. The Burgess *et al.* (1948) inventory contains a section that gives information about the respondents' attitudes toward themselves and the environment. Seven scales are included, each of which contains seven items. Each scale was scored so that a score of four reflects average satisfaction or acceptance, while lower scores indicate dissatisfaction and higher scores above-average satisfaction. Table XXVI

TABLE XXIV

ANALYSIS OF VARIANCE OF SEX AND AGE DIFFERENCES ON THE EPPS

Variable	Age MS	Age F	Sex MS	Sex F	Interaction MS	Interaction F	Residual MS
Achievement	46.24	2.25	289.00	14.08[a]	0.36		20.53
Deference	1142.44	111.89[a]	38.44	3.76	0.64		10.21
Order	1474.56	96.95[a]	1.44		40.96	2.69	15.21
Exhibition	198.81	15.98[a]	34.81	2.80	1.21		12.44
Autonomy	15.21		12.25		13.69		22.70
Affiliation	0.36		207.36	11.71[a]	12.96		17.71
Introception	3.61		100.41	4.30[b]	13.69		23.33
Succorance	51.84	3.09	169.00	10.09[a]	0.64		16.75
Dominance	98.01	4.55[b]	320.41	14.86[a]	0.01		21.56
Abasement	116.64	4.60[b]	112.36	4.43[b]	1.44		25.34
Nurturance	22.09	1.09	246.49	12.20[a]	7.29		20.20
Change	77.44	3.60	5.76		27.04	1.26	21.51
Endurance	1108.89	61.40[a]	2.89		1.69		18.06
Sex	4316.49	26.76[a]	102.01		161.29	7.07[a]	22.81
Aggression	4.84		237.16	14.79[a]	1.00		16.04
Consistency	0.09		6.25	1.97	0.09		3.17

[a] Significant at or beyond 5% level of confidence.

[b] Significant at or beyond 1% level of confidence.

gives means and standard deviations on these scales. The results suggest that our Ss are reasonably satisfied with their current state of health, their friendships, the satisfaction they derive from their family, their feelings of economic security, and their sense of continued usefulness. Only average satisfaction is expressed with respect to their ability to carry on useful work, feelings of happiness, and acceptance of religious experience. Significant sex differences were found in satisfaction derived from the family, which was higher for the male than female Ss, and in the acceptance of religious experience, which was much lower for the men than for the women. The latter finding coincides with the sex difference in religious participation reported in the section on environmental interaction. It is unclear, of course, whether lower satisfaction leads to reduced environmental interaction or whether the reported low satisfaction from religious experience is a consequence of a tendency to withdraw from relevant experiences.

b. Self-Ratings of Happiness and Success. As a concluding indication of our Ss' views of their life experiences, Tables XXVII and XXVIII provide data on their retrospective ratings of their life in terms of happiness and accomplishment. Only one member of the group described her life as having been unhappy, whereas over three fourths of the Ss considered their lives to have been at least moderately happy. Moreover, 90% of the Ss

TABLE XXV

MEANS AND STANDARD DEVIATIONS ON THE EPPS

Need	Total		Male		Female		$t_{m/f}$
	Mean	SD	Mean	SD	Mean	SD	
Achievement	15.04	4.20	16.68	3.95	13.40	3.85	2.97[a]
Deference	17.06	3.39	16.52	3.33	17.60	3.43	1.13
Order	16.48	3.69	15.96	3.79	17.00	3.58	0.97
Exhibition	11.40	3.70	11.88	4.21	10.92	3.14	0.92
Autonomy	15.06	4.74	15.04	5.59	15.08	3.83	0.03
Affiliation	16.28	4.65	14.48	4.68	18.08	3.93	2.64[b]
Introception	16.18	4.58	15.84	4.62	16.52	4.61	0.44
Succorance	10.02	4.47	8.64	3.97	11.40	4.60	2.27[b]
Dominance	12.90	5.04	14.68	5.20	11.12	4.28	2.65[b]
Abasement	13.62	5.32	12.44	5.27	14.80	5.20	1.59
Nurturance	15.28	4.62	13.44	4.95	17.12	3.47	3.04[a]
Change	15.48	4.57	15.76	4.54	15.20	4.68	0.43
Endurance	19.58	3.65	19.28	3.10	19.88	4.17	0.58
Sex	4.56	4.67	6.84	5.16	2.67	7.13	3.92[a]
Aggression	11.04	4.09	12.48	4.10	9.60	3.59	2.64[b]
Consistency	11.96	1.47	12.24	1.59	11.68	1.31	1.36

[a]Significant at or beyond 1% level of confidence.
[b]Significant at or beyond 5% level of confidence.

TABLE XXVI

POSITIVE ATTITUDES TOWARD SELF AND ENVIRONMENT
EXPRESSED ON BURGESS ATTITUDE SCALE[a]

	Total		Male		Female		$t_{m/f}$
	Mean	SD	Mean	SD	Mean	SD	
Health	4.38	1.23	4.52	1.16	4.24	1.31	0.80
Friends	4.98	1.02	4.92	1.16	5.04	0.89	0.41
Work	3.96	1.18	4.12	1.17	3.80	1.19	0.96
Economic security	4.52	0.95	4.52	1.12	4.52	0.76	0.00
Religion	4.16	1.93	3.44	2.22	4.88	1.27	2.82[b]
Usefulness	4.46	0.95	4.44	0.96	4.48	0.96	0.15
Happiness	4.00	1.07	4.24	1.02	3.76	1.10	1.60
Family	4.72	0.76	5.00	0.76	4.44	0.65	2.80[b]

[a]Burgess et al. (1948).
[b]Significant at or beyond 1% level of confidence.

TABLE XXVII

SELF-RATING OF RESPONDENT'S LIFE IN RETROSPECT

	Male	Female	Total
Very happy	10 (40%)	10 (40%)	20 (40%)
Moderately happy	11 (44%)	8 (32%)	19 (38%)
Average	4 (16%)	6 (24%)	10 (20%)
Unhappy	0 (0%)	1 (4%)	1 (2%)

TABLE XXVIII

SELF-RATING OF RESPONDENT'S ACCOMPLISHMENT IN LIFE

	Male	Female	Total
Well satisfied	8 (32%)	6 (24%)	14 (28%)
Reasonably satisfied	14 (56%)	17 (68%)	31 (62%)
Dissatisfied	3 (12%)	2 (8%)	5 (10%)

considered themselves at least reasonably satisfied with their lifetime accomplishment. No significant sex differences occurred in these global self-descriptions.

E. Effects of Confounding Variables on Performance on the Cognitive and Personality Variables

1. *Effect of Speed, Memory, and Motor-Cognitive Rigidity on the Primary Mental Abilities*

When the performance of our sample is compared with that of young reference groups, it becomes readily apparent that maximum decrement was found on the variables of psychomotor speed, memory, and motor-cognitive rigidity. An attempt was therefore made to adjust scores on the Thurstone Primary Mental Abilities Test for the effect of these three variables. Table XXIX gives the correlations between the PMA scores and the variables assumed to have a confounding effect, and reports mean *T* scores for the total group before and after the effects of speed, memory, and motor-cognitive rigidity have been removed.

The means on the PMA tests have been adjusted to the level that would obtain if there had been no age decrement on the confounding, and possibly peripherally determined, factors. After such adjustment, group means are raised to about 1 SD above the average performance in young *S*s for verbal meaning, number, and word fluency. The adjusted mean score on reasoning is at the mean of the young population, but the space score remains approximately 1 SD below the mean of the young reference group. Further details

TABLE XXIX

CORRELATIONS BETWEEN SCORES ON THE PMA TEST AND THE VARIABLES
OF PSYCHOMOTOR SPEED, MEMORY, AND MOTOR-COGNITIVE RIGIDITY

Variable	Verbal Meaning	Space	Reasoning	Number	Word fluency
Psychomotor speed (TBR)	.68	.14	.67	.41	.40
Overall memory score (WMS[a])	.38	.31	.57	.31	.45
Motor-cognitive rigidity (TBR)	.50	.26	.46	.32	.02
MEAN T SCORES ON PMA TEST BEFORE AND AFTER ADJUSTMENT FOR EFFECT OF SPEED, MEMORY, AND MOTOR-COGNITIVE RIGIDITY					
Before	48	39	43	53	51
After	62	42	52	60	59

[a]Wechsler Memory Scale.

on the method and results of the PMA score adjustment have been reported elsewhere (Strother, Schaie, & Horst, 1957).

2. Effects of Activities and Attitudes on Cognitive and Personality Variables

No attempt was made to adjust test scores for the effects of attitudinal variables and the level of environmental interaction shown by our Ss, since information on these variables was lacking for a comparable population at the young adult age level. However, several significant correlations were found in our sample that might have warranted appropriate adjustments if they had been feasible. Thus, correlations significant at the 5% level of confidence were found between the overall index of environmental interaction and the verbal meaning score on the PMA. Positive correlations were further found between the amount of leisure activity and the PMA scores for verbal meaning, reasoning, and number. An intriguing finding is a negative correlation between the PMA space score and expressed feelings of security. Apparently the greater the remaining ability to orient oneself in space, the greater one's feeling of security.

A positive correlation was found between the overall activity index and need for deference, while the correlations were negative between this index and the need for autonomy and that for aggression. Those of our Ss who were most active apparently had resolved conflicts that led to high need scores on the EPPS. Several correlations were significant also for the relationship between the composite score summarizing the attitude measures on the Burgess et al. (1948) activities inventory and the EPPS. Thus positive correlations were found between positive attitudes and needs for deference and order, and negative correlations occurred between the expression of positive attitudes about the self and needs for autonomy and dominance.

IV. Concluding Remarks

The results reported in this chapter on the assessment of a carefully selected and highly motivated sample of individuals of advanced age lend strong support to the proposition that psychological age decrements reported in the literature cannot be criticized or refuted simply by referring to low motivation or artifacts of sampling. Our group reported generally satisfying environmental and social conditions, and all our *S*s had attained a high level of education and related professional use of their abilities throughout their adult life. Nevertheless, the state of psychological functioning of this highly selected group was at best at or slightly below the population average for young adults. The results of our physical and social studies suggest that this obvious decrement from peak performance is most likely related to a physiological decrement, particularly of a sensory nature, and probably to the general slowing down of response speed as well.

Psychological decrement is most apparent in functions that require visual-motor response or where speed is of importance, but some decrement is also clearly apparent in most other cognitive processes, even though the range of individual differences is quite large. Although there are clearly changes in cognitive processes in the direction of reduced ability, these are not necessarily accompanied by a corresponding reduction in needs or an acceptance of reduced interaction with the environment. It is the relation of the older individual's continuing needs and aspirations to the limiting conditions of his physiological apparatus and the resulting environmental constraints that require most urgent attention and further study.

ACKNOWLEDGMENTS

This research was conceptualized by a University of Washington faculty group known as the Committee on Gerontology and was supported by a grant from the Agnes H. Anderson Fund. The authors are indebted to Joseph Cohen, Benjamin Houghton, and Norman Kunde, who were active members of the Committee on Gerontology, and to Mary Marjorie Campbell and Beverly Frasure, who assisted in the data collection and analysis.

REFERENCES

Brodman, K. Cornell medical index-health questionnaire. In A. Weider (Ed.), *Contributions towards medical psychology.* New York: Ronald, 1953.

Burgess, E. W., Cavan, Ruth S., & Havighurst, R. J. *Your activities and attitudes.* Chicago: Science Research Associates, 1948.

Chown, Sheila M. Rigidity—a flexible concept. *Psychol. Bull.*, 1959, **56**, 197–223.

Cohen, J. Supplementary living arrangement schedule for the aged. Mimeographed survey instrument, Univer. of Washington, 1954.

Cummings, Elaine, & Henry, W. E. *Growing old.* New York: Basic Books, 1961.

Edwards, A. L. *Manual for the Edwards personal preference schedule.* New York: Psychol. Corp., 1954.

Jones, H. E. Intelligence and problem solving. In J. E. Birren (Ed.), *Handbook of aging and the individual.* Chicago, Ill.: Univer. of Chicago Press, 1959.

Kunde, N. Recreational factfinding inventory for the aged. Mimeographed survey instrument, Univer. of Washington, 1954.

Schaie, K. W. A test of behavioral rigidity. *J. abnorm. soc. Psychol.*, 1955, **51**, 604–610.

Schaie, K. W. Cross-sectional methods in the study of psychological aspects of aging. *J. Geront.*, 1959, **14**, 208–215.

Schaie, K. W. *Manual for the test of behavioral rigidity*. Palo Alto: Consulting Psychologists Press, 1960.

Schaie, K. W. A field-theory approach to age changes in cognitive behavior. *Vita humana*, 1962, **5**, 129–141.

Schaie, K. W. A general model for the study of developmental problems. *Psychol. Bull.*, 1965, **64**, 92–107.

Schaie, K. W., Baltes, P., & Strother, C. R. A study of auditory sensitivity in advanced age. *J. Geront.*, 1964, **19**, 453–457.

Schaie, K. W., Rosenthal, F., & Perlman, R. M. Differential mental deterioration of factorially "pure" functions in later maturity. *J. Geront.*, 1953, **8**, 191–196.

Stein, K. I. The effect of brain damage upon speed, accuracy and improvement in visual motor functioning. *J. consult. Psychol.*, 1961, **25**, 171–177.

Strother, C. R., Schaie, K. W., & Horst, P. The relationship between advanced age and mental abilities. *J. abnorm. soc. Psychol.*, 1957, **55**, 166–170.

Sward, K. Age and mental ability in superior men. *Amer. J. Psychol.*, 1945, **58**, 443–479.

Terman, L. M., & Miles, C. C. *Sex and personality: studies in masculinity and femininity.* New York: McGraw-Hill, 1936.

Thurstone, L. L., & Thurstone, T. G. *Primary mental abilities test*. Chicago: Science Research Associates, 1947.

Wechsler, D. A standardized memory scale for clinical use. *J. Psychol.*, 1945, **19**, 87–95.

Author Index

Numbers in italics refer to pages on which the complete references are listed.

A

Aaron, R., 112, *129*
Aborn, M., 84, *91*
Allanson, J. T., 68, *71*
Allison, R. S., 137, *167*
Anderson, E. C., 41, 68, *73*
Anderson, N. S., 83, 89, *91*, 98, *127*
Andrews, H. L., 13, 27, *34*
Andrews, W., 184, *186*
Ankus, M. N., 125, *128*, 136, *167*, 190, *216*
Anliker, J., 27, *32*
Arenberg, D., 5, *32*, 94, 126, *127*, 170, *186*
Arnhoff, F. N., 227, 236, *236*
Attneave, F., 81, 83, 89, *91*, 148, *166*
Averbach, E., 170, *186*
Axelrod, S., 5, *33*, 169, *186*, 190, 198, *216*, 219, *237*

B

Baddeley, A. D., 84, *91*
Baltes, O., 287, *308*
Barker, R. G., 241, *278*
Barlow, H. B., 48, 50, *71*
Barnes, A. H., 184, *187*
Bartlett, F. C., 38, 40, 41, 69, 70, *71*
Bartley, S. H., 13, *32*
Basowitz, H., 94, *128*, 132, 139, *167*, 183, *187*, 190, 198, 211, *216*
Bates, J. A. V., 13, *32*
Beardshall, A., 233, *237*
Beck, L. H., 218, *238*
Beerstecher, D. M., 10, 16, *34*
Bekesy, G. von, 44, 47, 58, *71*
Bell, C. R., 26, *32*
Bellis, C. J., 2, *32*
Berger, H., 9, *32*
Bernstein, F., 69, *72*
Bernstein, M., 69, *72*

Bertelson, P., 76, *91*
Birdsall, T. G., 89, *92*
Birren, J. E., 2, 4, 7, 8, *32*, 40, 68, 70, *72*, 78, 79, 80, 88, 89, *91*, 92, 131, 138, 145, *166*, *168*, 217, *236*, 248, 259, 274, *278*
Bishop, G. H., 13, *32, 33*
Bogdonoff, M. D., 202, 207, *215*, *216*, 219, *237*
Boreham, J. L., 13, *34*
Botwinick, J., 2, 4, 8, *32*, *33*, 78, 79, 88, *91*, 101, 119, *127*, 145, *166*, 211, *215*, 217, *236*
Bousfield, W. A., 240, 248, *278*
Bragg, V. C., 58, *72*
Bransome, E. D., Jr., 218, *238*
Braun, H. W., 94, *128*, 132, 135, 137, *167*
Brazier, Mary A. B., 10, *33*
Brebner, J., 60, 65, *72*
Bregman, E. O., 190, *216*
Brener, L. R., 117, *127*
Brinley, J. F., 78, 79, 88, *91*, 101, *127*
Broadbent, D. E., 48, 65, *72*, 82, *91*, 101, 125, *127*, 134, 135, 136, *166, 167*, 233, *236, 237*
Brodman, K., 285, *307*
Bromley, D. B., 102, *127*, 133, 134, 138, *167*, 174, *186*
Bruckner, R., 46, *72*
Brunswik, E., 241, *278*
Burgess, E. W., 285, 302, 307, *307*
Burns, W., 51, *72*
Buschke, H., 98, *127*
Busse, E. W., 10, *33*, 184, *187*
Butler, R. N., 25, *34*, 68, *72*

C

Caird, W. K., 103, *127*, 136, 138, 153, *167*, 190, *215*
Cairnie, J., 88, *92*
Callaway, E., III, 15, *33*
Canestrari, R. E., Jr., 5, *33*, 94, 126, *127*,

309

Subject Index